.50

FOSSILS

the text of this book is printed on 100% recycled paper

FOSSILS

An Introduction to Prehistoric Life

by

WILLIAM H. MATTHEWS III
Professor of Geology
Lamar University
Beaumont, Texas

BARNES & NOBLE BOOKS
A DIVISION OF HARPER & ROW, PUBLISHERS
New York, Hagerstown, San Francisco, London

L. C. Catalogue Card Number: 62-12996

Hardbound Edition SBN 389 02940 8
Paperback Edition SBN 389 00246 1

79 80 12 11 10 9 8 7

Manufactured in the United States of America

To My Wife, Jennie

PREFACE

Almost everyone has seen the fossilized remains of prehistoric plants or animals—perhaps the skeleton of a huge dinosaur, the petrified trunk of an ancient tree, or the shells of clams or snails that lived in the great seas that covered the continents millions of years ago.

Each year more and more people are learning that these fossils are not mere curiosities. They realize that a good collection of fossils provides the geologist with much-needed information about the early history of our earth and the development of life throughout geologic time. In addition, many people are learning that the collection of fossils can be a most enjoyable, fascinating, and rewarding hobby. It is for these people that *Fossils* was written.

Designed primarily as an amateur collector's handbook, this book offers many suggestions and aids to those who would pursue the hobby of fossil-collecting. It will, moreover, provide the reader with a general background in earth history and acquaint him with the many types of plants and animals that inhabited the earth in prehistoric times. For the reader who wishes to know more about earth history and paleontology, there are selected, annotated references in the back of the book.

This publication should also prove helpful to students of paleontology and historical geology; certain sections of the book have been prepared with this group of readers in mind.

It would not be possible to list all of the people who contributed to the preparation and completion of *Fossils*. They include, however, Dr. H. E. Eveland, Dr. Russell Smith, Dr. Claude Boren, and Professor Charles Butler of Lamar State College of Technology, Dr. John A. Wilson, The University of Texas, and Dr. L. Frank Brown, Jr., Baylor University; also Dr. Peter U. Rodda, Miss Josephine Casey, and the late Dr. John T. Lonsdale of the Bureau of Economic Geology of The University of Texas. Each of the above read portions of the manuscript, offered criticisms and suggestions, or otherwise aided in the preparation of the manuscript.

The author is especially indebted to Dr. Peter T. Flawn, Director of the Bureau of Economic Geology, The University of Texas, for permission to use illustrations from *Texas Fossils, An Amateur*

Collector's Handbook and to Mrs. Sarah Louise Smith for her tireless and painstaking efforts in preparing the many drawings which illustrate the book. Certain of the charts were prepared by Mr. J. W. Macon of the Bureau of Economic Geology.

Photographs were furnished by Dr. W. W. Newcomb, Jr., Texas Memorial Museum; Drs. G. A. Cooper, C. L. Gazin, and Nicholas Hotton III, United States National Museum; Mr. J. H. Madsen, Geology Museum, University of Utah; Mr. E. Leland Webber, Chicago Natural History Museum; Dr. Irving G. Reimann, the Exhibit Museum, University of Michigan; Mr. E. T. Boardman, Rochester Museum of Arts and Sciences; Mr. M. V. Walker, Fort Hays Kansas State College Museum; Mr. Robert E. Logan and Mr. R. T. Bird, American Museum of Natural History; Mr. V. H. Cahalane, New York State Museum and Science Service; Mr. Fred T. Hall, Buffalo Museum of Science; Mr. Fred Amos and Mr. David Jensen, Ward's Natural Science Establishment; the Los Angeles County Museum; and the Hughes Tool Company.

The following publishers permitted the use of copyrighted quotations and/or illustrations, each of which is acknowledged at the appropriate place in the book: Harper and Bros.; John Wiley and Sons; W. H. Freeman and Company; McGraw-Hill Book Company; Spring Books Ltd., London; Dover Publications, Inc.; Ginn and Company; University of Chicago Press; The University of Texas; Harcourt, Brace, and World, Inc.; Illinois State Geological Survey; and Lamar State College of Technology Press.

Special thanks are due Miss Nancy Cone of the Barnes and Noble editorial staff for general guidance and invaluable help in the preparation of the manuscript. In addition, Dr. Samuel Smith, Editor-in-Chief, and Dr. Laurence Hawkins of the publisher's editorial staff provided valuable editorial assistance. I am especially grateful to Dr. Saul Aronow of the Lamar Tech Geology Department, who read much of the manuscript, offered numerous suggestions, and contributed greatly to the presentation of the material. The manuscript was typed by Miss Beth Crocker and Miss Annie Lee Tibbits, students at Lamar State College of Technology.

Finally, I would like to express deep gratitude to my wife, Jennie, and to my sons, Jim and Bill. Without their continued encouragement, patience, and understanding the story of *Fossils* might have never been told.

W. H. M. III

TABLE OF CONTENTS

FOSSILS

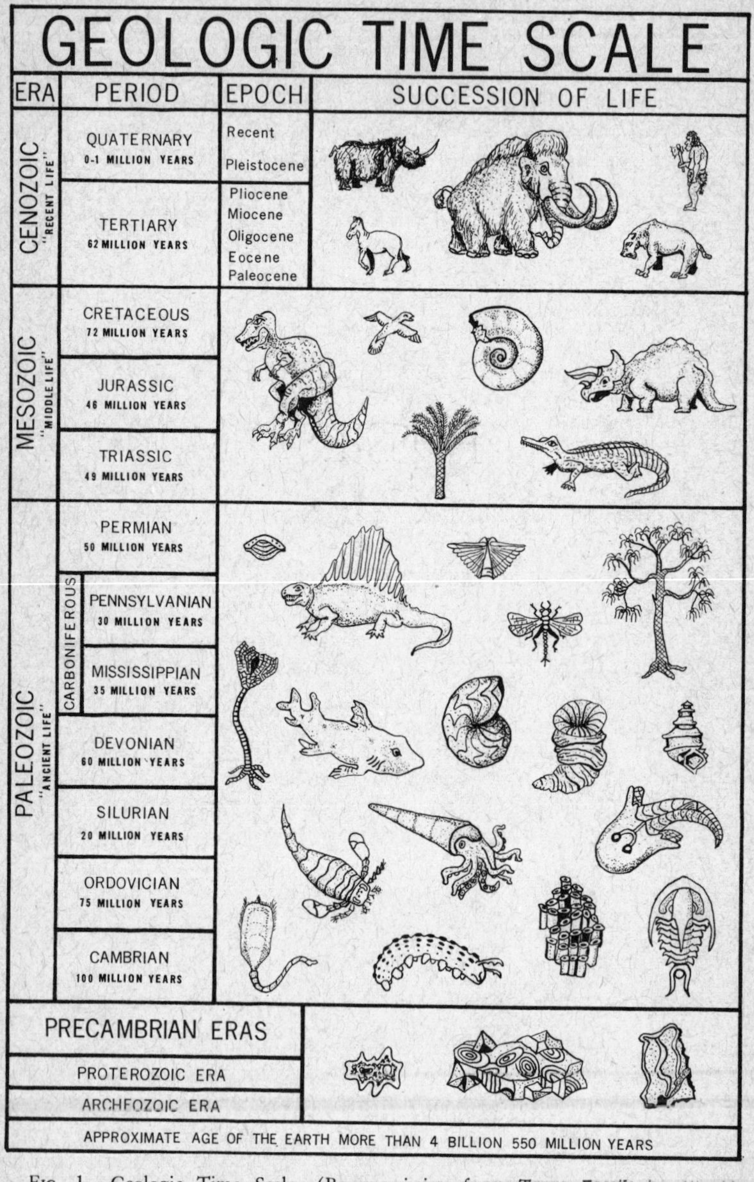

Fig. 1.—Geologic Time Scale. (By permission from *Texas Fossils* by W. H. Matthews III, Bureau of Economic Geology, University of Texas, Austin.)

Chapter I

AN INTRODUCTION TO FOSSILS AND FOSSIL-COLLECTING

Traces of ancient plant and animal life probably began to interest man at a very early time. Fossil shells, bones, and teeth have been found buried with the remains of primitive and prehistoric men. The collectors probably believed that these objects possessed supernatural powers such as healing properties or the ability to remove curses. Even today in some of the more primitive cultures, the tribal medicine men believe that fossils possess special healing powers and include them among the many strange articles to be found in their kits.

Within historic times the early Greek and Roman philosophers noted the occurrence of marine shells far from and high above the sea. As early as 500 B.C., one of these scholars reported the presence of fossil fish high above sea level and concluded that they were the forerunners of all life (see p. 144). While certain of these ancients recognized that fossils indicated the presence of former life, they were unable to explain how these remains had arrived there. A few came to the opinion that the sea had once covered the area in which they were found. During the Middle Ages fossils were variously explained as freaks of nature, remnants of attempts at special creation, or devices of the devil placed in the earth to lead men astray. (See Chapter XI for a detailed account of the way in which the modern science evolved from these early speculations.)

DEFINITIONS OF FOSSIL AND PALEONTOLOGY

Today we define a *fossil* as the remains or trace of any organism that lived prior to Recent time (see Geologic Time Scale, p. xii). The word *fossil* is derived from the Latin word *fossilis,* meaning "dug up," and for many years any object that was dug out of the ground was considered to be a "fossil." Consequently, many of the earlier books dealing with fossils discuss rocks, minerals, and other inorganic matter. By the late eighteenth century, however, this term had been reserved for objects indicating the presence of prehistoric organisms and giving some evidence of their size, shape, and habits.

The study of fossils is called *paleontology* (from the Greek *palaios,* ancient + *onta,* existing things + *logos,* word or discourse). The paleontologist attempts to decipher the history of life on earth by analyzing the remains of these ancient organisms and tracing their development through geologic time.

In working with and studying fossils the paleontologist uses many of the methods and principles of the biologist. He assumes that the plants and animals of the past lived under conditions similar to those of modern organisms. This idea has come to be known as the principle of *uniformitarianism,* which may be simply stated: "The present is the key to the past" (see p. 151). It is interesting to note that this fundamental geologic principle was formulated and proposed by a Scottish physician, James Hutton, who was attracted to geology through interests developed as an amateur collector of rocks, minerals, and fossils.

DIVISIONS OF PALEONTOLOGY

Some fossils represent the remains of extinct dinosaurs weighing as much as thirty-five tons and measuring as much as seventy feet. Others may be in the form of minute one-celled plants or animals or the shells of prehistoric clams or snails. With such a diversity of ancient organisms, it is only natural that the paleontologist has found it helpful to make certain divisions within his science. In this manner similar fossils may be studied together.

Paleobotany. Paleobotany is the study of fossil plants to obtain a record of the history of the plant kingdom. Most paleobotanical studies are approached from the viewpoint of botany; however, a geological background is also necessary.

One of the more recent practical applications of paleobotany has been in the field of *palynology,* the study of fossil spores and pollen. These microscopic plant elements are especially valuable to the petroleum geologist in his search for oil.

Many professional and amateur botanists are avid collectors of fossil plants and have added much to what is known about plant life of the past.

Paleozoology. The study of fossil animals is called *paleozoology.* The subdivisions of paleozoology (usually referred to by the general term *paleontology*) are invertebrate paleontology and vertebrate paleontology.

1. *Invertebrate paleontology* is the study of fossil animals without a spinal column, or backbone. These include such diverse organisms as protozoans (tiny one-celled animals), snails, corals, and starfishes. Since this is the type of fossil usually collected by the amateur, several chapters of this book are devoted to a discussion of invertebrate forms and of techniques for collecting them.

2. *Vertebrate paleontology* is the study of ancient animals possessing a backbone, or spinal column. They include such forms as fishes, reptiles, and mammals. Many amateur collectors are interested in collecting vertebrate remains, particularly bones and teeth. In fact, some important discoveries have been made by amateurs and reported to professional paleontologists on museum or university staffs who have then prepared and described the fossils. One such amateur find was made in 1811 by the twelve-year-old English girl Mary Anning. Mary's father was a cabinet-maker who supplemented his income by selling fossils and sea shells. It was on a shell- and fossil-collecting expedition that Mary made her first great fossil discovery: the petrified skeleton of a large swimming reptile that was later named *Ichthyosaurus* (see p. 261 and Fig. 155). Since no such animal had been described previously, this discovery created much excitement among scientists. In 1821 Mary Anning collected the remains of another great swimming reptile, *Plesiosaurus* (see p. 263 and Fig. 156). Seven years later, she discovered, for the first time in England, the skeleton of a *pterodactyl*—one of the large flying reptiles known as *pterosaurs* (see p. 267 and Fig. 160). Thus, although Mary Anning was not a scientist, she did much to advance scientific knowledge. Her vertebrate fossil discoveries are among the most important on record.

Another amateur fossil-collector who made significant fossil discoveries was the English surgeon Dr. Gideon A. Mantell. In 1812 he published *The Fossils of the South Downs; or, Illustrations of the Geology of Sussex.* In that year Dr. Mantell's wife discovered some unusual teeth embedded in the rocks at Sussex, England. These specimens were first identified as rhinoceros teeth, but this explanation did not satisfy Dr. Mantell. Later returning to the locality where the teeth had been found, he collected a number of bones which he studied in great detail; in 1825 he reported his conclusion that these teeth closely resembled a tooth of the living lizard *Iguana,* and so he named his fossil *Iguanadon*. Dr. Mantell later discovered many other vertebrate fossils and in 1827 published another important paleontological work.

Readers interested in collecting vertebrate fossils should note that vertebrate remains require special collecting and preparation techniques (discussed in Chapter VII).

From an economic viewpoint, the field of vertebrate paleontology is of rather limited use, but it has proved valuable in providing proof of organic evolution (see Chapter XI) and in the correlation of certain Tertiary and Quaternary strata (see Geologic Time Scale, p. xii).

Micropaleontology. *Micropaleontology* is the study of fossils that are so small that their distinguishing characteristics are best studied under the microscope. It is in this field that the science of paleontology attains its greatest practical application. Micropaleontology is used both in paleobotany with its study of one-celled plants, spores, and pollen and in paleozoology with its study of minute animals and animal fragments. These remains, like spores and pollen, are very small and may be brought to the surface intact and unharmed by the mechanics of drilling or coring.

Microfossils, like vertebrate fossils, require special collecting and mounting techniques and unfortunately are not usually collected by the amateur fossil enthusiast. These small fossils are very interesting, however, and have the advantage of presenting few storage problems to the collector. They may be studied in much the same manner as the micromounts of the mineral-collector. (Instructions for collecting, storing, and preparing this type of material are discussed in Chapter VII.)

A relatively young branch of paleontology, commercial micropaleontology is less than fifty years old, but today it is the most active branch of the science from the standpoint of industrial application and employment (see Chapter IV).

FOSSIL-COLLECTING AS A HOBBY

Amateur fossil-collectors are increasing in numbers each year as more people become acquainted with these relics of past life. Much of this growth has been associated with a tendency on the part of "rockhounds" (amateur mineral, rock, and gem collectors) to become increasingly interested in fossils. This is a perfectly natural development, as rock and mineral hobbyists often become fairly proficient in the sciences of mineralogy, petrology, and gemology; and it is only logical that they should desire to broaden the scope of their geologic interest to include paleontology. It is but a short step from the techniques and terminology of mineralogy to the field of paleontology and the fascinating game of unraveling the history of life upon the earth. Minerals and fossils are often found together in sedimentary rocks under the same conditions. Many of the methods of hunting, collecting, preparing, and labeling are common to minerals and the collection of both types of materials may be carried on simultaneously.

Earth-science hobbyists are drawn from all walks of life: they include students, housewives, and professional people of all ages. This hobby enables the collector to work outdoors and to become acquainted with the many wonders of the earth and to learn how they were formed. It affords equal opportunity for indoor activity, as many fine collections have been obtained by trading with other collectors or purchasing specimens from dealers.

As a result of this increased interest in fossils, a number of state geological surveys, museums, and universities have prepared publications dealing with the fossils of their respective states. Texas, Ohio, Illinois, Washington, Indiana, Missouri, and New York are among states which have made contributions of this sort. Several other states are planning such publications. These books help to provide the collector with basic paleontological knowledge, information on possible collecting localities, and reference material pertaining to those areas. (For a list of these and other helpful publications, see p. 309.)

The beginning collector can usually find ready help from many sources. Colleges and universities with geology departments have nontechnical books in their libraries, and the geology faculty members of these schools are usually happy to identify fossils brought to them. Most of the state museums and geological surveys also extend this courtesy to the amateur; many of them will allow him to compare his specimens with those in the institutional collections. These institutions usually have members on their staffs who are willing to give talks on fossils and fossil-collecting and to conduct field trips for rock and mineral clubs, nature-study groups, etc.

With the assistance, information, and encouragement that are available to most individuals and groups, the typical collector can soon become a competent amateur paleontologist, thereby participating in the pleasures of one of the world's most fascinating hobbies.

This book is designed to guide both the veteran "rockhound" and the person who is simply interested in learning something about fossils. Subsequent chapters will deal with such basic topics as how fossils are collected; the geologic time scale; a review of historical geology; a brief history of paleontology; a discussion of organic evolution; and the major divisions of the organic world.

CHAPTER II

HOW FOSSILS ARE FORMED AND PRESERVED

Many people have been attracted to fossil-collecting because of the great number and variety of specimens to be found. Yet, as numerous and diversified as the fossil record appears to be, it has been estimated that only one out of each thousand species of prehistoric organisms has been found (see Fig. 2).

What has happened to the myriads of plants and animals that have inhabited the earth in the many millions of years since life first appeared on our planet? Why are the shells of oysters, corals, and other marine animals found embedded in rocks hundreds of miles from the sea and thousands of feet above sea level? Why were these shell remains preserved while countless others were destroyed by the forces of nature? These are but a few of the many questions that must be answered in order to explain the process of fossilization.

THE REQUIREMENTS FOR FOSSILIZATION

We have already noted that the majority of organisms that lived in the past have left no record of their existence. Organisms normally become fossilized only under certain conditions favoring preservation. Numerous factors may determine whether these conditions are met, but only the three basic requirements will be discussed here.

Possession of Hard Parts. Forms containing hard parts are much more likely to become fossilized than are those lacking a skeleton. These hard body parts typically consist of bones, teeth, shell, chitin (see p. 161), or the woody tissue of plants. Under exceptionally favorable conditions, however, even the most delicate organisms may be preserved as impressions, carbon residues, or petrifactions.

Escape from Immediate Destruction. Out of the estimated million or more species of living animals, it is safe to assume that only a very small percentage will be preserved as fossils. The remains of most of these organisms will be destroyed by the work of the atmosphere, mechanical forces such as wave action or crushing, and biological agents such as predators, scavengers, and bacteria. Nevertheless, although the possibility that any given animal will leave a fossil record is quite small, the large number of animals involved results in an essentially adequate record of past life.

Group	Number of Species				Per Cent of Total Species in Grand Total
	Living	Extinct	Total	With Hard Parts	
Protozoa	27,000	9,000	36,000	29,000	3.2
Porifera	2,240	1,760	4,000	3,500	0.4
Coelenterata	9,500	4,500	14,000	10,700	1.2
Worms	36,000	1,000	37,000	10,000	3.3
Bryozoa	3,050	3,000	6,050	5,500	0.5
Brachiopoda	225	15,000	15,225	15,225	1.3
Mollusca	81,150	40,400	121,550	121,000	10.7
Gastropoda	*69,000*	*15,000*	*84,000*	*83,800*	*7.4*
Pelecypoda	*11,000*	*15,000*	*26,000*	*26,000*	*2.3*
Cephalopoda	*300*	*10,000*	*10,300*	*10,200*	*0.9*
Other	*850*	*400*	*1,250*	*1,000*	*0.1*
Arthropoda	804,898	16,400	821,298	821,298	72.5
Insecta	*746,298*	*12,000*	*758,298*	*758,298*	*66.9*
Other	*58,600*	*4,400*	*63,000*	*63,000*	*5.6*
Echinodermata	5,344	14,329	19,813	19,700	1.7
Crinoidea	*800*	*5,000*	*5,800*	*5,800*	*0.5*
Echinoidea	*867*	*7,200*	*8,067*	*8,067*	*0.8*
Stelleroidea	*3,700*	*479*	*4,179*	*4,179*	*0.3*
Other	*117*	*1,650*	*1,767*	*1,767*	*0.1*
Chordata	33,640	24,360	58,000	56,000	5.1
Grand totals	1,106,749 (1,105,000)	129,749 (130,000)	1,132,796 (1,135,000)	1,091,923 (1,090,000)	99.9

FIG. 2.—Composition of Animal Kingdom. Mostly from data by MacGinitie and MacGinitie, 1949; Mayr, Linsley, and Usinger, 1933; Shrock and Twenhofel, 1953, Muller and Campbell, 1954; Durham, 1954; Hyman, 1955. (By permission from *Invertebrate Paleontology* by W. H. Easton, Harper & Brothers, 1960.)

Rapid Burial in a Medium Capable of Retarding Decomposition. The type of protective material that the fossil is buried in usually depends upon the environment inhabited by the organism while it was living. Marine animals are more apt to be preserved, for they tend to accumulate on relatively shallow sea bottoms away from wave and tidal action and in association with the remains of other organisms of similar size and weight. These concentrations of shell material are then covered and enclosed by the soft marine sediments that will be the shales and limestones of the future. In general, the finer the sediment, the better are the chances that an organism will be preserved. In the famous Solnhofen quarries of Bavaria fine-grained marine limestones have kept fossils in a remarkable state of preservation. In addition to such rare forms as fossil jellyfishes and dragonflies, a large number of reptiles and the earliest known bird (see p. 121) have been collected from the sediments laid down in this ancient lagoon.

Organisms living on the land are not so likely to be preserved as are those from marine habitats. The remains of terrestrial faunas are usually found in lake, swamp, or wind-blown sand deposits. Land-dwelling animals that live in very dry regions may be preserved by *dessication* (extreme drying). Such remains are usually referred to as *natural mummies*. Many extinct insects and spiders have been described from specimens that are encased in fossil resin, or *amber* (see p. 12). These early insects were trapped in the sticky antiseptic resin exuding from coniferous trees that once occupied the Baltic region. The ancient forests are now buried beneath the Baltic Sea, but the amber is cast upon the beach by the waves.

Larger animals have been trapped in tar pits and oil seeps. One of the most famous localities of this type is at Rancho La Brea in Los Angeles (Fig. 3). Here an ancient oil seep, through loss of its volatile materials, has been transformed into a pool of asphalt. Many unwary prehistoric animals were trapped in the asphalt (Fig. 65) and their accumulated bones have been removed from the pit in large numbers and in an excellent state of preservation.

Volcanic ash, dust, and, in rare instances, lava may also serve as a protective medium in fossilization. The mineralized bones and teeth of an early rhinoceros have been found encased in *basalt* (a typical solidified lava); and the remains of many plants have been preserved after being buried by lava flows and falling ash.

The protective material producing the most remarkable preservation is ice or frozen soil. Animals living in periods of glacial cold were frozen and incorporated into ice or frozen ground. Their remains are found in such a remarkable state of preservation that even the flesh, hair, and contents of the stomach have been perfectly preserved (see p. 12).

Courtesy of Los Angeles County Museum

FIG. 3.—Typical excavation at Rancho La Brea tar pits (note well-preserved bones).

DEFICIENCIES IN THE FOSSIL RECORD

Though there have been untold numbers of organisms present on the face of the earth, only a minute fraction of them are available for study by the paleontologist. This fact is easily understood in view of the rigorous requirements of fossilization outlined above.

Even if the requirements for preservation have been met, there are other factors which might prevent fossils from being discovered. Many fossils have been destroyed by the processes of erosion, by being dissolved out of the enclosing rocks, or by having undergone recrystallization. Other fossils may have been preserved in rocks that have been subjected to violent physical changes, such as folding, fracturing, or melting. Under these circumstances a fossiliferous marine limestone may be changed into a marble, and any traces of organisms that were present in the original rock are either completely or almost completely obliterated. Much of the record is doubtless contained in fossiliferous deposits that are so deeply buried beneath the land or the sea that they are inaccessible for study. In addition, there must be some well-exposed fossiliferous rocks in portions of the world which have not been studied geologically. In other areas fossils may go undetected in some formations because of poor outcrops of the formation or the scarcity of specimens. Another problem frequently encountered is that we often find what appear to be organic remains, but the specimen is fragmentary or poorly preserved and does not adequately represent the organism.

It is only reasonable to assume that these gaps in the fossil record increase as we go backward into geologic time. Because of their great age, the older rocks have had more opportunity to be subjected to the various destructive forces that tend to obscure the paleontological record. The record of life in these rocks is further complicated by the fact that many of the earlier organisms are difficult to classify because they were so different from organisms living today.

THE DIFFERENT KINDS OF FOSSILS

The record of past life is found in many forms, each being somewhat dependent upon the original character of the organism, the type of material in which it was embedded, and the chemical action or forces which affected it after burial.

The beginning collector of fossils is often confused by the different ways in which plants and animals may become fossilized and by the various forms in which the fossil record occurs in the rocks. Once he learns these methods, however, they help him better to understand his specimens and their geological significance.

For convenience in classification, fossils are arranged into four major groups according to their method of preservation. These methods do not actually represent four distinct and separate kinds of fossil-making; rather, they generally work in combination, several frequently being involved in the preservation of any given fossil. The reader should again be reminded, however, that as broad as this classification appears to be, the sum total of the fossils known today represents only a small fraction of the plants and animals of the geologic past.

Original Soft Parts of Organisms. Usually only the hard parts of organisms are fossilized; the fossilization of unaltered soft parts takes place only under exceptionally favorable conditions. Organisms may be preserved intact in a medium that protects them from decay by bacterial action, thereby producing some rare and interesting fossilizations. Examples of such special media are frozen soil or ice, oil-saturated soil, and amber. As already mentioned, extreme aridity may produce natural mummies by the process of desiccation (see p. 9).

Probably the best-known examples of fossils preserved *in toto* (in their entirety) are frozen woolly mammoths of Siberia and Alaska. These huge mammals apparently succumbed to the extreme cold and were buried many thousands of years ago. The first such find was reported from the Lena River Delta, Siberia, in 1799. More than fifty additional discoveries have been made in Siberia since that time. The flesh of certain of these fossil elephants is so well preserved that it may be eaten by wild animals; the tusks are in such excellent condition that they have been much sought after by ivory traders. The Natural History Museum of Leningrad, Russia, has on display the mounted skins and skeletons of two specimens. The American Museum of Natural History in New York (Fig. 4) and the United States National Museum in Washington, D. C., have parts of the almost perfectly preserved remains of such mammoths.

The remains of an extinct rhinoceros have been obtained from waxy, oil-saturated soils in eastern Poland. This is a rather uncommon medium of preservation, but it has resulted in well-preserved skin and flesh.

In 1928 an unusual specimen of a ground sloth was found remarkably well preserved in an extinct volcanic crater in New Mexico. The skeleton of this Pleistocene (see Geologic Time Scale, p. xii) mammal is complete, the bones being held together by the original sinews and tendons. Portions of dried skin, as well as the claws, are well preserved. The desert atmosphere probably caused dehydration of the body before decomposition set in, and further desiccation resulted in a natural mummy. In rare instances dinosaurs have also been preserved as natural mummies (Fig. 5).

Another interesting and unusual method of preservation occurs in amber, or fossil resin. Prehistoric insects became trapped in the sticky gum and were enclosed in this transparent, antiseptic material. The resin hardened with the passing of time, leaving the insect undamaged and in a perfect state of preservation (Fig. 6). Spiders and insects thus trapped have been found with wings, hairs, legs, and muscle tissue so well preserved that they may be studied under the microscope. Even fossil spider silk has been preserved and studied in this manner. Preservations of this sort have been responsible for

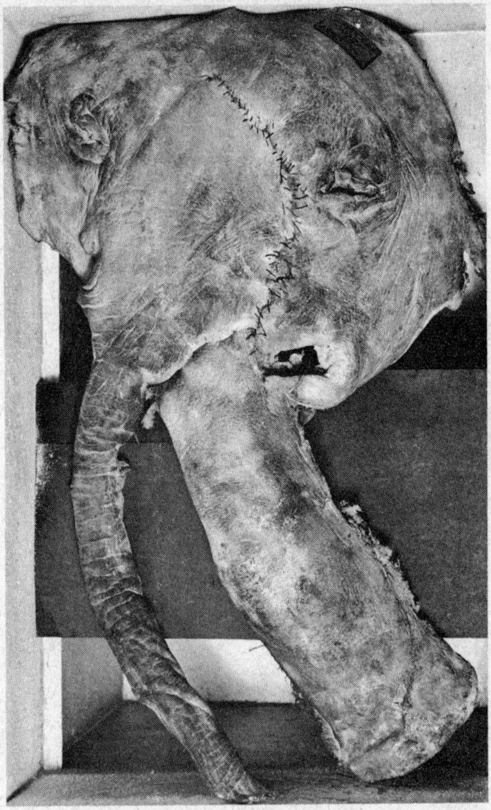

Courtesy of American Museum of Natural History

FIG. 4.—Trunk, head, and forelimb of well-preserved baby woolly mammoth dug out of frozen ground in Alaska.

much of our knowledge about extinct insects and spiders. Many of these insects embedded in amber have become so dehydrated and shrunken that only minute fragments of the original tissue remain. In this type of preservation a delicate but lifelike mold of the original insect is visible; if the amber is dissolved, almost no residue will be left.

While the preservation of unaltered soft parts of organisms may result in unusual and often spectacular fossils, the total number of such occurrences is quite small in comparison with the products of other methods of fossilization.

Original Hard Parts of Organism. Most plants and animals have some hard parts capable of fossilization. Many invertebrate animals possess protective coverings or supporting structures composed of common mineral substances. These may be in the form of the calcitic or aragonitic shells of mollusks, the phosphatic shells

Courtesy of American Museum of Natural History

FIG. 5.—A natural "mummy" of *Trachodon*, a Cretaceous duck-billed dinosaur. This unusual specimen shows that the duck-billed dinosaurs had skins of leathery texture and that there were webs between the toes of the front feet.

of brachiopods, or the chitinous exoskeletons of arthropods. The hard bones and teeth of vertebrates are commonly found in a virtually unaltered condition. Diatoms, single-celled aquatic plants possessing

Courtesy of Ward's Natural Science Establishment

FIG. 6.—Insect preserved in amber (fossil resin). From Oligocene deposits of the south Baltic coast.

siliceous skeletons, are preserved under all but the most adverse conditions.

CALCITIC REMAINS. The mineral calcite $CaCO_3$* is one of the more common constituents of the skeletal parts of invertebrates. The *tests* (shells) of echinoderms, many foraminifers, corals, bryozoans, brachiopods, and certain mollusks and crustaceans are composed of calcite. The calcitic hard parts of these organisms are frequently preserved in an unaltered state despite the loss of some or all of the unstable organic matter (Fig. 7).

ARAGONITIC REMAINS. The shells of most mollusks (gastropods, pelecypods, and cephalopods) are composed of aragonite, a relatively

* Richard M. Pearl, *Rocks and Minerals* (New York: Barnes and Noble, Inc., 1956), p. 210. The reader is referred to this excellent book for background material on the characteristics and composition of rocks and minerals.

unstable form of calcite ($CaCO_3$). Unaltered aragonitic shells are common in rocks of Cenozoic age (see Geologic Time Scale, p. xii), but they are relatively rare in older rocks because of the removal of aragonite by solution or by recrystallization to the more stable calcite.

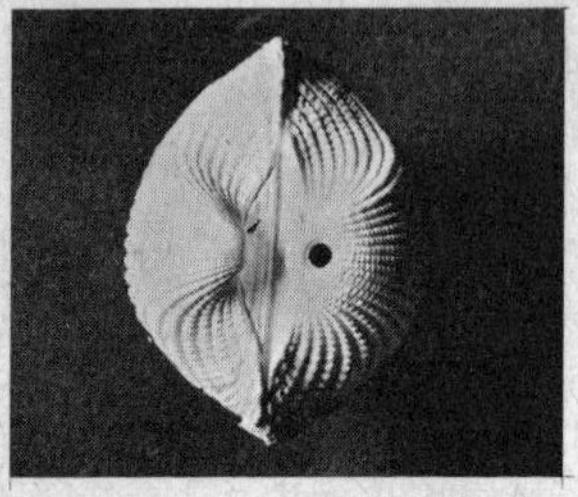

Fig. 7.—Boring made by a carnivorous gastropod on clam shell (about one half natural size).

Phosphatic Remains. The shells of many brachiopods, the exoskeletons of certain arthropods, all conodonts, and the bones of vertebrates contain large amounts of calcium phosphate [$Ca_3(PO_4)_2$]. Because of the unusually strong chemical resistance of this compound, it is found virtually unaltered in fossils of all ages.

Siliceous Remains. Many organisms have hard parts composed of silica or silicon dioxide (SiO_2). Siliceous skeltons are composed of hydrous silica, which upon dehydration may become chalcedony and may ultimately crystallize into quartz. Among the invertebrates such animals as certain sponges, radiolarians, and other protozoans possess siliceous skeletal parts. Hydrous silica is soluble in alkaline waters. In older specimens the siliceous skeletons may have been converted to more stable varieties of silica, such as chert. It is not uncommon to find original siliceous parts replaced by calcite, leaving a calcareous *pseudomorph* (a natural cast in which the replacing mineral is calcite).

Chitinous Remains. These are the remains of animals with an exoskeleton composed of a nitrogenous substance called *chitin,* a material similar in composition to our fingernails. The chitinous skins of certain animals have been preserved intact when buried immediately in an airtight medium. The chitinous exoskeletons of arthropods, graptolites, certain foraminifers, sponges, and hydrozoans are often preserved as carbon residues because of their chitinous composition and method of burial.

Altered Hard Parts of Organisms. The original hard structures of many organisms may undergo considerable alteration with the passing of long periods of time. These changes may come about in many different ways, depending upon the body materials of the organism, the environment in which the organism lived, and the conditions under which the remains of the organism deposited.

Carbonization or Distillation. As organic matter slowly decomposes under water or sediment, it gradually loses its organic constituents. During this process of *distillation* the oxygen, hydrogen, and nitrogen present in the original tissues are decreased to the extent that only a thin film of carbonaceous material remains. This *carbon residue* may retain many of the characteristics of the form of the original organism. Large numbers of plants, graptolites, arthropods, and fish (Fig. 8–7) have been preserved in this manner. Plants that have undergone this type of preservation are often referred to as *impressions* or *compressions* because of the compressive forces that brought about carbonization. Probably the best-known and most important carbonized remains are those of the Burgess Shale fauna of western Canada. This locality was discovered in 1910 by Charles D. Walcott, an American paleontologist. The fossils are found in a layer of black shale of Middle Cambrian age (see Geologic Time Scale, p. xii) on Mt. Wapta in British Columbia. Even the most delicate specimens are preserved in minute detail. Included in this fauna are such forms as sponges, jellyfish, arthropods, and annelid worms (see Fig. 9). Animals of this type are seldom found in a fossil state because of their lack of preservable hard parts and are especially rare in rocks as old as those described above. This important fossil discovery furnished paleontologists with much valuable information about early soft-bodied forms and provided important clues as to what types of life may have been present in the Precambrian.

Permineralization or Petrifaction. The hard parts of many organisms have been preserved by mineral-bearing solutions after burial in sediment. These solutions, usually in the form of percolating ground water, infiltrate porous bones and shells, depositing their mineral content in the pores and open spaces of the skeletal parts. Infiltration may take place (1) at the time of burial; (2) after burial, as a result of invasion of minerals from the surrounding rock; or (3) during the weathering of the enclosing formation. This process has been called *permineralization* or *petrifaction,* and a fossil produced in this manner is referred to as a *petrifaction,* as it has literally turned to stone. The addition of these minerals (which may be chemically similar or dissimilar to the substance being preserved) tends to make the original hard parts of the organism even harder

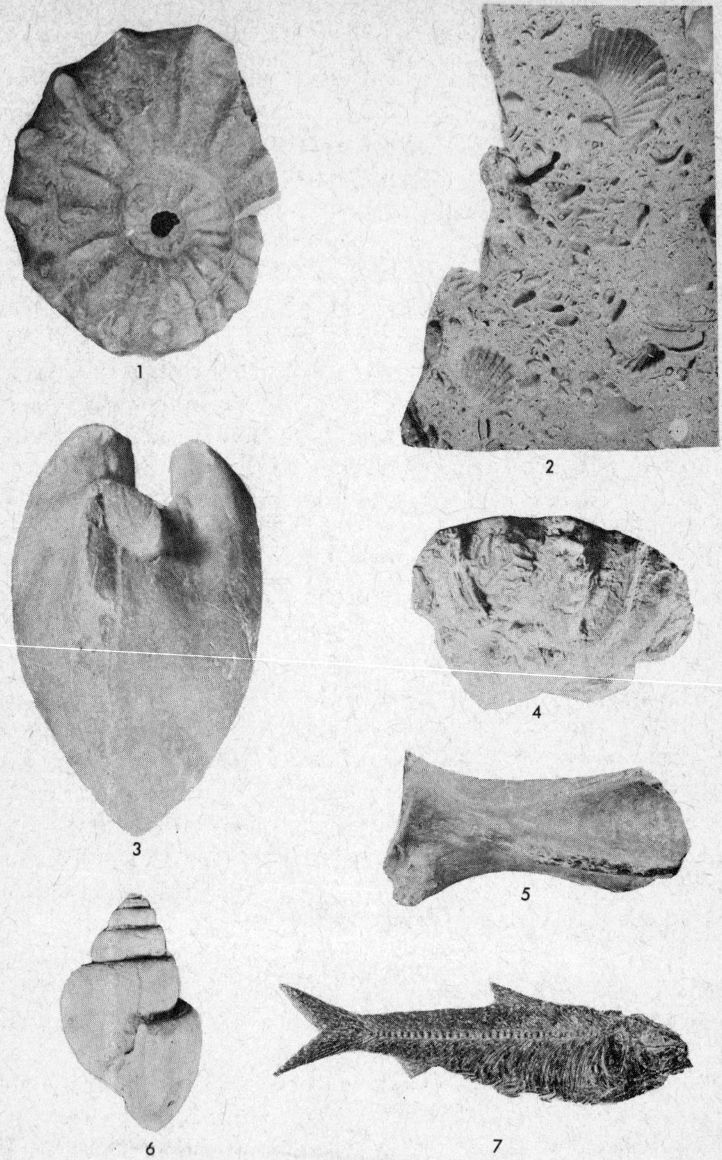

FIG. 8.—Types of fossil preservation. (*1*) Internal mold of ammonite. (*2*) Internal and external molds of gastropods and pelecypods in Cretaceous limestone. (*3*) Internal mold of pelecypod. (*4*) Fossil worm tubes attached to ammonite. (*5*) Petrified or permineralized bone of Tertiary age. (*6*) Steinkern of Cretaceous gastropod. (*7*) Carbon residue of Tertiary fish. (By permission from *Texas Fossils* by W. H. Matthews III, Bureau of Economic Geology, University of Texas, Austin.)

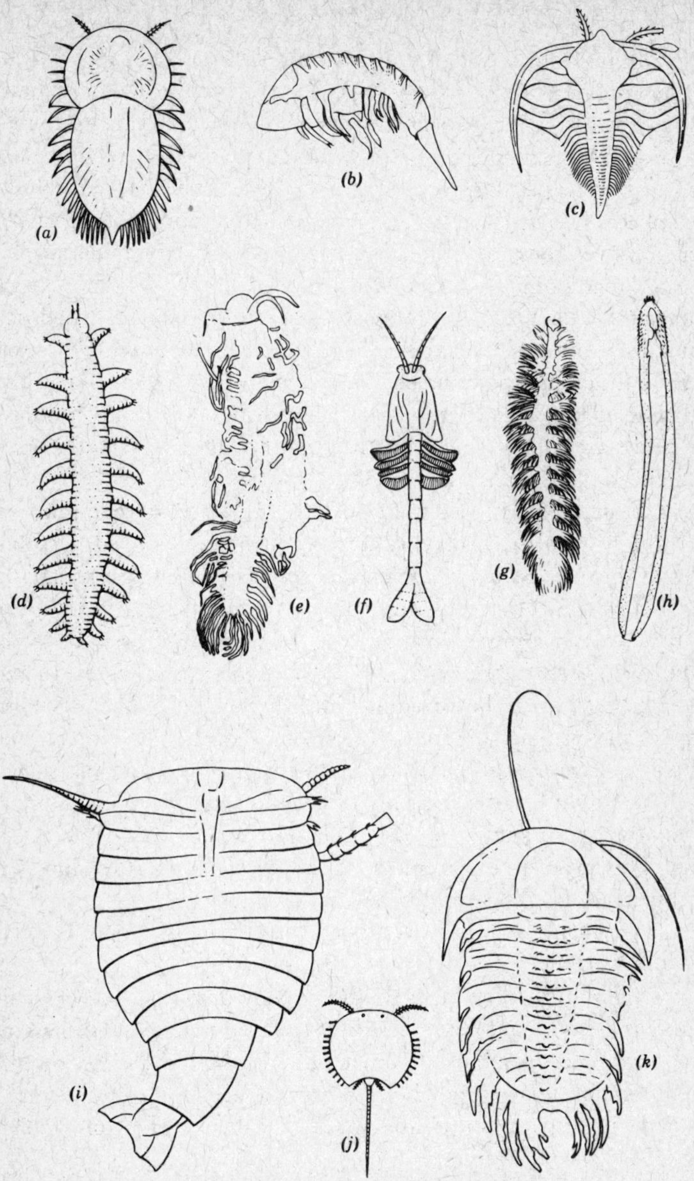

FIG. 9.—Fossils from the Burgess Shale, partly restored: (*a*), (*c*), (*f*), (*i*), (*j*), (*k*), trilobitelike; (*b*) eurypteridlike; (*d*) onychoporid; (*e*) holothurian; (*g*), (*h*) annelidlike worms. (Reprinted with permission from R. A. Stirton, *Time, Life, and Man*, copyright 1959, John Wiley & Sons, Inc.)

and more resistant to weathering or other destructive agents. Fossils that have undergone this type of preservation are true petrifactions and may be correctly referred to as "petrified wood," "petrified bone," etc. (Fig. 8–5). (Though it is a common practice to refer to any fossil as being "petrified" or "turned to stone," these terms should be applied only to remains that have been permineralized. Silica, calcite, and various iron compounds are the usual permineralizers, although many others are known.) Petrified wood is the most common example of this type of preservation. After a piece of wood has been buried by sediments, circulating ground waters tend to completely saturate its woody tissues. These waters fill all the pore spaces and some of the surrounding material with minerals, usually silica. The process results in increased weight and durability of the permineralized plant material.

Replacement or Mineralization. This type of preservation occurs when the original hard parts of an organism are removed by solution and this process is accompanied by almost simultaneous deposition of some other mineral substance in the resulting voids. As in the process of permineralization, the minerals are derived from ground waters that are saturated with the replacing mineral. In replacement, however, the invading minerals not only fill pores and voids in the original organic matter, but they totally replace the original structure. In some instances the original microscopic structure of the organism may be preserved, affording the paleontologist an opportunity to study the tissues of the plant or animal in great detail. This type of replacement must precede even the slightest decomposition of the remains; hence it is much more common in plants, in which the processes of decay set in much more slowly than in animals.

More than fifty minerals have been known to replace original organic material, and each of the replacing minerals discussed below may later become altered to other substances. The resulting alterations may produce changes of such magnitude that the original organic structure of the fossil may be completely obliterated.

Replacement by Calcite. In this type the hard parts of organisms are replaced by calcium carbonate ($CaCO_3$) in the form of calcite or aragonite. Alteration by *calcification* is common among the corals, brachiopods, echinoderms, and certain mollusks. The siliceous skeletal parts of animals (such as sponge spicules) may also be replaced by calcite.

Replacement by Dolomite. Here the original hard parts are replaced by dolomite [calcium magnesium carbonate, $CaMg(CO_3)_2$]. *Dolomitization* is particularly common in remains that were originally composed of calcite or aragonite. The calcareous exoskeletons of corals, brachiopods, and echinoderms, or the aragonitic shells of mollusks are often altered by the substitution of magnesium carbonate for some of the original calcium carbonate.

Replacement by Silica. When the original organic hard parts are replaced by silica (SiO_2), the process of alteration is referred to as *silicification.* This type of replacement may result from the filling of cavities and tissue with ground water saturated (or supersaturated) with silica or from the solution of the original hard parts and the deposition of silica in their place. The silica is frequently deposited around a central nucleus and deposited in concentric rings known as *beekite rings.* Siliceous replacement usually produces fine-grained quartz, chalcedony, or opal. This type of preservation may result in an almost perfect specimen. More frequently, however, silicification obliterates many details of the original structure.

Striking examples may be seen in the silicified Permian fauna (see Geologic Time Scale, p. xii) described by Dr. G. A. Cooper of the United States National Museum in Washington, D. C. Upon digestion in acid, large blocks of limestone from the Glass Mountains of western Texas have yielded an amazing variety of perfectly silicified brachiopods, crinoids, bryozoans, and mollusks. Due to the high degree of replacement, even the most delicate ornamental and morphological features are unchanged (Fig. 10).

Another interesting occurrence of silicification has recently been reported from ancient lake deposits on the Mojave Desert in California. Here limestone nodules have yielded perfectly preserved insects, spiders, and other arthropods, many of which are silicified. These fossils are so perfectly preserved that even the body appendages and hairs may be studied.

Replacement by Pyrite. Pyritization occurs when the original hard parts are replaced by pyrite (iron disulfide, FeS_2). This type of replacement is common in calcareous remains. The replacing mineral may be pyrite or marcasite, the latter becoming pyrite under certain conditions. The iron disulfide is probably formed from the sulfur of the decomposing organisms and the iron that is present in the sediments. The remains of many brachiopods, of crustaceans, and of some mollusks are found in a pyritized condition.

Courtesy of Dr. G. A. Cooper, U. S. National Museum

FIG. 10.—Silicified brachiopods. All specimens from Permian limestones of the Glass Mountains, Brewster County, Texas.

Replacement by Hematite. Less common than pyritization, *hematization* occurs when hard parts are replaced by hematite (iron oxide, Fe_2O_3), a common ore of iron. This type of replacement usually results from deposition of the iron around the fossil. The shells of bryozoans, brachiopods, trilobites, and crinoid fragments may be preserved in this manner. Certain of the older North American iron ores are known to be fossiliferous.

Replacement by Limonite. Limonite (brown hydrous iron oxide, $Fe_2O_3 \cdot nH_2O$) is also known as "bog iron ore" and is often found replacing plant material, a process called *limonitization.*

Replacement by Glauconite. Glauconitization is common in certain formations containing large amounts of glauconite (a complex hydrous potassium iron silicate). The tests of many foraminifers and occasionally the shells of mollusks are found replaced by glauconite.

Traces of Organisms. In addition to the actual remains of organisms, certain traces of former plants and animals are also considered to be fossils. In this type of preservation none of the original organic material and no replacement of it remains, but a trace or impression of the organisms provides evidence as to the structure of the plant or animal responsible for it. The more common types of evidence will be discussed here.

Molds and Casts. A *mold* is the impression of an organism or an organic structure (bone, shell, teeth, etc.) in the surrounding material. If the shell of an animal was pressed down into the sediment before it hardened into rock, it may have left an *impression* of the outside of the shell which would be known as an *external mold.* This type of mold reflects the *morphology* (form or shape) and characteristics of the outer surface of the original organic remains (see Fig. 8–2). An *internal mold* (Fig. 8–*1*) represents the morphology and characteristics of the inner surface of the original organic remains. Internal molds, frequently referred to as *steinkerns* (stone-kernel) or *cores* are produced in nature when the shell of an animal becomes filled with sediment and the shell material is later removed by solution or erosion (Fig. 8–*6*). This leaves behind the hardened sediment to reflect the internal structures of the animal.

Artificial external molds may be produced by pressing the outside of a shell or other object, into soft plaster of Paris and allowing the plaster to harden. When the shell is removed the external impression will be left in the hardened plaster. An artificial core can be made by filling a shell with plaster of Paris and allowing the plaster to harden inside the shell. When the hardened plaster is removed, it will reflect the features of the interior of the shell. (Detailed instructions for preparing molds and casts are discussed in Chapter VII.)

A *cast* is the positive representation of organic remains that is derived from various types of molds. It results when any substance, mineral or artificial, fills the mold formed by solution of the original hard parts. A *natural cast* occurs when a natural mold is filled under natural conditions while still embedded in the surrounding rocks. An *artificial cast* or *replica* is produced when the mold is filled with a substance such as liquid rubber, plaster of Paris, or wax.

The formation of molds and casts has resulted in the preservation of numerous fossils, and specimens of this type make up a large part of many collections. This manner of preservation is particularly characteristic of fossil clams and snails because their aragonitic shells are easily dissolved.

External impressions showing the skins of dinosaurs have been made when the animal died and the body settled into soft sediments (Fig. 59). Decomposition of the skin leaves hollow spaces which may become filled with fine-grained sediments such as sand. Upon hardening, the sandstone produces a surface which shows in minute detail the characteristics of the reptilian skin.

Vertebrate paleontologists frequently use casting techniques in their studies. They can sometimes learn more from a good cast of a fossil bone than they can from the poorly preserved original. Casts of brain cavities have also been useful in certain vertebrate studies.

Under special conditions, such as those of the fine-grained Solnhofen limestones mentioned previously (see p. 9), impressions of jellyfishes and of other soft-bodied organisms may be formed.

TRACKS AND TRAILS. Both vertebrate and invertebrate animals have left records of their movements over dry land or sea bottom; these often provide valuable information for the paleontologist.

Tracks are footprints made by animals as they walk over the substratum (see Fig. 11). These tracks are more likely to be preserved in arid and semiarid areas, where the footprints are not apt to be destroyed by rain before being buried. As bones and footprints usually do not occur together, identification or description of the animal making the tracks may be difficult. Footprints occurring in a series, however, may indicate not only the size and shape of the foot but length of the limbs, posture, and type of gait.

The Triassic (see Geologic Time Scale, p. xii) rocks of the Connecticut Valley contain large numbers of reptile tracks. These tracks not only provide information about the animals that made them but also give some evidence of the climatic conditions and the environment in which they were made.

Trails are impressions made by the bodies, tails, or other appendages of organisms as they crawl over the substratum. The trails made on or just below the surface of soft sediments may become filled

FIG. 11.—Dinosaur tracks in Cretaceous limestone in bed of Paluxy Creek, near Glen Rose, Texas. (Photograph courtesy of the American Museum of Natural History. Permission to reproduce by R. T. Bird.)

with finer sediments and may later be recovered as fossils. The fossil trails of mollusks, worms, sea urchins, crabs, etc., have been found in many sedimentary rocks (Figs. 12 and 38). Irregular markings believed to have been made by the tentacles of jellyfishes or the leaves of floating plants have also been found.

Burrows and Borings. These types of holes have furnished useful information about numerous organisms.

Tubes or holes in the ground, in wood, in rock, or in some other substance which have been made by an animal for shelter or in search

Fig. 12.—Tracks of Pennsylvanian invertebrates as preserved in sandstone from West Texas.

of food are referred to as *burrows*. These tubes may later become filled with fine sediments and preserved. On rare occasions the remains of the animal making the burrow have been found in the sediments filling the tubes.

Burrows are made on soft sea bottoms by worms, arthropods, mollusks, and other animals. The fossil burrows or borings of such species of mollusks as *Teredo,* a wood-boring clam, and *Lithodomus,* a rock-boring clam, are also frequently found.

Structures believed to be worm burrows are among the oldest known fossils, and many of the most ancient sandstones contain large numbers of tubes which are regarded as worm burrows.

Borings are holes made by animals on other organisms for the sake of food, attachment, or possibly shelter. Such holes frequently occur on fossil shells, wood, and other organic objects, and are considered to be fossils.

Carnivorous boring snails drill through the shells of other mollusks in order to reach the soft parts of the animal. The neatly countersunk holes bored by similar fossil snails are common on many ancient mollusk shells (see Fig. 7).

The boring sponge *Cliona* is frequently found, today, attached to shells. Similar holes left by fossil boring sponges are present on many fossil oyster shells.

COPROLITES. *Coprolites* (Greek *kopros*, dung + *ites,* having to do with) are fossil fecal pellets, or castings, of animals. This fossil excrement is usually nodular, tubular, or pelletlike in shape and phosphatic in chemical composition (see Fig. 13). Coprolites are frequently found in association with the animals that made them,

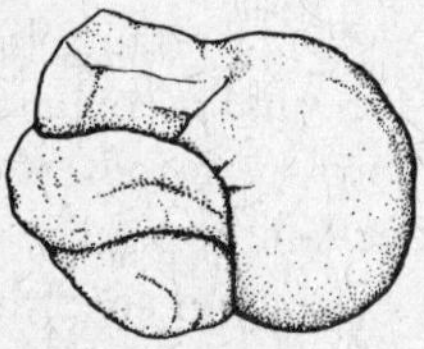

FIG. 13.—Sketch of a coprolite—fossilized animal excrement (about natural size).

FIG. 14.—Sketch of a gastrolith—the "gizzard stone" of an ancient reptile (about natural size).

and a study of the fossil excreta may provide valuable information pertaining to the food habits and anatomical structure of these organisms.

Many fossil worms have left castings similar to those of today's earthworms. These consist of soil particles which have passed through the worm's intestinal tract and have been excreted as small masses of molded sediment.

The coprolites of marine reptiles have been found to contain the remains of fossil squids, fish scales, and bones. The external markings of many coprolites, such as grooves and spirals, give evidence of unusual characteristics of the alimentary tract of the animal making them.

GASTROLITHS. *Gastroliths* (Greek *gastros,* stomach + *lithos,* stone) are highly polished, rounded stones believed to have been of aid in grinding the stomach contents of extinct reptiles (see Fig. 14).

Gastroliths are found in abundance in the body cavities of certain reptiles. They almost invariably accompany the remains of plesiosaurs (extinct long-necked, small-headed swimming reptiles). The remains of one large plesiosaur contained half a bushel of these stones, the largest of which was four inches in diameter.

The collector purchasing gastroliths should make certain that he obtains them from reliable dealers, as many so-called "stomach stones" are merely polished rocks.

Pseudofossils. Many objects of inorganic origin closely resemble forms of organic origin. These false fossils are often found in sedimentary and metamorphic rocks. A few of the more common pseudofossils are listed here in order that the amateur collector may be better able to distinguish such inorganic objects from those that are organic in origin.

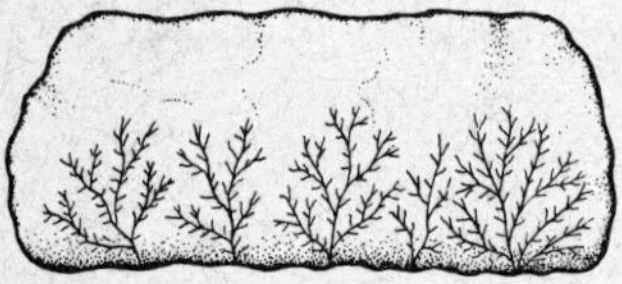

FIG. 15.—Dendrites. These thin branching mineral deposits bear a marked resemblance to plants, hence they are called pseudofossils (about one half natural size).(Reprinted by permission from *Texas Fossils* by W. H. Matthews III, Bureau of Economic Geology, University of Texas, Austin.)

1. *Dendrites.* Certain limestones bear, on the surface, branching patterns which superficially resemble a fern or some other plant form. These mineral incrustations are produced on or in a rock by such minerals as manganese dioxide (MnO_2) or pyrite (see Fig. 15). Dendrites are usually rather small in comparison to most ferns, and are sometimes also found in igneous rocks which normally would not have fossils in them.

2. *Slickensides.* These are vertical striations, produced by rock surfaces as they move against each other after having been fractured. They bear superficial resemblance to some of the ancient coal-forming plants. But since slickensides are commonly at an angle to the surface of the rock layers whereas plant remains lie parallel to the bedding plane, the two are usually easily distinguished.

3. *Concretions.* Many sandstones, marls, and shales contain hardened masses of mineral substances which are commonly mistaken for fossils. Under unusual conditions of weathering, these have been sculptured into shapes resembling plants or animals. Careful inspection will reveal the absence of organic structures.

4. *Weathering Phenomena.* Rocks undergoing differential erosion

due to unevenly distributed constituents such as flint may weather into patterns which resemble algae, sponges, etc. However, close examination of concretions and weathering phenomena will usually reveal the absence of any organic structures that would relate them to true fossils.

Chapter III

HOW OLD ARE FOSSILS?—AN EXPLANATION OF GEOLOGIC TIME

The preceding discussion has indicated that all fossils are "old," but that some are much older than others. Statements are commonly made that fossils are "ancient," "prehistoric," or "more than 20,000 years old," or "lived prior to recent time." Before continuing our discussion of these ancient organic remains it will be helpful to learn something about geologic time and to look at some of the methods used to date the rocks that contain fossils.

THE GEOLOGIC TIME SCALE

The study of fossils is actually a subdivision of *historical geology* —the history of the earth and its inhabitants as it is recorded in the rocks of the earth's crust.* The earth historian, like the historian dealing with the development of civilization, must have some method of relating important events to each other. For this purpose the geologist has developed a special *time scale* (see Fig. 1) consisting of large and small units of geologic time. These time units, or divisions of geologic time, are arranged on the time scale in the order of their age. Thus, the geologist may speak of an animal that lived during the Paleozoic era in much the same manner that a historian might speak of a general who served during the Civil War. Each of these time terms gives us an idea as to when the animal lived or the general served, but in terms of *relative time* rather than *absolute time.*

In constructing this time scale and naming its units, geologists developed another subdivision of historical geology, namely, *stratigraphy.* Stratigraphy is concerned with the composition, arrange-

* Richard M. Pearl, *Geology* (New York: Barnes and Noble, Inc., 3rd ed., 1963), p. 165. This comprehensive College Outline will further acquaint the reader with the various phases of geology.

ment, and correlation (or "matching up") of the rock layers of the earth's crust. The arrangement of these layers in an orderly sequence is based upon the *law of superposition*. This law states that *in a normal sequence of beds, younger rocks are always found on top of older rocks,* since that was the original order of their deposition. What this means, of course, is that in order to read earth history from its beginning we must read from the *bottom* of the scale upward. Just as history books start with the earliest known historical events, the earliest known geologic events are in the earliest "chapters" of earth history. These first "chapters" are located at the bottom of the time scale.

Another difficulty, for the beginner, of the geologic time scale is the odd and unusual names that have been given these time units. Why not use simple English words that would be easy to spell and pronounce? The answer is to be found in the words themselves. In looking at the terms, we find that many of them have been derived from Greek and Latin words. There are two reasons for this: first, ancient Greek and Latin are both "dead" languages and hence are not subject to change as a modern language would be; second, they are international languages and mean much the same thing to geologists all over the world. Therefore, in order to understand and use geologic and paleontologic terminology, it is most helpful to learn certain Greek stems, prefixes, and suffixes. For example, if we look up the meaning of the word *Paleozoic,* we find that it is derived from the Greek words *palaios* meaning "ancient" and *zoikos,* pertaining to life (*zoe*). This is the geologist's way of saying that the Paleozoic era was the time of ancient life. He expresses all of this in a single word that can be understood all over the world! Pronunciation? Simply break it into syllables: Pay′-lee-o-zo″ik.*

Later in this chapter we shall consider the rest of the terms in the time scale, but first we shall explain how the scale is divided and indicate the relative importance of each of the divisions.

Divisions of the Geologic Column and Geologic Time Scale. When the geologist speaks of the *geologic column* he means the total succession of rocks, from the oldest to the most recent, that are found in the entire earth or in a given area. Thus, the geologic column of Texas, California, or New York consists of all rock divisions known to be present in those states. By referring to

* The principal accent is indicated by double accent marks (″), and the secondary accent by a single mark (′).

the geologic column previously worked out for a given area, the geologist can determine what type of rocks he might expect to find there.

The *geologic time scale* is composed of named intervals of geologic time, during which similarly named groups of rocks were deposited in the geologic column. As noted earlier, these *time units* are used to refer to events that have taken place in the geologic past. Unlike years, however, geologic time units are arbitrary and of unequal duration; the geologist cannot be positive about the exact amount of time involved in each unit. The time scale does, however, provide a standard by which he can discuss the age of the rocks and the fossils they contain.

ERAS. The largest units of geologic time are called *eras* (see Fig. 16). These immense units of time are marked by large physical breaks in the geologic record. Such breaks may be caused by extensive uplifts of the land and periods of mountain-building disturbances. In addition to the physical changes in the record, there is also much evidence of great changes in the plant and animal life from one era to another.

There are five great eras, each of which has been given a name descriptive of the stage of development of the life of that time—for example, Paleozoic ("ancient life"), because the most common animals of that time were primitive invertebrates. Since an era may extend over several hundred million years, the boundary lines of the eras are necessarily somewhat vague.

The five geologic eras and the pronunciation and meaning of their names are:

Cenozoic (see′-no-zo″-ik)—"recent life"
Mesozoic (mess′-o-zo″-ik)—"middle life"
Paleozoic (pay′-lee-o-zo″-ik)—"ancient life"
Proterozoic (prot′-er-o-zo″-ik)—"fore life"
Archeozoic (ar′-kee-o-zo″-ik)—"beginning life"

Archeozoic and Proterozoic rocks are commonly grouped together and referred to as *Precambrian* in age. Since the Precambrian rocks have been greatly contorted and altered, the record of this time is most difficult to interpret. Precambrian time is that part of geologic time from the beginning of earth history until the deposition of the earliest fossiliferous Cambrian strata. If the earth is as old as is believed, it may represent as much as 85 per cent of all geologic time. (This portion of geologic time has also been referred to as the

Azoic (ay′-zo″-ik)—"without life," a term which has fallen into disuse in the United States.)

Periods and Systems. Each of the eras has been subdivided into smaller units of time called *periods.* The rocks deposited during a period are known as a *system.* The period is, then, a *time unit,* whereas the system is a *time-rock unit*—a unit of rock deposited during a certain period of geologic time (see Fig. 16). Hence, we may refer to the Pennsylvanian period (of time) and the Pennsylvanian system (the rocks that were deposited during that period). The names of most of the periods and systems have been derived from the names of the areas in which the rocks were first studied and described. Thus, the Pennsylvanian period is named for the state of Pennsylvania, where there are many exposures of rocks of this system. It should be noted that although these names were derived from specific localities, rocks of similar age may occur in many parts of the world.

Time Units	*Time-Rock Units*
Era	Erathem
Period	System
Epoch	Series
Age	Stage

Rock Units
Group
Formation
Member
Bed, etc.

Fig. 16.—The above chart indicates the relationship between time and time-rock units. Rock units are placed below these, as they do not, in any way, correspond to the upper units.

The Paleozoic has been divided into seven periods of geologic time, each with its corresponding system of rocks. With the oldest at the bottom of the list, these periods, the origin of their names, and a guide to their pronunciation are listed below:

Permian (pur″-mee-un)—for the province of Perm in the Ural Mountains of Russia

Pennsylvanian (pen′-sil-vain″-yun)—for the State of Pennsylvania

Mississippian (miss′-i-sip″-i-un)—for the Upper Mississippi Valley

Devonian (dee′-vo″-nee-un)—for Devonshire, England

Silurian (si-lu″-ri-un)—for the Silures, an ancient tribe of Wales

Ordovician (or′-doe-vish″-un)—for an ancient Celtic tribe which lived near the type locality in Wales

Cambrian (kam″-bri-un)—from the Latin word *Cambria,* meaning Wales

The term *Carboniferous* is used by European geologists to designate a geologic period which is equivalent to the Mississippian and Pennsylvanian periods of North America. Although this classification is no longer used in the United States, the Carboniferous period is referred to in many of our earlier geological publications and on many of the earlier geologic maps.

The periods of the Mesozoic and the source of their names are:

Cretaceous (kree-tay″-shus)—from the Latin word *creta,* meaning "chalk"; refers to chalky limestones such as those exposed in the White Cliffs of Dover on the English Channel

Jurassic (joo-rass″-ik)—for the Jura Mountains between France and Switzerland

Triassic (try-ass″-ik)—from the Latin word *trias,* meaning "three"; refers to the natural threefold division of these rocks in Germany

The Cenozoic periods have derived their names from an old outdated system of classification which divided all of the earth's rocks into four groups. The two divisions listed below are the only names from this system which are still in use:

Quaternary (kwah-tur″-nuh-ri)—implying "fourth derivation"

Tertiary (tur″-shi′-ri)—implying "third derivation"

Each of the geologic systems is characterized by the types of plants and animals living during that time. For example, the Tertiary system is characterized by a large number of modern organisms. In addition to typical life forms, the system may also be marked by recognizable breaks between it and adjoining systems.

Epochs or Series. Periods are divided into smaller units called *epochs,* while the rocks deposited during an epoch are referred to as a *series*. Epochs or series usually represent the upper, middle, and lower parts of a period or system.

The only epochs and series that will be referred to in this book are the five subdivisions of the Tertiary period and the two of the Quaternary period. Listed below are these epochs, a guide to their pronunciation, and an explanation of their names. The two epochs at the top of the list are in the Quaternary.

Recent—the latest time division; the geologic present
Pleistocene (plice″-toe-seen)—"most recent"
Pliocene (ply″-o-seen)—"more recent"
Miocene (my″-o-seen)—"less recent"
Oligocene (oll″-i-go′-seen)—"little recent"
Eocene (ee″-o-seen)—"dawn of recent"
Paleocene (pay″-lee-o-seen)—"ancient recent"

The above epochs are based on the relationships between the life forms of those times and the present forms of life.

Epochs and series may be further divided into smaller units called *ages* and *stages,* but these need not concern us in this book.

ROCK UNITS. There are certain other units of the geologic column which are based on the physical and chemical characteristics of rocks and not on geologic time. The basic rock unit is the *formation,* which may be defined as a recognizable unit of similar rocks useful for mapping (see Fig. 16). The names of formations are commonly derived from geographic names of places where they were first described, combined with the names of the predominant rock that makes up the bulk of the formation; for example, Beaumont clay, Oriskany sandstone, St. Louis limestone. If, however, the formation is composed of varied types of rocks (such as alternating sands, clays, and limestones) it is referred to as the San Joaquin formation, etc.

Formations may be subdivided into *members,* which may also be given geographic and/or lithologic (rock type) names. Other smaller units are *lentils* (smaller lens-shaped rock bodies within the formation), *tongues* (interfingering or intertonguing bodies of different lithology), and *beds* (individual rock layers).

If several formations have certain definite characteristics in common, they may be spoken of as a *group*. The group is the largest rock unit that is recognized.

Gaps in the Geologic Column. As might be suspected, a record involving such an immensity of time cannot be complete. At many points in the geologic column there are missing "pages" in earth history, and where these occur the geologist must attempt to reconstruct them. Such a break in the continuity of the geologic record is called an *unconformity*. Unconformities may be the result of certain rocks being removed by erosion before later sediments were deposited. Or there may have been no deposition at all during a certain interval of geologic time. Unconformities, then, represent surfaces of erosion or nondeposition which indicate interruptions or gaps in the normal sequence of geological events. These breaks may vary in magnitude from a relatively minor interruption in sedimentation to the complete absence of an entire geologic system.

HOW GEOLOGIC TIME IS MEASURED

The age of the earth has been estimated by several different methods. Some of these, such as computing the salinity of the sea or the rate of erosion, only serve to indicate that our planet is very, very old. On the other hand, the so-called "radioactive clock" can give us rather accurate age determinations based upon the rate of disintegration of certain radioactive minerals. The oldest rocks yet tested by the latter method indicate that the earth is between three and five billion years old.

Salt Content of the Sea. It is believed by many geologists that the oceans were originally composed of fresh water and that the salt was dissolved from the soil and carried to the sea by streams. The conversion of such large bodies of fresh water to salt water must, of course, have taken a long period of time. Age estimates based on this method indicate that it must have taken approximately one hundred million years for the oceans to reach their present degree of salinity.

This method cannot be used with any degree of accuracy because (1) much of the salt has been subjected to several cycles of deposition; (2) much of the original salt is in water locked deeply in buried marine sedimentary rocks; and (3) the age of the oceans is necessarily less than the age of the earth.

Rate of Deposition of Sediments. This method assumes that if the rate of deposition of sediments is known, the total thickness of these sediments will give some indication as to the age of the earth. Estimates derived by this method range from one hundred to six hundred million years.

There are three major disadvantages to this type of estimate: (1) different types of sediments accumulate at different rates; (2) typical rates of deposition for different rock types are not known with any accuracy; and (3) no allowance is made for rocks that were not deposited or that were deposited and were later removed by erosion.

Rate of Erosion. This method, based on attempts to determine how long ago erosion began on the earth, is the reverse of the sedimentation method discussed above. The main procedure is to determine the number of years required to erode one foot of rock from the earth. The estimated number of years divided into the number of feet calculated to have been removed in the past will give some idea as to how long the earth's surface has been subjected to erosion. Although this estimate can provide no accurate indication of the earth's age, it does indicate that the earth is extremely old.

The principal disadvantages of this method are: (1) there is no way of knowing the total amount of sedimentary rock in the earth's crust; (2) much of the sediment derived from sedimentary rocks has been eroded and redeposited many times; and (3) the present rate of erosion is not necessarily the average rate of erosion for all geologic time.

Disintegration of Radioactive Minerals. In the application of this method, rocks containing radioactive minerals are used. These radioactive minerals, such as uranium or thorium, have large unstable atoms which undergo slow, spontaneous disintegration. The rate of disintegration, or "decay," is not affected by changes in temperature, pressure, or chemical conditions. As the mineral disintegrates, helium is released and a series of new elements is formed, the last of which is lead. Using a mathematical formula whereby the ratio between the radioactive lead and the remaining amount of uranium can be calculated, it is possible to determine the age of the radioactive mineral. The oldest rock definitely dated by this means is one from the St. Peter and St. Paul rocks about 700 miles northeast of Brazil which indicates an age of 4,550 million years.

While this method is the most accurate yet developed, it is, of course, limited to those rocks containing radioactive minerals. These rocks are usually difficult to correlate with fossil-bearing sedimentary rocks, and the latter must therefore be dated indirectly.

The radioactive minerals mentioned above are useful in dating the more ancient rocks, but they disintegrate so slowly as to be useless in dating younger deposits. The discovery of *radiocarbon dating* by the Carbon-14 method (C^{14}) has provided scientists with a valuable means of obtaining relatively precise measurements of rocks less than thirty to forty thousand years old.

Radiocarbon dating is based on the discovery that all organisms contain a constant amount of Carbon-14, a radioactive isotope. However, when an organism dies radiocarbon is gradually lost, and the disintegration of this radioactive carbon proceeds at a known rate. This rate is such that one-half of the radioactive material has decayed at the end of about 5,568 years. In using this method the amount of Carbon-14 remaining in the sample is measured, and the approximate age of the specimen is ascertained by comparing the ratio of radioactive carbon remaining in the specimen to the amount present in most living things.

This method was discovered by Dr. W. F. Libby, who was awarded the Nobel prize in chemistry for his outstanding work in this field. The radiocarbon technique has been of particular value in dating archaeological objects, as well as wood, bone, or shells of less than forty thousand years in age.

The following quotation will help us to appreciate the enormous amount of time involved in the history of the earth.

> If we imagine the whole of earth's history compressed into a single year, then on this scale, the first eight months would be completely without life. The following two months would be devoted to the most primitive creatures ranging from viruses and single-celled bacteria to jellyfish, while mammals would not have appeared until the second week in December. Man, as we know him, would have strutted onto the stage at about 11:45 p.m. on December 31. The age of written history would have occupied little more than the last sixty seconds on the clock.*

* Richard Carrington, *The Story of Our Earth* (Harper & Brothers, 1956), pp. 47–48. Reprinted by permission of the publisher.

CHAPTER IV

HOW FOSSILS ARE USED

Fossils are useful in a number of ways. It has been mentioned that prehistoric man utilized fossils in an attempt to ward off evil spirits, also that the medicine men of certain primitive cultures of today use fossils in the belief that they possess some mysterious power of healing. The scientist, however, uses these ancient remains in order to recreate the geologic history of the earth. Fossils are also of practical use in a number of modern industries.

Perhaps the chief importance of fossils is in the tracing of the development of plants and animals. The fossils in the older rocks are primitive and relatively simple, but similar specimens that lived in later geologic time are more complex and more advanced. Every fossil provides some information about when it lived, where it lived, and how it lived.

J. W. Powell, the second Director of the United States Geological Survey, had this to say about the importance of paleontology:

> Paleontology, the science of fossils, is the geologist's clock by which he determines the times in earth history when the beds containing the fossils were deposited. Geological time is divided into periods which are characterized by the existence of certain plants and animals. Without paleontology the geologic classification of formations, their correlation, and the determination of their mutual relations would be impossible. In fact, real and symmetrical progress in geology would be impossible without corresponding interrelated development and refinement in its handmaid, paleontology. The study of the economic geology of any region of complicated structure is blind and inconsequent unless the time relations are known. These relations are indicated by the fossils which the strata contain.

FOSSILS AS STRATIGRAPHIC INDICATORS

Fossils are one of the most valuable tools of the stratigrapher (see p. 30) and can provide important clues to the age of the rocks containing them. It is possible to use fossils for this purpose because it has long been known that there is a definite relation between the fossil content of the rocks and the position of these rocks in the geologic column.

According to the principle of superposition (see p. 31) we know that in a normal sequence of sedimentary rocks younger strata are laid down on top of older strata. Hence it follows that older fossils will normally be found at the bottom of the geologic column, with younger fossils near the top of the column.

In some areas, however, the rocks have been disturbed by crustal deformation. In these regions the beds may have been overturned or older rocks thrust on top of younger ones. If the strata in the area are fossiliferous and if the geologist knows the order in which the fossils normally occur in the section, he can then work out the proper stratigraphic sequence. This is possible because of the *law of faunal and floral succession,* which states that assemblages of fossil plants (*floras*) and animals (*faunas*) succeed one another in a definite and determinable order. The floras and faunas are distinctive for each portion of earth history, and a comparison of these fossil assemblages often enables the geologist to recognize deposits of the same age. This is frequently possible even when the deposits are in widely separated areas.

The use of fossils to demonstrate the relationships of certain rock units is called *biologic,* or *paleontologic, correlation.* This is the most valuable and common use that is made of fossils. There are several methods of paleontologic correlation, but only three of these will be briefly considered here.

Correlation by Guide, or Index, Fossils. Some fossils are so characteristic of certain strata that they have been called *guide,* or *index, fossils.* These are the remains of rapidly evolving species that lived only a short time in geologic history but while alive attained widespread distribution (Fig. 17). The usefulness of guide fossils is enhanced if the species is abundant and possesses distinctive features making it easy to identify.

Correlation by Fossil Assemblages. Paleontologic correlations are usually more reliable if more than one species of fossils is used as a basis for comparison. When correlating by fossil assemblages, the stratigrapher must first determine the types of organisms that lived during the time that the rock was deposited. Also helpful to know is the relative abundance of each of the species. With this information at hand, the stratigrapher can study two or more geologic sections and attempt to correlate them by comparing the assemblages of fossils in each section (Fig. 18).

Correlation by Stage of Evolutionary Development. Another method of paleontologic correlation is to attempt to "match"

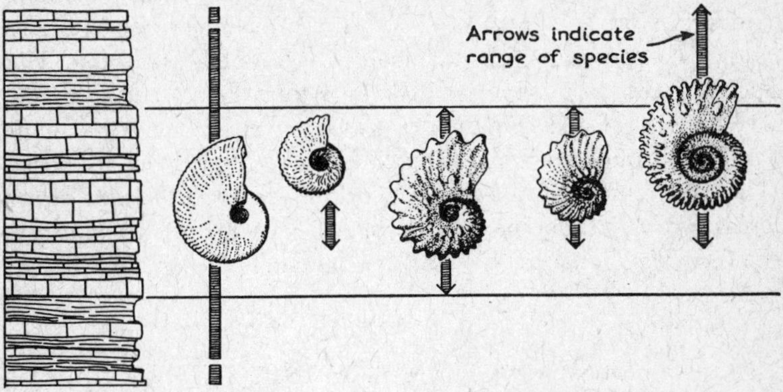

FIG. 17.—Using fossils to date beds. The long-ranging species on the left is of no value in dating the limestone bed between the two horizontal lines, but the short ranges of the other species make them good time markers. The actual specimens were collected in England. (Data from S. W. Muller. Reprinted by permission from *Principles of Geology,* Second Edition, by James Gilluly, Aaron C. Waters, and A. O. Woodford. San Francisco: W. H. Freeman and Company, 1960.)

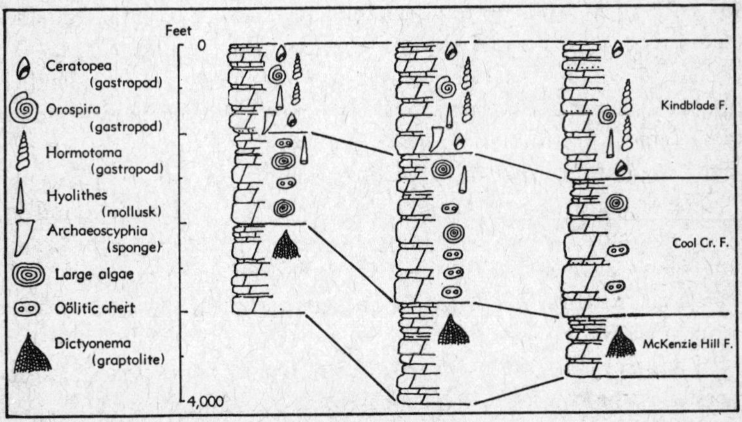

FIG. 18.—Correlation by fossil assemblages. Successions of lithologically similar rocks of the Lower Ordovician in southern Oklahoma can be divided and correlated on the basis of fossils, even though these are scanty and not highly specialized. (By permission from Moore's *Introduction to Historical Geology,* after C. E. Decker, Oklahoma Geological Survey.)

the strata on the basis of similarity of evolutionary development between groups of animals. This technique is particularly useful in the case of rocks containing fossils of certain vertebrate animals. One of the more commonly used groups in this type of correlation is the horse. The development of the horse is well known, and the record clearly indicates a gradual evolution of the size, limbs, feet, and teeth (Fig. 19). The record begins with *Hyracotherium* (known also as *Eohippus*), which was about the size of a small dog. This species is the most primitive of known fossil horses and is indicative of rocks of early Eocene age. Fossil horses become increasingly larger and more complex in successively younger Cenozoic rocks. Thus, the remains of the relatively primitive *Hyracotherium* can be used to correlate Eocene strata, while the remains of the more advanced *Pliohippus* can be used to correlate beds of the Pliocene series.

FOSSILS AS CLIMATIC INDICATORS

Fossils have been successfully used to demonstrate the existence of different climatic conditions in the geologic past. If we find the remains of tropical plants or animals in a region that has a temperate or cold climate today, we may assume that a tropical climate prevailed in that area at one time. For example, the fossil ferns found in Antarctica and the fossil magnolias reported from Greenland indicate a much warmer climate for these areas in other times.

Coal deposits commonly contain the remains of ferns and other plants which suggest warm, swampy conditions; yet many of these coal deposits are found in parts of the world that are much too cold and/or dry to support this type of vegetation today.

The remains of Silurian reef-building corals have been found in the New Siberian Islands within the Arctic Circle. Since these animals have always apparently lived in warm seas, their fossils indicate that the climate was tropical to subtropical in this area at least during the Silurian period.

Glacial, or colder, climates may be inferred by the presence of such fossils as the musk ox, which has been found in New York and Arkansas, and of fossil reindeer, which have been reported from France. These typical Arctic animals could not, of course, inhabit these areas today.

It should be remembered that certain fossil species may have been

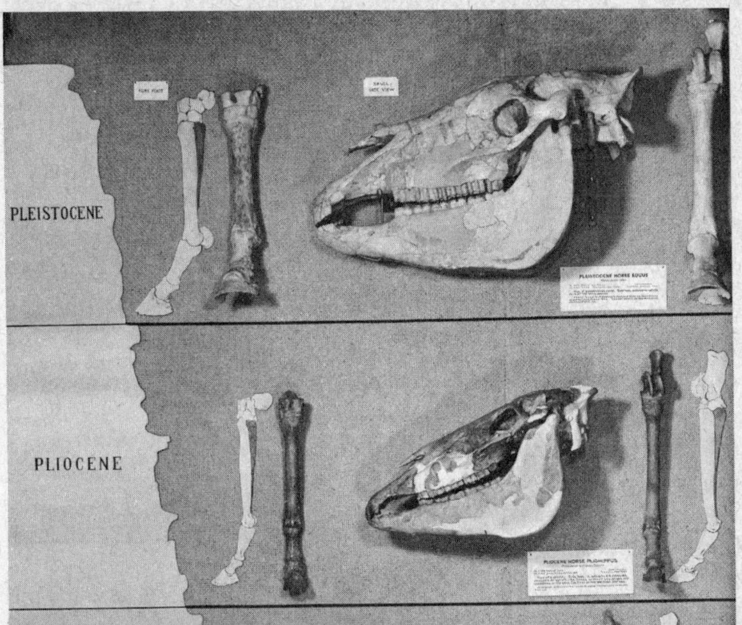

Courtesy of American Museum of Natural History

FIG. 19.—Evolution of the horse as illustrated by the feet and skulls of Cenozoic horses. The changes from the Eocene *Hyracotherium* (*Eohippus*) to *Equus*, the modern horse, can be traced because of the excellence of the fossil record.

adapted to different living conditions from those of their modern counterparts. For this reason one should use caution in interpreting climatic conditions from the evidence of fossils. Moreover, as in the case of paleontologic correlation, it is safer to use an entire fossil assemblage than to infer climatic conditions from a single species.

FOSSILS AS EVIDENCE OF CHANGING GEOGRAPHIC PATTERNS

Fossils have provided us with much information about the distribution of the seas and land masses of the past. Certain animals, such as the corals, echinoderms, brachiopods, and cephalopods, have always lived in the sea. The presence of fossils of this type indicates marine deposition for the rocks containing them. By plotting the distribution of these fossiliferous marine strata, the outlines of past seas can then be determined. The outlines of these ancient continents and oceans are shown by means of *paleogeographic maps*. These are maps that portray the ancient geography of an area and show such features as the positions of past shore lines, mountains, lakes, rivers, and oceans (Fig. 20).

The presence of fossil trees or stumps *in place* (that is, where they originally grew) would suggest a land environment, as would the bones of land animals. These remains indicate continental deposition, and the paleogeographer would, therefore, infer the presence of a land mass in an area where they are found.

Many ancient marine organisms were restricted to certain environments, and their fossils often provide some information as to the temperature, depth, and other properties of the sea water. Still other types of plant and animal remains suggest swamp or marsh conditions, during which time the land was barely above sea level. The geologist sometimes finds numerous fresh-water clam and snail shells mingled with the leaves of land plants. Fossil assemblages of this type could be typical of deposition in lakes and streams. Deltaic deposition may be indicated by the mingling of marine and land faunas and floras. This mixing occurs when a fresh-water stream enters a body of salt water.

Fossils, therefore, not only are valuable as evidence of the changing geographic patterns of our earth but also provide much information as to the type of environment in which these prehistoric organisms lived.

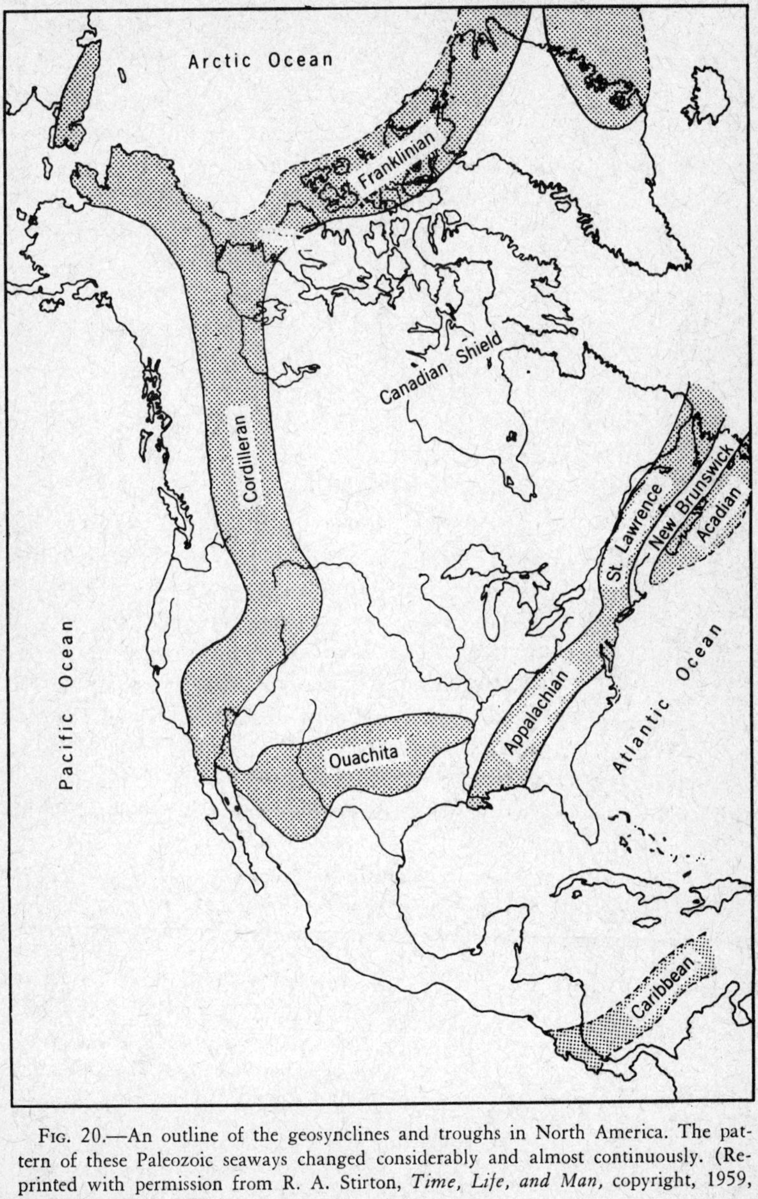

FIG. 20.—An outline of the geosynclines and troughs in North America. The pattern of these Paleozoic seaways changed considerably and almost continuously. (Reprinted with permission from R. A. Stirton, *Time, Life, and Man,* copyright, 1959, John Wiley & Sons, Inc.)

FOSSILS AS RECORDS OF PREHISTORIC LIFE

The study of fossil plants and animals has given us much information about the origin and evolution of organisms living today. This knowledge is possible because all modern plants and animals have descended from their more primitive ancestors which populated the earth in times past. By studying the record of the changes that organisms have undergone, the paleontologist is able to work out a family tree or evolutionary pattern for most forms of present-day life. It is thus possible to determine the relationships between different plant and animal groups and to see how life has slowly, but continually, become progressively complex.

Some forms, like the dinosaurs, ammonoids, and trilobites, have become extinct. All that is known of these animals has been learned from a study of their fossil remains. Some information has, however, been derived from a study of living animals which appear to be closely related to these extinct forms. For example, certain living reptiles have provided information which has been helpful in the reconstruction of the body form and life habits of the dinosaurs. The pearly nautilus has provided the paleontologist with much needed information about the soft parts of the extinct ammonoids. The construction and form of the ammonoid shell (Fig. 123–*1*) are quite similar to the shell of *Nautilus* (Fig. 120), and it is inferred that the soft parts of the ammonoid animal were also similar to those of *Nautilus*. A study of certain recent arthropods such as the horseshoe crab has thrown some light on the nature of the trilobites, which have been extinct since the end of the Permian period.

A comparison of living and fossil specimens is also important in the reconstruction or restoration of extinct animals. The reconstruction of the skeleton or soft parts of a dinosaur must be preceded by a careful study and comparison of the anatomical relationships of the dinosaurs with similar reptiles that are living today. Skeletal reconstructions are, for the most part, based on sound, scientific anatomical principles. The soft parts, however, present more of a problem, because they are much less likely to leave any record of their characteristics. A small number of fossil skin impressions have been found (Figs. 5 and 59), and some fossils, like the woolly mammoth, have been preserved in an almost perfect state (Fig. 4). Such forms are, of course, of considerable scientific importance, as they permit a most accurate re-creation of the soft parts of the animal. Unfortunately such occurrences are exceptional, and most restorations of soft tissues and coloration are based on what might be termed "scientific imagination."

FOSSILS AS EVIDENCE OF ORGANIC EVOLUTION

Fossils provide one of the strongest lines of evidence to support the theory of *organic evolution.* This theory states that the more advanced forms of modern life have evolved from simpler and more primitive ancestral forms of the geologic past. The transformation has been gradual and has been brought about by such factors as heredity, changes in environment, the struggle for existence, and adaptability of the species. (Evolution is discussed in some detail in Chapter XI.)

The older rocks contain the remains of organisms which differ considerably from living forms, and younger rocks contain fossils that appear to be more closely related to the plants and animals that are living today. This succession of fossils clearly indicates that life has slowly evolved from a few simple ancestors to the many different types of organisms that inhabit the earth today.

One of the best-known records of evolutionary change is found in the series of fossil horses from Cenozoic rocks (Fig. 19). This record begins with the small, primitive, four-toed *Hyracotherium* (*Eohippus*) of early Eocene time, and continues for some 60 million years through the Oligocene, Miocene, Pliocene, and Pleistocene, and up to the present time. This series culminates in our modern horse, *Equus,* with its relatively large size and one-toed hoofs.

The fossil record contains many such examples of evolutionary documentation, and it is little wonder that paleontology has been considered one of the foundation stones of the theory of organic evolution.

FOSSILS AS ECONOMIC TOOLS

Fossils not only are of value in conducting purely scientific studies but have extensive practical uses as well.

Since many of our more important resources are associated with sedimentary rocks, fossils, when present, may be of help in locating ores, coal, oil, and gas. For example, mining geologists use fossils to date the strata above and below the rocks that contain valuable minerals. In addition, fossiliferous rocks may also provide clues as to where these ore-bearing rocks may be found. Coal deposits, which are commonly associated with fossil plants, have been found in much the same way. Valuable deposits of radioactive minerals have been discovered in sedimentary rocks, and in some of these strata the ore concentrations are found closely associated with fossils. In fact, some specimens of fossil wood and the bones of certain fossil reptiles and mammals have been found to contain uranium.

Some fossiliferous limestones and sandstones are in considerable demand as building stones. The "Trigonia stone" of the Lower Cretaceous is an example of such a stone. This richly fossiliferous limestone (Fig. 8–2), quarried near Austin, Texas, contains large numbers of casts and molds of marine clams and snails, the most abundant of which is *Trigonia,* a clam. The presence of these fossils in the cream-colored rock has produced a most attractive stone which has been used in many buildings and monuments throughout the United States. It is also quite popular for interior and exterior ornamentation purposes. Another well-known fossiliferous building stone is the Salem limestone of Mississippian age, which is quarried near Bedford, Indiana. Other fossiliferous rocks have been quarried for similar purposes in many parts of the country.

The economic utilization of fossils has become increasingly widespread with the expansion of the petroleum industry. A great many geologists and paleontologists are actively engaged in the search for geologic formations that may contain profitable accumulations of oil and gas. A knowledge of fossils is basic in the search for these oil-bearing rocks, and most major oil companies have large, well-equipped paleontological laboratories.

Although larger fossils may be used in surface mapping projects, microfossils are most commonly used by the petroleum geologist. These fossils are particularly useful since they are of many different types and, because of their small size, are not likely to be broken by the drill bit. The majority of these tiny fossils are the remains of invertebrate animals, particularly one-celled forms called protozoans; but plant and other animal microfossils also occur.

Some of the more common invertebrate fossils are foraminifers, radiolarians, sponge spicules, echinoid and holothurian fragments, scolecodonts, conodonts, bryozoans, ostracodes, and microscopic brachiopods and mollusks.

Vertebrate fossils that are sometimes found as microfossils include various kinds of small bones and teeth, as well as fish scales. Among the plant microfossils are such forms as diatoms, algae, and plant spores, pollens, and seeds. Each of the above groups is discussed in Appendix A.

By far the most important group of microfossils are the foraminifers (commonly called "forams"). These small, one-celled animals are abundant in many fossiliferous rocks, and certain species, or assemblages of species, are characteristic of different formations. For this reason some types of forams are especially important in

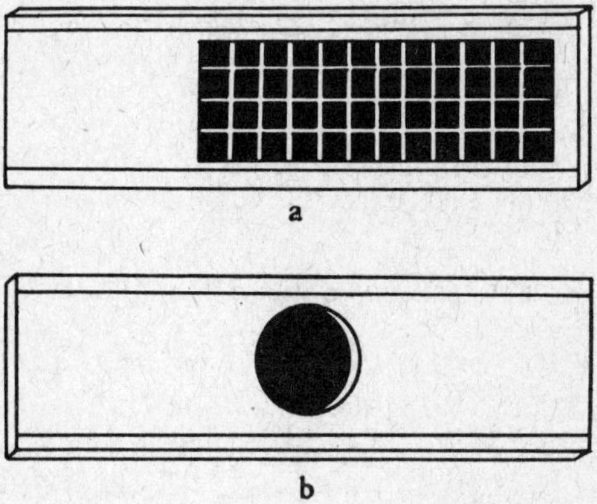

FIG. 21.—Two types of slides used to mount microfossils. (*a*) Multiple space faunal slide. (*b*) Single-hole slide for individual specimens. (By permission from *Texas Fossils* by W. H. Matthews III, Bureau of Economic Geology, University of Texas, Austin.)

subsurface mapping. In order to examine microfossils, the micropaleontologist washes rock samples taken from the drill hole and separates the fossils from the rock cuttings. The specimens are then mounted on special slides (Fig. 21) and studied under the microscope.

Forams are particularly important in the oil fields of California and the Atlantic and Gulf coastal regions of the United States. In fact, some of the oil-producing zones of Texas and Louisiana have been named for certain key forams; for example, the "het" zone of Oligocene age is named for *Heterostegina*. *Marginulina* and *Discorbis* are other species of forams that are especially useful as guide fossils in subsurface mapping. Other microfossils, such as fusulinids, ostracodes, conodonts, spores, and pollens, are also used to identify subsurface formations in many parts of the world.

Information derived from these minute fossils provides valuable data for the subsurface geologist. They may tell, for example, the geologic age of the deeply buried formation from which the fossils came. In *wildcat* (exploratory) wells they also serve as stratigraphic markers which help tell the geologist something about the subsurface section that is being drilled.

Chapter V

COLLECTING AND PREPARING FOSSILS

In fossil-collecting, as in other collecting hobbies, the key to success lies in knowing what equipment to take, where to look, and how to use the most effective methods of collecting. It is also important that the collector make every attempt to clean and prepare the fossils properly in order that they may be displayed in an attractive manner.

One of the best ways to start collecting is to take a field trip with an organized group such as a rock and mineral club or museum class. This should provide the beginner with basic information about the type of locality where fossils are most likely to be found, and also acquaint him with the fundamentals of field-collecting.

Only time, experience, and experimentation will provide the collector with the necessary background to properly prepare fossils for display. Displaying one's fossils is, to many collectors, one of the more gratifying aspects of the hobby of fossil-collecting, for it makes it possible for the collector to share his hobby and his enjoyment with others (see Chapter VII).

COLLECTING EQUIPMENT

Fossil-collecting is not an expensive hobby; it requires a minimum of supplies and equipment. Moreover, most fossil-collecting equipment may be found in the household belongings of the average family. As in most hobbies, however, there are certain basic items that must be purchased.

The *hammer* is the basic tool in the fossil-collector's field kit. Almost any hammer will do, but the type most commonly used is the *geologist's hammer* or *prospector's pick*. These hammers are of two basic kinds; one with a flat square head on one end and a pick on the other (Fig. 22–*1*); the other (Fig. 22–*2*) similar to a stonemason's or bricklayer's hammer with chisel-type end. The

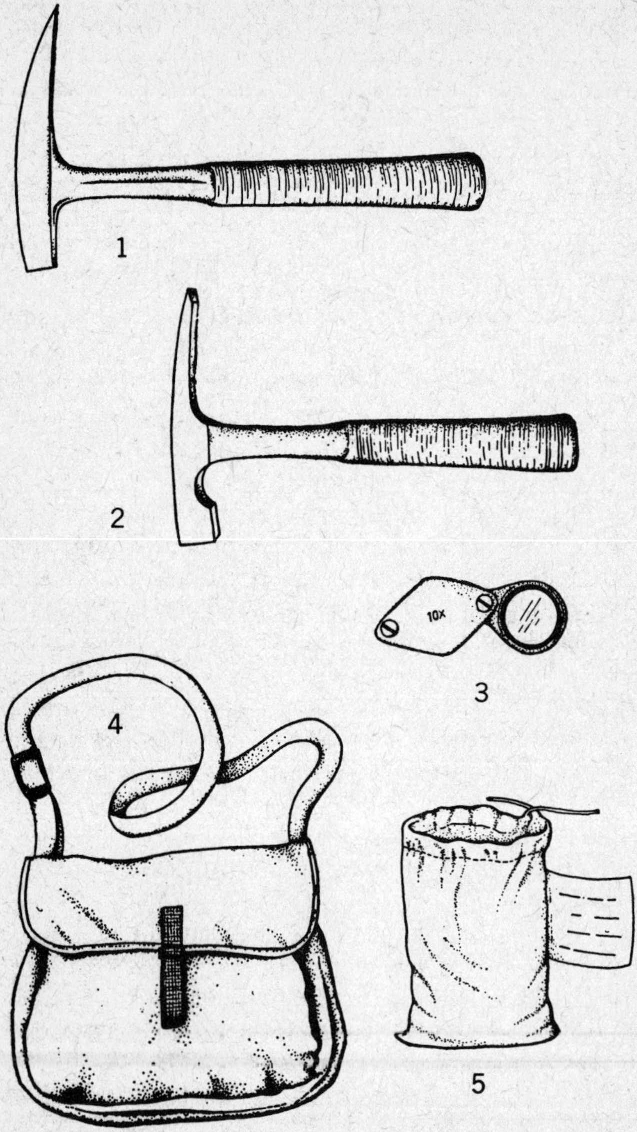

FIG. 22.—Fossil-collecting equipment. (*1*) Geological hammer with pick end. (*2*) Geological hammer with chisel end. (*3*) Magnifying glass or hand lens. (*4*) Collecting bag with shoulder strap. (*5*) Cloth sample bag with label. (By permission from *Texas Fossils* by W. H. Matthews III, Bureau of Economic Geology, University of Texas, Austin.)

square face of the hammer is useful for breaking and chipping harder rocks, and the chisel or pick end is handy for digging, prying, and splitting up soft rocks. Geology hammers can be bought at some hardware stores or from a geological supply dealer (see p. 323). A bricklayer's or stonemason's hammer, available at most hardware stores, is a satisfactory and less expensive substitute for the geologist's hammer.

Some type of collecting bag is needed to carry collecting equipment, fossils, and other supplies. A boy-scout knapsack, musette bag (Fig. 22–4), hunting bag, or similar canvas or leather bag is suitable. A bag with a shoulder strap leaves both hands free for collecting and is much less apt to be lost in the field. Bags of this type can be secured from most sporting goods dealers, geological supply houses, or army surplus stores.

A pair of *chisels* will be most useful when fossils must be chipped out of the surrounding rock. Two sizes, preferably ½ and 1 inch, will usually suffice. A small, sharp punch, or awl, is effective for removing smaller or more delicate fossils from softer rocks.

Wrapping materials, such as newspaper, tissue, or cotton, should always be kept in the collecting bag. Larger specimens should be wrapped in newspaper and placed in the bottom of the bag. Smaller or more fragile specimens may be wrapped in tissue paper or cotton, or placed in small plastic pill vials filled with cotton. These should, if possible, be placed in a separate pocket of the collecting bag or on top of the heavier material. Such precautions in the field will usually prevent fine specimens from being broken or otherwise damaged. If desired, twine or rubber bands may be used to hold the wrappings in place.

Paper or *cloth bags* can be used to separate specimens from different collecting localities. Heavy-duty hardware or nail bags should be used for large, rough material, while medium-weight grocery bags are satisfactory for smaller fossils. Locality data may be written on the side of the bag or on a label placed inside with the fossils. As an added precaution, many collectors do both. Some collectors prefer the cloth geological sample bag (Fig. 22–5) which is used by the professional geologist. This type of bag, which may be purchased from geological supply houses, has an opening equipped with a drawstring and a cloth-backed label sewn along one side.

Small paper *labels* are quite handy to have along. These are used to record data such as name of the collector, collecting locality, geologic formation, and the date of collection. These labels, properly filled in, should be placed in each bag of fossils collected from the locality described on the label. The labels should be about 2 by 3 inches and may be cut from writing paper, a small scratch pad, or index cards.

Finally, the collector should never be without a *notebook, pencil,* and a suitable type of *map*. These are most important, for every collecting locality must be completely and accurately recorded. It is quite easy to forget where fossils were collected, and one should never rely on memory. A small, pocket-sized notebook will serve for notes on field trips. A highway or county map should be used to find the geographic location of each collecting locality. Maps of this type can be obtained from most state highway departments. They are usually reasonably priced and available for each county of the state. A scale of one-half inch to a mile is the best-sized map for most purposes. If there is a small-scale geologic map available for your state, this will help determine the age of the rocks that are exposed at each locality. To find out if such a map has been prepared for your state, write your state geological survey (a list of the state geological surveys and their addresses will be found on p. 313).

The items described above constitute the basic equipment of fossil-collectors; they are all that is usually carried in the field. However, the more serious amateur may wish to have access to certain additional items which will place his collecting on a more professional basis. Some of these accessory items are:

1. *Magnifying Glass.* A magnifying glass or hand lens (Fig. 22–3) is useful for examining small specimens and will also be helpful in examining the finer details of larger fossils. A 10-power magnification is satisfactory for most purposes; several inexpensive models are available from sporting goods or geological supply dealers.

2. *Topographic Maps.* These are maps that show the position, relation, size, and shape of the physical features of an area. They also show valleys, rivers, hills, and mountains, as well as roads, towns, houses, and other artificial features of the region. They are useful in planning collecting trips and in findings one's location in the field. These maps are available for many parts of the United States and can be purchased from the United States Geological Survey, Washington 25, D. C., or Denver, Colorado. They may be purchased at a nominal cost, and the Survey will supply, without charge, a key

sheet showing all of the maps available for each state. For special information about maps, write the Office of Map Information, Washington 25, D. C.

3. *Fossil Guide.* If a guide to the fossils of your state has been published, this will be extremely helpful. Fossil guides are presently available for Texas, Washington, Illinois, Ohio, Missouri, New York, and Indiana (see "Publications about Fossils," in the back of this book). Several other states have publications of this nature in preparation, and your state geological survey can provide information about the availability of these or similar bulletins. These guidebooks provide the amateur with information about the various kinds of fossils, possible collecting sites, collecting and preparation techniques, and background information about the geology of the respective states. In addition, most have illustrations which will assist in the identification of the more common fossils.

4. *Compass.* A compass is most helpful when working in unfamiliar areas, and can be used for accurate finding and recording of fossil localities.

5. *Adhesive,* or *Masking, Tape.* Tape of this sort can be applied directly to larger fossils or rock specimens, and locality data can be recorded on the tape.

6. *Stiff-Bristle Paint Brush* or *Whisk Broom.* Brushes can be used to clean loose dirt or rock chippings from around embedded specimens and to clean off rock exposures.

7. *Sledge Hammer* and *Shovel.* An 8 to 10-pound sledge hammer is handy in collecting slabs or very heavy specimens. A shovel is often desirable when working in loose, unconsolidated rocks such as sand, clay, or shale.

8. *Camera.* Many collectors like to take pictures of their fossil-collecting localities. Photographs are often very helpful when one wishes to return to a collecting locality after a long absence, for a picture will call to mind certain landmarks and other distinguishing features of the area.

The beginning collector should own one or two of the basic books on geology and paleontology listed on p. 303. He should also read a rock and mineral magazine (p. 311) that has a section devoted to fossils. Such a publication will provide a broader and more meaningful understanding of earth science, and thus bring additional enjoyment to the hobby of rock-, mineral-, and fossil-collecting.

WHERE TO LOOK

One of the first things the beginning collector must learn is where to look for fossils. The best and quickest way to learn is to go to the field with an experienced collector and carefully observe the manner in which he selects a collecting site. If this is not possible, it is still a relatively simple matter to find good collecting localities if there are fossiliferous rocks in the area.

It has already been mentioned that igneous and metamorphic rocks are not likely to contain fossils and that most fossils are found in marine sedimentary rocks. The sediments from which these rocks were formed were deposited under conditions which were favorable for organisms during life and which facilitated their preservation after death. Limestones, limy shales, marls, and certain types of sandstones are typically deposited under such conditions.

One should look especially for areas where marine sedimentary rocks lie relatively flat and have not been greatly disturbed by heat, pressure, and other physical and chemical agencies. If the rocks appear to have undergone considerable folding and fracturing, there is great likelihood that any fossils that may have been present will have been destroyed or damaged.

Quarries are often choice collecting areas. (One should be sure to get permission from the operators before entering their property.) Rock exposures in quarries are relatively fresh but have still undergone some weathering. Fossils are often found in the thin shale or marl layers which may be present between the thicker and harder limestone beds. These shale beds weather more readily than the more resistant limestone, and any fossils that are present can be recovered with a minimum of difficulty. When working the face of a quarry or cliff, one should be particularly careful not to dislodge loose rock material or boulders that might be hazardous to fellow collectors working below.

Limestone quarries for building-stone and cement materials have been opened in many states, and fossiliferous strata have been exposed by a large number of these operations. Sand and gravel quarries may also prove to be profitable collecting localities. This type of quarry has produced many exposures rich in vertebrate fossils, such as the bones and teeth of mammoths, mastodons, camels, and horses.

Particular attention should be directed to all railroad and highway cuts, since rocks exposed in this way are usually still in their original position and are fairly well weathered. Recent cuts will probably be more productive after they have undergone some weathering, for weathering helps to separate the fossils from the surrounding rocks.

Canyons, gullies, and stream beds are also good places to examine. These areas are continuously subjected to the procesess of erosion or stream action, and so new fossils may be uncovered year after year.

Fossils, as well as Indian relics, may also be found in freshly ploughed fields, particularly in areas where the topsoil is thin and the underlying bedrock is fossiliferous.

If there are abandoned coal mines nearby, it may be worth while to check the dumps of waste rock around the shafts. A careful examination of this waste may reveal fine specimens of well-preserved plant fossils. (The collector should, as always, obtain permission before collecting on private property and should *never* go into an abandoned mining shaft.)

With a little practice and field experience, the amateur will soon learn to recognize promising collecting areas and to evaluate their potentialities.

Collecting in the field, however, is not the only way to acquire a fossil collection. Many earth-science hobbyists augment their specimens with fossils obtained by trading. Still others purchase specimens from fossil dealers or natural science establishments.

Trading is best done on a person-to-person basis in order that both parties may see exactly what material is being offered in the exchange and so that there will be no danger that fragile material will be broken in transit. However, some very satisfactory trades have been effected by mail; therefore, this method of exchange is not to be discounted completely. Many rock and mineral clubs have regularly scheduled "swap nights" or trading meetings where members can exchange duplicate material for other desired specimens. This is but another of the many advantages that come from being a member of your local rock and mineral society.

Many collectors purchase at least a few specimens, because it is impossible to build a truly representative collection through finding or exchanging fossils. Fossil dealers advertise in many of the rock and mineral magazines, some of which are listed on p. 311 and a partial list of fossil dealers may be found on p. 323. Some collectors buy representative selections of the fossils found in their areas to use in learning to recognize and identify similar specimens in the field.

HOW TO COLLECT

When a likely collecting spot has been located, the ground should be examined very carefully to see whether there is any evidence of fossil remains. Such evidence will usually be in the form of pieces of shell, bone, or rock fragments bearing impressions of shells, leaves, or other organic material.

If the rocks are fossiliferous and the fossils have been freed by weathering, they may simply be picked up and placed in the collecting bag. Often, however, it will be necessary to take the hammer and carefully remove the rock surrounding the fossils. Smaller fossils may be more safely freed with the careful use of the proper-sized chisel. The chisel should be gently tapped in order to gradually chip away the *matrix*—the rock that is holding the specimen. After most of the matrix has been removed, the fossil should be carefully wrapped and placed in the collecting bag.

Before leaving a collecting locality, you should be sure to record its geographic location and, if possible, the geologic age of the rocks in which the fossils were found. (The geologic age of the formation can be determined by referring to a geologic map of the area if one is available.) An attempt should be made to locate the place on a map and then the locality data should be written in the field notebook. Locality information must be recorded in such a manner that you, or another collector, could easily return to the site for additional collecting. If a county or topographic map is available, it would be wise to mark the locality directly on the map. You should then write the geographic data (name of county, highway number, etc.) on a label and drop it into the bag of fossils collected at that particular locality. As an added precaution, many collectors also find it advisable to write locality data on the outside of each bag of fossils. This is a safety factor in case labels become lost, and it also facilitates handling the material upon return from the field.

Fossils from separate localities should be kept in individual cloth or paper bags, and the collector should make every attempt to keep the labels with their respective fossils. It is most important to remember that *a fossil without a locality is little more than an oddity and hardly worth the paper it is wrapped in.*

To repeat, collecting ethics demand that one should always obtain the landowner's permission before entering or collecting on private property. One should respect all property and not litter the area with newspaper, lunch wrappings, and similar trash. It is also important to close all gates after passing through them. If these precautions are observed, collectors will probably be welcome to return for additional fossil-hunting.

The Collection and Preparation of Larger Invertebrate Fossils. The larger invertebrate fossils are commonly referred to as *macrofossils* or *megafossils*. These are fossils that are large enough to be studied with the naked eye, and include such forms as fossil sponges, corals, snails, clams, and other larger organic remains. Fossils of this type are common in many of the marine sedimentary rocks throughout the United States, and for this reason macrofossils comprise the bulk of most fossil collections.

Fossils embedded in shales, clays, or loose sands are often freed by weathering and need only to be picked up, wrapped, labeled, and placed in the collecting bag. Often, however, fine specimens are found still embedded in the rock, and these require particular care if they are to be safely collected. Shells encased in somewhat loose, unconsolidated sands can often be freed by brushing the matrix away with a stiff-bristled paintbrush. If the specimen is fractured or crumbling, it will be advisable to coat the shell with shellac, varnish, or collodion. When the protective coating has dried, the specimen can be removed by undercutting with pick or chisel. It is usually a good idea to leave part of the matrix on the underside of the fossil, to serve as additional support and protection. Later, this part can be removed and the underside of the specimen coated. Such specimens should be carefully wrapped and carefully placed in the collecting bag.

Fossils embedded in harder rocks such as sandstones and limestones are best freed by means of the hammer and chisel. Many times, however, fossils are so firmly embedded as to be impossible to remove. If the specimen should break, the pieces can be wrapped together, placed in a paper bag, and reassembled later. If a particularly fine specimen should be found, it may be advisable to bring in a large section of the rock. The fossil can be removed from the block at home, where more suitable tools and working conditions are available.

Slabs of fossiliferous sandstone and limestone can be broken into convenient sizes, wrapped in newspaper, and brought home with a minimum of difficulty. Individual fossils can then be removed from the slab, or the entire rock can be prepared for display. Fossiliferous shales and slates can be split along *bedding planes* (the dividing planes or surfaces which separate individual layers of sedimentary rock), and those pieces that bear fossils or impressions can be saved. In situations of this sort it is wise to save both sides of the impression.

If the original shell material has decayed, leaving a mold, it may be desirable to make a plaster cast of the specimen. The mold should be cleaned out, coated with light-weight machine oil, and filled with a mixture of plaster of Paris and water. The plaster mixture should be about the consistency of thick cream and should be poured in such a manner as to fill all parts of the mold. After the plaster has hardened, the matrix can be gently broken away, leaving the plaster cast of the original fossil. Although internal molds are usually found loose on the ground, external molds provide much more information about the organism.

Macrofossils should always be carefully packed for transportation from the field. Larger fossils should be wrapped in paper, and a properly filled-in label should accompany each specimen. Smaller or more delicate specimens should be placed in matchboxes or pill vials, with cotton above and below the fossil.

In some instances it may be advisable to collect shales, marls, sands, and clays in bulk and to pick out and sort the fossils later. The loose sediment tends to act as a cushion for the more fragile fossils and gives the collector a large amount of material for later study.

It is usually necessary to do the final cleaning and preparation of fossils at home or in the laboratory. Most fossils brought in from the field require considerable preparation before they are ready to display. This important phase of the work should be done when a sufficient amount of time and the proper instruments are available. The basic requirements for good preparatory work are a comfortable work table, good lighting, an assortment of simple tools, and considerable patience.

After the specimens have been unwrapped, the fossils should be checked to see whether the identifying labels are still with them. These labels should remain with the fossils until the collection number has been written on each specimen with India ink (Fig. 25). Before starting the final cleaning, it is helpful to place the fossils in water and allow them to soak overnight (place the label underneath or alongside the pan). This will loosen much of the excess rock, and most of the softer material can be removed with

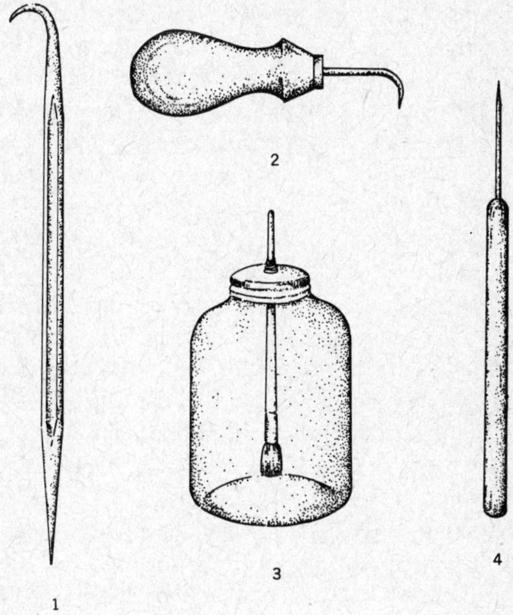

FIG. 23.—Fossil preparation equipment. (*1*) Dental tool for working between surface structures, etc. (*2*) Awl for removing fossils from matrix. (*3*) Shellac bottle made from common jar, paintbrush, and rubber bands. (*4*) Teasing needle for cleaning smaller structures, separating microfossils, etc.

a small stiff-bristled scrub brush or toothbrush. A wire brush may be needed on larger specimens, but care should be taken not to damage the surface of the fossil.

Long needles, tweezers, awls, and old dental tools (Fig. 23) can be used to clean the more delicate fossils, or to clean around the smaller structures of larger specimens. It may be advisable to use a magnifying glass when working with smaller fossils or with the delicate surface features of larger forms.

Excess matrix should be cautiously removed with a light hammer or mallet and a chisel of the proper size. The blows should always be directed away from the fossil. Stout long-nosed pliers are particularly useful in breaking away small pieces of excess matrix. Any broken surfaces of matrix that might remain on the fossil can be smoothed with a wire brush, steel wool, or sandpaper.

Dilute hydrochloric acid may be used to remove silicified fossils from calcareous rocks. After the preliminary washing, the fossils should be placed in a glass or pottery container and covered with water. Acid should then be added to the water very slowly until large numbers of bubbles are given off. Each time the bubbling ceases (when the acid has become exhausted), more acid should be added and this process repeated until the fossils are free of matrix. The fossils should then be thoroughly washed to remove all traces of the acid solution. *This procedure should be carried out in a well-ventilated place, and the acid and acid solution should be handled with extreme caution.* Hydochloric acid can cause damage or serious injury to the skin, and the corrosive fumes are extremely dangerous to breathe. It is also poisonous and should be kept carefully locked up when not in use. Before using this technique, one should place a small drop of dilute hydrochloric acid on the fossils to be sure that they will not be dissolved by the acid solution.

After they have been cleaned, the fossils, with their labels should be placed in shallow wooden or cardboard trays. Each fossil should then be assigned a collection number (see "Labeling," p. 80), which should be written on the specimen in India ink.

Fragments of broken specimens should be kept together in the same tray; you should work with the various parts until they have been properly fitted together. The broken surfaces should then be cleaned and strong household cement or glue applied to both surfaces. Pressure should be exerted until the cement has had time to make its initial set. Specimens that are crumbling or otherwise deteriorating should be given a protective coating of shellac, varnish, clear plastic, or collodion.

The Collection and Preparation of Microfossils. Microfossils are those fossils that are so small that they are best studied under a microscope. Because of their small size, they are not collected by most amateurs. Quite a few more experienced collectors, however, have microscopes and are interested in collecting microfossils.

Foraminifers (Fig. 88) are the most common microfossils, but ostracodes (Fig. 130) and conodonts (Fig. 151) are also often collected by the amateur.

Many fossiliferous marls, shales, and limestones yield microfossils, in addition to the remains of larger invertebrates. It is often worth while to inspect the surfaces of the rock with a hand lens, because microfossils, if present, can often be seen in this manner. It is, of course, easier to collect microfossils from soft rocks, such as marls, shales, and clays, than from hard rocks. Those embedded in harder rocks require special equipment and preparation techniques that are not available to the amateur.

Samples that are suspected of containing a microfauna should be carefully collected, with special care being taken to prevent their contamination by other rock samples. When collecting in softer rock, the weathered surface material should be removed and the sample taken well below the zone of weathering. The pick or chisel end of the geology hammer or a small entrenching pick is well suited for collecting this type of material. The sample should be placed in a double paper pag, with the top folded down, and secured by means of twine or heavy rubber bands. Slabs of limestone containing larger foraminifers such as fusulinids can be wrapped in newspaper. Locality data should be included with all samples.

After the material has been collected, special treatment is necessary before the microfossils can be conveniently studied. First, the sample should be thoroughly dried, either at room temperature or—more quickly—in an oven set at about 325°. Next, you must break up or crush the rock so that the fossils will become separated from the matrix. In general, the rock fragments should average from ⅛ to ½ inch in diameter after they have been broken. The sample should then be placed in a pan of water and allowed to soak for several hours. This soaking will usually result in complete disintegration of the sample, but it is sometimes necessary to boil a sample to hasten the disintegration process. After the sample has been completely broken down, the material should be stirred and water continually added and poured off until the liquid is finally clear. The remaining part of the sample should then be dried and passed through a 20-mesh screen. The screened sample can then be placed in a small coin or seed envelope or plastic pill vial, with the locality written on the outside of the container. Larger amounts of washed residue may be stored in glass jars, coffee cans, or ice-cream containers.

A binocular-type microscope is preferred for most micropaleontological work, but a simple biological microscope is satisfactory for many microfossils. The sample to be examined should be spread out in a thin layer on a small tray about the size of the microscope stage. Such a tray should have a dark background. It can be made from any small cardboard box and then painted black. When a fossil has been located through the microscope, it can be picked up with the end of a slightly moistened camel's-hair paintbrush or long needle. The specimen is then mounted on a special micropaleontology slide (Fig. 21) by means of a tiny drop of water-soluble glue, such as gum tragacanth, gum arabic, or glycerin. Micropaleontology slides can be purchased from scientific-supply houses or made from two strips of cardboard. A 1- by 3-inch piece of black cardboard is used to form the base of the slide. The second piece of cardboard (also 1 by 3 inches) should be white and have a hole ½-inch in diameter punched in its center. These two pieces are glued together and covered with a 1- by 3-inch glass microscope slide or a strip of celluloid or clear photographic film of the same size. The transparent cover should be mounted in such a way that it can be removed to add additional specimens if so desired.

The slides should be numbered, and when the fossil has been identified the name of the specimen should be written directly on the cardboard portion of the slide. Slides of microfossils from the same locality can then be filed together in a cigar box or other suitable container.

The Collection and Preparation of Fossil Plants. Fossil plants are usually fragmental and poorly preserved, and this fact tends to discourage most amateurs from an active interest in paleobotany. Nevertheless, the evolution of plants is, intrinsically, of as much interest and importance as is the evolution of animals. In addition, certain plants are of considerable value as indicators of ancient climatic conditions, and their remains have played a large part in the formation of our vast coal deposits. There is, therefore, considerable interest in fossil plants.

Leaf impressions are sometimes found associated with sandstones, shales, lignitic clays, and volcanic ash. These imprints are likely to be found along bedding-plane surfaces, and frequently occur as carbon residues. The rocks containing leaf impressions are commonly quite soft and must be handled with considerable care to prevent crumbling and damage to the fossils. In working in this type of rock, the chisel end of the hammer or a broad-bladed knife can be used to split clays and shales along bedding planes.

If leaf impressions are found, it is often necessary to apply white shellac or clear plastic to the specimen. This will protect it from damage and bring out its fine details. The protective coating should be applied thinly in order not to mask any of the delicate leaf structure. Shellac may be thinned by diluting it with alcohol or shellac-thinner. A coating of shellac will also help to hold the rock together and prevent its crumbling after it has dried. It may be necessary to coat the entire rock sample if it is very crumbly.

Specimens treated in this manner will, of course, require special care if they are to be safely transported. To minimize breakage they should be wrapped in tissue and placed in a cotton-filled box if possible.

Shellac can be conveniently carried in the field in almost any bottle. To prevent the brush from drying out, the lid of the bottle should be pierced and the brush handle inserted in the hole. The brush can be held in place by wrapping rubber bands or tape around the handle (Fig. 23–*3*).

Silicified, or "petrified," wood is common in many parts of the country and offers no particular problem to the collector. For purposes of identification, however, the specimen must be cut across the grain and the surface polished. This exposes what is left of the original woody tissue of the plant.

The Collection and Preparation of Vertebrate Fossils. The average amateur finds relatively few, if any, vertebrate fossils. However, fossils of this type are frequently discovered in the United States, and some amateur paleontologists have become interested in collecting and preparing vertebrate material.

The remains of fish, amphibians, and reptiles are to be found in Paleozoic and Mesozoic rocks in many parts of the country. Teeth and bones of fish, horses, camels, mammoths, mastodons, and many other vertebrates are also numerous in certain Cenozoic deposits.

Vertebrate remains usually require special techniques and considerable time to collect. If the collector thinks he has made an important find, he should not disturb the specimen but report it to a professional paleontologist who can supervise its excavation. The inexperienced collector can easily ruin a valuable specimen.

When bones or bone fragments are found on the surface, these are usually hard and dry and can easily be collected. If the bone is broken into several pieces, each fragment should be marked and kept in proper relation to the others. After wrapping and labeling loose material, you should carefully search the surrounding area for traces of bones that are still embedded in the rock. When discovered, these must be carefully uncovered with pick and shovel to remove heavy *overburden* (the rock or loose soil that overlies the bones), and a hand awl (Fig. 23–2) and whisk broom must be used for the final cleaning. Care must be taken not to damage the bone by rough handling. After part of the matrix has been removed, the bone should be gently brushed clean, and after it has dried it should be coated with shellac or plastic. Next, a trench should be dug around the block containing the bone, and then the rock should be undercut so that the entire block can be freed. The block should then be wrapped well in newspaper, excelsior, or similar material and placed in a sturdy container suitable for transportation.

Certain larger specimens, such as the bones of dinosaurs or of the larger mammals, may need to be jacketed in a plaster of Paris block. The application of a jacket enables the collector to remove the bone in one piece and has the added advantage of protecting the bone in transit. The jacket is made after the bone has been cleared of overlying rock, allowed to dry, and coated with shellac. When the shellac has dried, the surrounding rock should be removed and then undercut in such a manner that the specimen rests on pedestals of rock. Next, the fossil should be covered with strips of wet newspaper or cotton cloth to prevent the plaster of Paris from sticking to the bone. A burlap bag should then be cut into 2- or 3-inch strips and these should be soaked in water. While the burlap strips are soaking, plaster of Paris and water should be mixed to the consistency of thick cream. The burlap strips are then wrung out, soaked in the plaster, and laid across the block in overlapping layers. The plaster should be worked into the surface of the block with the fingertips. Only small amounts of plaster should be mixed at one time, as it dries and sets quickly. After the upper surface has been completely covered with plaster strips, one long strip should be tied completely around the base of the block. This strip will serve to hold the loose ends of the other strips in place.

The plaster block should if possible be allowed to dry overnight before being moved. After the plaster has dried, the block containing the fossil should be completely undercut, turned over, and the matrix trimmed to within a few inches of the bone. If the undersurface of the block is soft, it too should be coated with shellac and covered with plaster strips. When it has dried, the plaster block should be packed in a sturdy wooden crate or packing box. To prevent shifting during transit, excelsior, straw, or newspaper should be carefully packed around the block.

Vertebrate fossils should be unpacked with special care. If the specimen is encased in plaster, one side should be moistened and the plaster cut away. The undersurface should remain encased in plaster until the specimen has been completely prepared for display.

A complete discussion of the numerous techniques and methods of restoration of vertebrate fossils is, of course, beyond the scope of this book. The interested collector, however, will find additional sources of information in the list of references on p. 309.

Chapter VI

HOW TO IDENTIFY FOSSILS

The identification of fossils is sometimes the most difficult task undertaken by the amateur collector. Yet it is an achievement that adds greatly to the over-all pleasure of fossil-collecting and can result in much personal satisfaction.

Some fossils, particularly common ones, are relatively easy to identify because they are often referred to in geological publications. Others are more difficult to identify and will require a diligent search of the *paleontological literature* (books, journals, and other publications dealing with fossils).

Before attempting to identify your fossils, it is necessary to know something about the method that is used to classify fossils. This is important because the references that you will be using usually list the fossils by their scientific names.

The number of plants and animals, both living and extinct, is so great (see Fig. 2) that some system of classification is needed to link them all together. The system created for this purpose is called *taxonomy* (Greek *taxis,* arrangement + *nomos,* law), which is the science of plant and animal classification.* Taxonomic classification permits an orderly scientific approach to the study and identification of fossils. Such a classification is used as a convenience in study, as well as to show the development of the various life forms through geologic time.

THE DUAL SYSTEM OF NAMING FOSSILS

The system of classification used in naming fossils is the same as that used by biologists in naming living organisms. The system, known as the system of *binomial nomenclature* (or "two-name system of naming"), was proposed by Linnaeus (see p. 150) in 1758.

* Gordon Alexander, *General Zoology* (New York: Barnes and Noble Inc., 4th ed., 1951), p. 220. This is an easy-to-use, readily understood review of basic zoology.

This dual-name system requires that the scientific name identifying an organism have two parts: the *generic* name (name of the *genus*) plus the *specific* name (name of the *species*). The specific name is also referred to as the *trivial* name. These names are usually derived from Greek or Latin words which describe the organism (living or fossil) that is being named. They may, however, be derived from the names of people or places, and in such instances the names are always Latinized. The classical languages are used in naming plants and animals for the same reasons that they were used to designate the units of the time chart: names established under this system are descriptive, unchanging, and mean the same to scientists all over the world.

The organic world of nature has been divided into the plant and animal *kingdoms,* which, in turn, have been divided into large divisions called *phyla* (singular, *phylum*), derived from the Greek *phylon,* meaning a race. Each phylum is composed of a large number of organisms with certain characteristics in common. For example, all animals with a spinal cord are assigned to the phylum Chordata (having a notochord or "back-string"). Each phylum is divided into *classes,* classes into *orders,* orders into *families,* families into *genera,* and genera into *species*—which may be divided into subspecies, varieties, or races. Thus, the common house cat belongs to the genus *Felis* and the species *domestica,* and all living men belong to the genus *Homo* and the species *sapiens.* It is obvious that there are a large number of variations among individual men and individual cats, but the general characteristics of each group are quite similar. In the writing of a scientific name, the generic name should always start with a capital letter, the species name should start with a lower-case letter, and both names should be italicized or underlined.

The table on page 70 shows the similarity in classification of man, the common domestic cat, and the zigzag scallop.

The name of the *author* (the person who first described the fossil) often forms part of the scientific name. Following this, may be the date of the publication containing the original description of the fossil. For example:

Apsotreta expansa Palmer 1954

The generic name of this Cambrian brachiopod is *Apsotreta;* the trivial, or specific, name is *expansa;* and the form was first described by A. R. Palmer in 1954.

Taxonomic Unit	Man	Cat	Clam
Kingdom	Animalia	Animalia	Animalia
Phylum *	Chordata	Chordata	Mollusca
Class	Mammalia	Mammalia	Pelecypoda
Order	Primates	Carnivora	Anisomyariida
Family	Hominidae	Felidae	Pectinidae
Genus	*Homo*	*Felis*	*Pecten*
Species	*sapiens*	*domestica*	*ziczac*

* In botanical classification the term Division is also used to designate plant groups of phylum rank.

TAXONOMY AS AN AID IN IDENTIFYING FOSSILS

The beginning collector is usually content to know that his fossil is an oyster or a snail, a fern or a bone; but as he collects more fossils and gains more experience he will want to know the scientific name of each specimen.

The Linnaean system of classification is a useful aid in identification because it requires that organisms with similar characteristics be put in the same category. For instance, all animals that produce milk to feed their young are placed in the class Mammalia. Those mammals whose anatomical structure indicates that they eat meat exclusively are placed in the order Carnivora. The carnivores are divided into families such as the Canidae, which includes the dogs, or the Felidae, which includes the cats. We all know that cats and dogs are different in many respects, but they are basically similar in that the females of both families produce milk and members of both families are meat-eaters.

In using taxonomy as a tool in identification it is usually best first to determine the phylum and class, and then try to trace the organism through the lower taxonomic units until the genus and species have been determined. We may not, for example, know the genus or species of a certain fossil, but we do know that it looks like a clam. So we call it a pelecypod (for class Pelecypoda, bivalved mollusks), and this is, at least, a start in determining the scientific name. The fossil clam in question may also have characteristics which suggest that it should be placed in a certain order or family. Once the family has been determined, a close study of the specimen in comparison with the reference material will probably lead you to the genus and species. See Appendix A for a detailed description of plant and animal groupings.

If possible, you should also try to determine the common name of the fossil. For example, *Lima wacoensis* is the scientific name of a small fossil clam, but it is also known as the "pigeon-wing clam" because of the shape of the animal's shell (Fig. 24). However, since some fossils have more than one common name, it is necessary to learn the scientific name to avoid confusion.

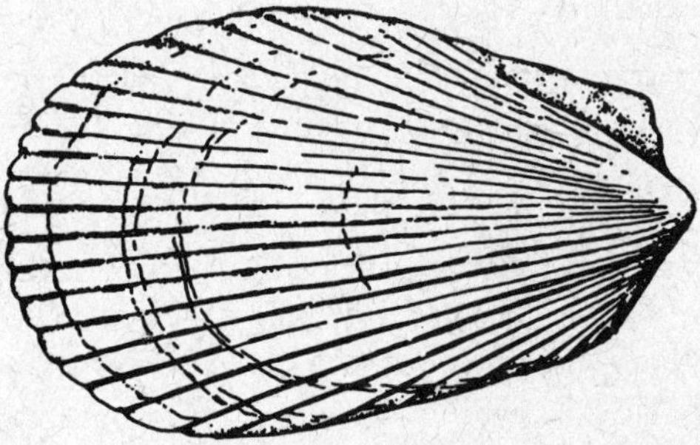

FIG. 24.—*Lima wacoensis,* the "pigeon-wing" clam from the Cretaceous of Texas (about normal size).

WHERE TO GET HELP

When the beginning collector makes his first attempt at identification, he is often bewildered by the profusion of scientific names and the great similarity between certain fossils. For this reason it is often wise to seek help from a geologist before searching the literature. Such assistance can be obtained from natural history museums, college or university geology departments, state geological surveys (see p. 313) practicing professional geologists, and other amateur paleontologists.

Natural History Museums. Museums of natural history are very good places to get help. If the museum has a geological collection, it will probably include specimens of fossil plants as well as of fossil vertebrate and invertebrate animals. It will be most helpful to compare your material with the fossils in the museum collections and to note any similarity between these specimens. Such comparisons should be carefully made, however, because many fossils bear superficial resemblances which can be most confusing.

As you study the museum collections, pay close attention to the collecting data on the label with each fossil. Note the geographic location. Was your specimen found in the same general area? Note the stratigraphic position (the age and name of the formation from which the fossil was collected). Did your fossil come from the same formation or from rocks of the same age? The locality data (the geographic and stratigraphic position) can often be a valuable indication as to whether you are working along the proper line. Needless to say, one would be wasting time comparing Cretaceous fossils with Devonian fossils in an attempt to determine the Cretaceous species.

The museum curator will probably be glad to offer advice on your specimens. If he is a paleontologist, he can often tell at a glance what specimen you have. Or he can give you some idea as to where you should start looking in the museum collections. He might, for instance, direct you to a case of Pennsylvanian ferns or Tertiary mollusks. This would be of considerable help, as it would then be unnecessary to look at ferns or mollusks of other geologic ages. The curator might also be willing to check your identification, once it has been made. Remember, however, that most museum curators are very busy people; so be sure to call at a time that is convenient to them.

On page 317 there is a list of natural history museums which display good collections of vertebrate, invertebrate, and plant fossils. This list includes, primarily, the larger museums and is by no means complete. Many cities have smaller museums with representative collections of fossils from the local area. Most colleges and universities also have fossils on display in their museums or geology buildings.

College and University Geology Departments. If you are located near a college or university which offers courses in geology, you may want to show your fossils to a geology professor. Most professors are glad to be of help, and will probably show you similar specimens in their own collections. These men are also familiar with the literature of the area, and they can offer suggestions as to where and how to collect. Not all colleges have departments of geology, but even those that do not will frequently offer at least an elementary course in geology or will have on their staffs science teachers with some geological training.

If there is no college or university nearby, contact one of the science teachers in your public schools. He may be familiar with fossils, or he may refer you to someone who is.

For many collectors who do not live near a town with a college or museum, it may be desirable to mail specimens to a paleontologist. Before doing this, however, you should exhaust all other sources of information that are available to you. Try also to come as close as possible to determining the scientific name of the fossil; at least try to determine the class or order to which the fossil belongs. If you decide to send your speciments to a specialist, first write and ask if you may send him some fossils for identification plus duplicates for his own collection. But do not send any material until you have received his permission. Remember that these men are very busy and you should not expect an immediate reply. If you are sending only a few specimens and you are sure that these are duplicated in your collection, you may tell the paleontologist to keep the specimens for his own collection. In this case, be sure to enclose a self-addressed envelope or postal card so that he can notify you of his identification.

When you have been granted the privilege of submitting your fossils for identification, the following suggestions should be observed:

1. Pack each specimen carefully with a label denoting (*a*) class or order to which the fossil belongs (if known), (*b*) locality date, including exact geographic location and the name of the geologic formation if possible, (*c*) name of the collector, and (*d*) date of collection. Pack the specimens in such a way that the fossils will not become separated from their accompanying label.

2. Place all fossils that you believe to belong to the same species in the same container or wrapping. Send at least two, preferably more, well-preserved representatives of each different type of fossil. (The number of specimens submitted may be limited by the high cost of shipping.)

3. Enclose a packing list in each shipment. This list should include (*a*) the number of specimens enclosed, (*b*) tentative identification, (*c*) geographic and geologic location, (*d*) collection date, and (*e*) collector's name.

4. Pack the shipment carefully and wrap it securely for safe mailing. The fossils should be wrapped in paper and placed in a durable cardboard carton with excelsior or newspaper as additional packing. The box should then be wrapped in heavy paper and securely tied with heavy cord. If the specimens are fragile, the package should

be so marked. But all packages should be marked "Handle With Care," as rough handling may cause the carton to come apart.

5. Before mailing the package, write a letter to the paleontologist or museum curator notifying him that the material is being sent. Tell him where the material was collected and what you want to know about it, and if you are enclosing duplicates for his collection, advise him as to the number he may keep. If you want some of the fossils returned to you, be sure to enclose enough postage to pay for the return shipment.

6. Do not become impatient or overanxious if it seems to take a long time to get your reply. Bear in mind that you are asking a favor of a very busy man, but you may be sure that he will reply just as soon as possible.

7. When you have received the information that you want, be sure to write and express your thanks.

Geological Surveys. Most states have some form of geological survey or division of geology which is concerned with geological research. It is usually located in the state capital and may be associated with one of the state universities. A list of the geological surveys of the United States will be found on page 313. Such an organization is charged with the responsibility of promoting the study of the geology of the state, and it also disseminates geological information to the general public.

If you are doing serious collecting, it would be advisable to contact your state survey and ask for their list of geological publications. By consulting this list you will be able to determine what literature is available for your general area. You can also learn what maps, geologic or topographic (see p. 54), are available. If a geological report has been prepared on the particular county that you are interested in, it should contain a geological map and a comprehensive list of all fossils that have been collected there. Check also to see if your state has published a nontechnical, or "popular," book on fossils or fossil-collecting (see p. 309). For specific references to these publications, see "Publications about Fossils" in the back of this book.

You may find it convenient to show your fossils to one of the state geologists and to ask his help in classifying your material. He will be familiar with the fossils and literature of the state and can offer valuable suggestions on many different aspects of fossil-collecting. If you cannot see a state geologist personally and should decide to send your fossils to him, be sure to follow the suggestions outlined above.

In addition to the various state geological surveys, the United States Geological Survey has published many valuable bulletins. It is possible that your public library will have some of the U. S. G. S. publications in its geology section. If not, you can write the United States Geological Survey, Washington 25, D. C., and inquire about the specific publication that you have in mind.

Practicing Professional Geologists. Most cities have practicing professional geologists who will be glad to talk to the amateur collector. They may be consulting geologists (in business for themselves) or they may be employed by an oil or mining company. Refer to the classified section of the telephone directory to see if there are any such geologists in your city.

These men can probably give you some idea as to the type of fossil that you have and where you can get additional information about it. If you should decide to call on one of these geologists, be sure to contact him well in advance and visit him at his convenience.

Other Amateur Collectors. Valuable and readily available help may come from your fellow fossil-collectors. If you are a member of the local rock and mineral club, you probably already know many of them. If there is a club of this type available and you do not already belong to it, you should, by all means, join. Many members of these clubs have been collecting for years and can make suggestions that may save you many hours of work. They may be able to identify a specimen for you or to refer you to the proper source of information. The exchange of ideas and the association with your fellow collectors can indeed be a rewarding experience for the earth science hobbyist or student.

To find out if there is a rock and mineral club in your vicinity, inquire of your local newspaper or chamber of commerce. If they do not have this information, write one of the rock and mineral magazines listed on page 311 and ask for the name of the club nearest you.

75

HOW TO USE THE PALEONTOLOGICAL LITERATURE

Although there are many publications dealing with fossils, this material is widely scattered and much of it is quite technical. If an experienced paleontologist can direct you to the proper paleontological literature, it will save you an untold amount of time. But if you are unable to get such assistance, you will have to start the search on your own.

First, check the publication list of your state geological survey for bulletins or reports dealing with the specific area in which you have collected. These publications supply valuable data on the geology of the area and provide lists of the fossils that have been reported from the various geological formations that are exposed there. Many of these reports have sections dealing with the paleontology of each formation and contain illustrations of the more common fossils. Then, too, the lists of references or bibliographies at the end of these reports contain additional books or reports which will be of further help to you.

The publications of the United States Geological Survey may be used in much the same way. Refer especially to the various editions of the *Bibliography of North American Geology* (see "Publications about Fossils" in the back of this book). In the index of each *Bibliography,* geologic publications are listed according to the respective states. Thus, a person in California can refer to the "Paleontology" entry under "California" and find out what has been written about the fossils of that state during the period covered by that particular edition. These bibliographies cover references that may not be listed in the state survey publication lists and are a very valuable source of information. Although these publications are relatively expensive, they may prove to be a worthwhile purchase for the more serious collector or student.

If you are a dedicated collector, you will probably want to buy certain of these publications, for most survey bulletins are moderately priced. Many times, however, this is not possible because some of the older publications are out of print and no longer available. In a situation of this sort you should attempt to borrow a copy from a public library or refer to it in a college or museum library. In using the literature, always try to find the latest material that is available, because of the frequent discovery of new fossils and the occasional changing of the names of old ones.

As you start to use a reference, look first at the illustrations to see if any of the figures are similar to your specimen. If you find an illustration of a fossil that resembles it, look at the caption under the figure and see where that fossil is discussed in the text of the report. Next turn to that page of the report and see what has been written about that particular specimen. It will usually be described in considerable detail, and the author will point out those features that distinguish it from similar forms. When reading descriptions of this type, you may find it helpful because of the somewhat technical terminology employed, to refer to the descriptive material pertaining to the main kinds of plants and animals in Appendix A. There you will also find illustrations (see, for example, Fig. 116) of some of the different structures and shell forms which are used by paleontologists. However, it is only with practice and continued use that you will become proficient in using the literature in identification.

In the reference section at the end of this book you will find the names of several publications that will be of considerable help in classifying your fossils. Most of these publications pertain to specific geographic areas or to rocks of a certain geologic age. One book that is particularly useful for rocks of all ages and that applies to most areas is *Index Fossils of North America* by H. W. Shimer and R. R. Shrock (published by John Wiley and Sons, New York). This useful, but rather expensive book contains descriptions and illustrations of many of the more common and important North American fossils. Included also are representatives of the major taxonomic groups which may be encountered by the average fossil-collector, plus a short section of fossil plants. All fossils are indexed according to both genus and species, and are illustrated by a large number of drawings and photographs. There is, in addition, an excellent list of general references in the introductory chapter, and more specific references under each general heading.

Of use also are the standard textbooks of paleontology and the more technical *Journal of Paleontology*. Some of the historical geology texts have a good treatment of the more common fossils as well as fine illustrations. For more detailed information about these and other publications, consult the list of references (p. 303).

Chapter VII

YOUR FOSSIL COLLECTION

One of the more enjoyable aspects of any hobby is sharing one's collection with others. You would like, of course, to display your collection in the most interesting and attractive manner. The specimens must be cleaned and provided with labels identifying each fossil and its locality.

CATALOGUING, LABELING, AND MOUNTING THE COLLECTION

The interest and scientific value of any display or exhibit depend to a large degree upon the care with which the fossils have been catalogued, labeled, and mounted.

Cataloguing. Each collector should keep some type of permanent record of all significant data pertaining to the fossil collection. This record is usually referred to as a *catalogue*. It does not matter greatly what type of cataloguing system is set up, but it is most important that such a system be adopted and conscientiously followed. Some collectors prefer a catalogue consisting of a notebook or spiral-bound composition book. Others prefer to use a filing system consisting of 3-by-5 or 5-by-7 index cards; this system is probably the most practical and most commonly used system and will be described here.

When a collection is first brought in from the field, it should be given a *locality number* which represents the geographic location where the fossils were collected. Locality numbers are used to set up the *locality catalogue*. The locality number should be written on the locality catalogue card (usually in the upper right-hand corner) and the locality data should be carefully recorded on the card (Fig. 25). (Locality information may be taken from the labels that were placed in each bag of fossils [see p. 80] or from information recorded in the field notebook.) It is sometimes useful to make a simple sketch map of the locality on the back of the card. There should also be recorded, on the face of the card, the name of the collector, date of collection, geologic age of the formation from which the fossils were collected, and any other significant information, such as notations about the different types of fossils found at this locality, their relative abundance, and their state of preservation. All such entries should be made in India ink in order that the record may be as permanent as possible.

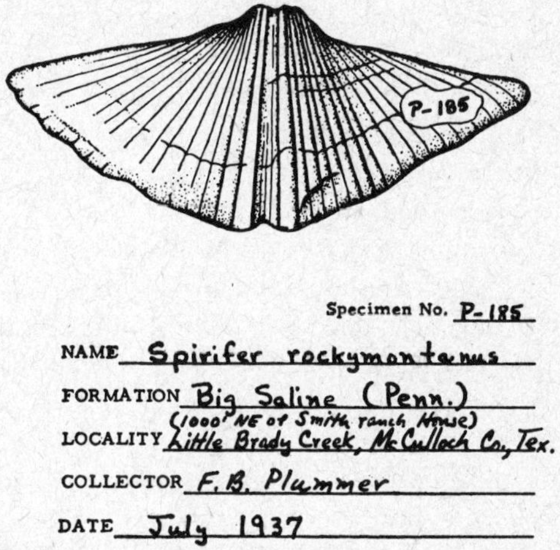

FIG. 25.—A Pennsylvanian brachiopod showing the catalogue number and the accompanying label. (By permission from *Texas Fossils* by W. H. Matthews III, Bureau of Economic Geology, University of Texas, Austin.)

Some collectors also assign a separate number to each specimen from the same locality. This specimen number should not be confused with the locality number. The specimen number should be written on the fossil with India ink, preferably on any remaining matrix or on some inconspicuous part of the specimen (Fig. 25). If the surface of the fossil is too coarse or porous for ink, the specimen number can be written on a small patch of white enamel or clear nail polish applied to the specimen. After the ink has dried, it should be coated with a dab of clear shellac or clear nail polish to help preserve the number. If each specimen is numbered it can easily be identified even if it should become separated from its label.

Many collectors find it helpful to keep, also, a *systematic catalogue* of their fossil specimens. In this catalogue there will be a card for each genus and species in the collection. The systematic catalogue should contain all known taxonomic data, such as the phylum, class, genus, species, and variety to which the specimen has been assigned. The name of the author (the scientist who first described this particular species) should be entered if it is known, and if possible this name should be followed by the date of the original description (as: *Turrilites worthensis* Adkins and Winton 1920). The locality number, specimen number (if one has been assigned), geologic age, collector, date of collection, name of the person who identified the fossil, and a brief description of the locality should also be noted. The names of any books or other publications that were used to identify the specimens can be given under the heading "References." The title, date, volume, and number of the publication, as well as references to specific pages, plate and figure numbers, etc., should also be recorded.

The locality catalogue cards should be filed numerically and the systematic catalogue cards should be filed systematically—that is, according to phylum, class, and so on. Thus, in the systematic card catalogue, cards referring to protozoan fossils would be found in the front part of the card file and cards referring to vertebrate fossils would be found in the back part of the file.

The adoption of a double cataloguing system provides a cross-check on the collection and preserves important information about each specimen. The methods described above are typical examples of fossil catalogues. Either of the above systems may be simplified or expanded to fit the needs of the collector.

Labeling. A fossil without an identifying label is little more than a curio. Because the proper labeling of each specimen is so important, all fossils should be accurately labeled just as soon as they have been cleaned and identified.

The label should contain, if possible, the scientific name of the specimen, and, even more important, the location and the geologic formation from which the specimen was collected (Fig. 25). This information can be obtained from the label that was placed in each bag of fossils at the time they were collected, or from the field notebook (it is a good practice to check one against the other). The information should then be recorded on a permanent label, which is placed in the tray or box containing the fossil. If the fossils are to be mounted on display boards, the label may be secured to the board beneath the proper specimen. Each label should contain such information as (1) the scientific name of the fossil, (2) the geologic formation from which the fossil was collected, (3) the exact collecting locality, (4) the name of the collector, (5) the date the fossil was collected, and (6) the specimen number, which is usually placed in the upper right-hand corner of the label (Fig. 25). The specimen number should correspond with the number previously placed on the fossil. Since the same number is on both fossil and label, it is a simple matter to reattach the proper labels if they should become separated from the fossils.

Courtesy of Ward's Natural Science Establishment

FIG. 26.—Compartmented collection box with fitted individual trays.

Labels should be typed or be printed with India ink; some collectors spray or paint the label with clear plastic to prevent fading and to discourage the attacks of silverfish.

Mounting. Fossils are usually exhibited on display boards or in trays or drawers, although special mountings are sometimes employed (see p. 89). If trays or boxes are compartmented (Fig. 26), it is not necessary to glue the specimens to the bottom of the tray. If you wish to attach the specimens permanently, glue them to cards and display boards with one of the white glues which dries clear. Such glues, for example Borden's or LePage's, may be obtained at most hardware, variety, or drug stores. These glues are very strong and may be used on wood, paper, cloth, and other porous material. Larger specimens may be attached to the board by means of fine wire. Small holes are drilled in the board; the wire is then passed over the specimen and the loose ends twisted together behind the board.

Suitable display boards can be made from Upson board, masonite, celotex, and plywood. It is a good idea to strengthen the board by means of a wooden border made of screen molding or some similar type of material; this border serves to hold the display board erect and to prevent it from warping. The display board may then be hung from the wall where it can be seen to its best advantage.

DISPLAYING THE COLLECTION

The way in which the collection is exhibited will probably depend upon the amount of time, space, and money that can be allotted to the display. A really good exhibit demands considerable thought and careful planning if it is to be shown to the best advantage.

Before setting up your first display it would be helpful to visit other collectors and see how their material is displayed. In this way it is possible to pick up new ideas and to profit from the experience of a veteran collector.

Although some collectors exhibit their specimens in special cabinets, many use china cabinets, chests of drawers, bookcases, and whatnot shelves. Still others build shelving or construct special display racks that will show their collection in an attractive manner and yet require a minimum of space. Another space-saving display method is the display board which holds both fossils and labels and can be hung from the wall (see p. 86).

Fossils may also be displayed on small wooden stands or bases which have sloping fronts to whch labels may be attached (Fig. 27). Display bases of this sort may be made by the collector or may be purchased from one of the supply houses. Cardboard collection boxes containing individual trays (Fig. 26) are also convenient for both storage and display.

Delicate or unusual specimens may be displayed in a *Riker Mount.* The Riker Mount is a shallow cardboard box, glass-topped and filled with cotton (Fig. 28). The specimen is placed on top of the cotton and is held in place by the pressure of the glass top

FIG. 27.—Fossils mounted on wooden display bases. (Left) *Asteroceras tuberosum* an ammonite from the Jurassic of England. (Right) *Juresania,* a Pennsylvanian brachiopod.

Courtesy of Ward's Natural Science Establishment

FIG. 28.—Fossil collection displayed in Riker Mount.

against the specimen and the cotton backing. The top of the mount is held in place by a pin on each side of the box. Some collectors apply adhesive picture-hangers to the back of the mount, thus transforming it into an attractive framed exhibit suitable for hanging on the wall. These mounts may be obtained in a variety of sizes ranging from 2½ by 3½ inches to 16 by 24 inches and can be purchased from one of the natural science supply establishments. The supply houses also offer a variety of other special storage and display equipment, such as cardboard trays, wooden and metal storage cases, and glass-panel museum-type display cases of all sizes. The latter may be equipped with fluorescent lighting fixtures if desired.

Regardless of the type of display decided upon, the specimens should always be as clean as possible, correctly and clearly labeled, and arranged in an attractive, orderly, and uncrowded manner.

SPECIAL EXHIBITS

Fossils can be exhibited in a number of special ways, each of which can tell a different story about the material that is shown.

Stratigraphic Display. In this type of exhibit the fossils are displayed in chronologic order, that is, according to their geologic age, with the oldest specimens in the collection mounted first, and these followed by representative species from successively older rocks. This type of display will also show how most life forms have become increasingly complex through geologic time. Each specimen should be labeled as to age, scientific name, and, where possible, the common name.

Phylogenetic Display. Other specimens might be arranged to show representative fossils in the probable order of their development through geologic time. These specimens would be shown in phylogenetic sequence (i.e., in the order of their probable descent), beginning with fossil protozoans and ending with vertebrate material such as bones or teeth (Fig. 29).

"What Is a Fossil?" Display. This exhibit is designed to answer the question "What is a Fossil?" Labels are used to define briefly the terms *paleontology* and *fossil* and the various paleontological subsciences—*paleobotany, invertebrate paleontology, vertebrate paleontology,* and *micropaleontology*. Representative specimens of plant fossils, microfossils, and vertebrate and invertebrate fossils should be shown under each of the above subdivisions (Fig. 30).

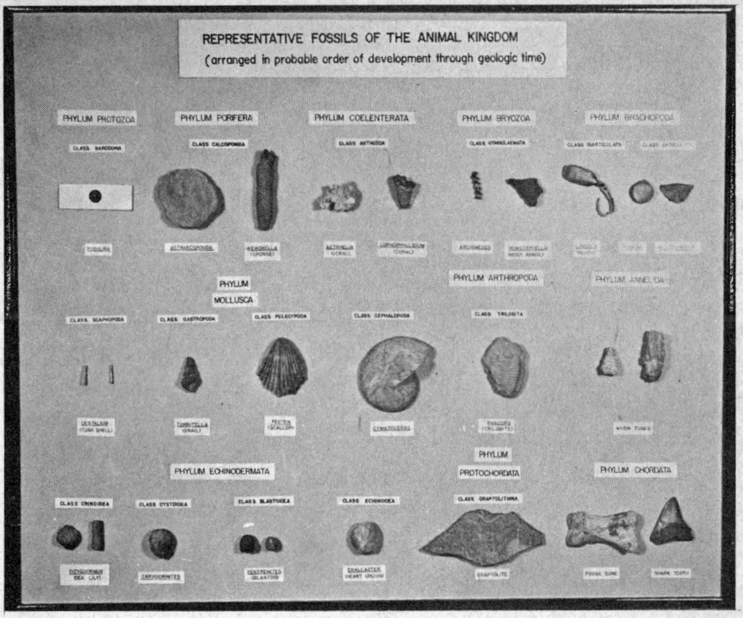

FIG. 29.—Fossil display board showing specimens arranged in phylogenetic order.

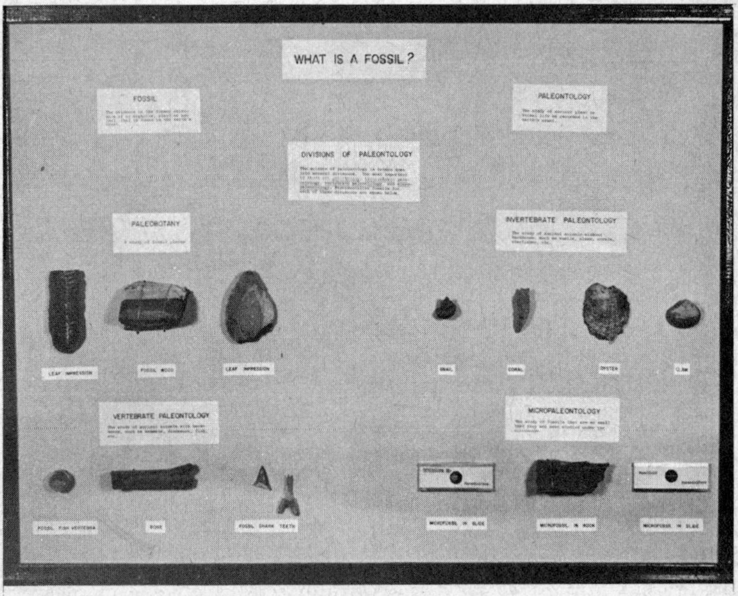

FIG. 30.—Display board that answers the question: "What is a Fossil?"

Types of Fossilization Display. This type of exhibit (Fig. 31) illustrates the ways in which organic remains can become fossilized. Specimens of each kind of fossilization (for example, "Unaltered Hard Parts," such as an oyster shell or fish tooth) are displayed; and each specimen is accompanied by a brief statement as to how it was preserved and what it represents. A combination of this exhibit and the "What Is a Fossil?" display will provide the viewer

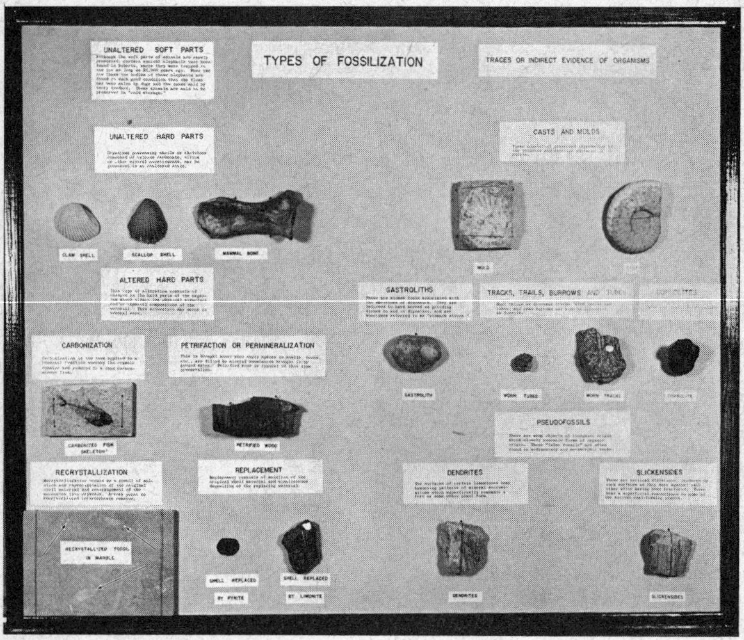

FIG. 31.—Fossil display board illustrating the various types of fossilization.

with a clear insight into what fossils are, how they may be recognized, and how they are preserved.

Display Comparing Fossil and Recent Specimens. It is also interesting to illustrate the relationships between fossils and the plants and animals of today (Fig. 32). This can be done by using specimens which will show a comparison between a fossil and the remains of a similar recent form. Thus, the fossil remains of a Tertiary gastropod might be mounted beside the shell of a recent gastropod of similar shape or size. Comparisons between fossil and recent clams, corals, brachiopods, nautiloids, plants, and many other forms can also be shown in this manner. The exhibit should be arranged in phylogenetic order and show as many different forms as possible. Recent shells may be collected at the beach; or they may be purchased in curio shops or from a shell dealer. Most of the natural science supply houses also carry this type of material.

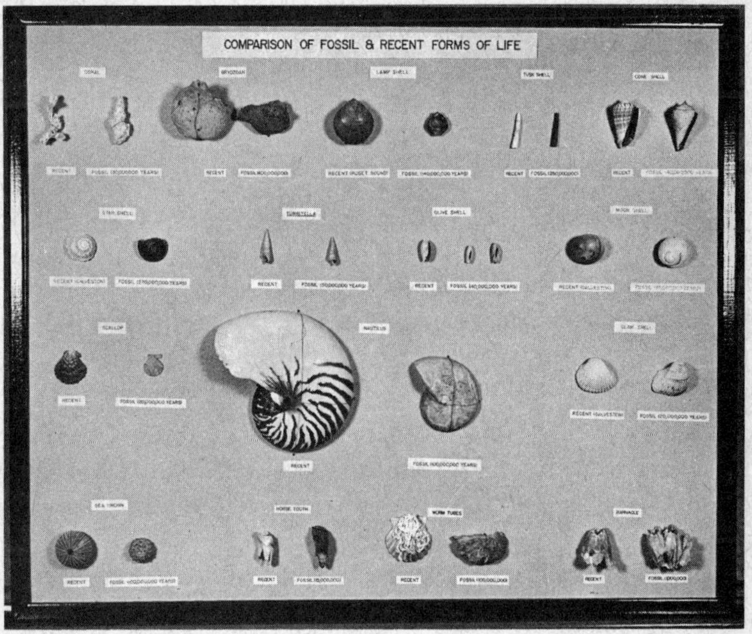

FIG. 32.—Display illustrating relationships of living forms to comparable fossil specimens.

Geographic or Regional Display. An unusual way to display fossils is to concentrate on the fossils that occur in a given area. You might wish to show, for example, representative fossils from a certain state or the particular locality from which most of the fossils were collected. This type of exhibit can be prepared in two ways. In the first, you can make a large outline map of the area to be covered and place it on heavy poster board or wall board. Key cities and/or counties should be designated on the map. Next, representative fossils can be glued to the map (see "Mounting," p. 81) in the approximate area from which they were collected. Care should be taken to show the more typical species; and, of course, large and heavy specimens should be avoided. The finished map should be strengthened with a wooden border to hold it erect and prevent warping, and the exhibit can be hung on the wall or placed on a table.

Still another way to display the fossils of a given area is to make the map as described above but place the fossils on a table and attach them to the map by means of colored strings or ribbons (Fig. 33). This type of exhibit requires more space than the wall type but has the added advantage of permitting a greater number and variety of specimens to be used. Then, too, because more space is

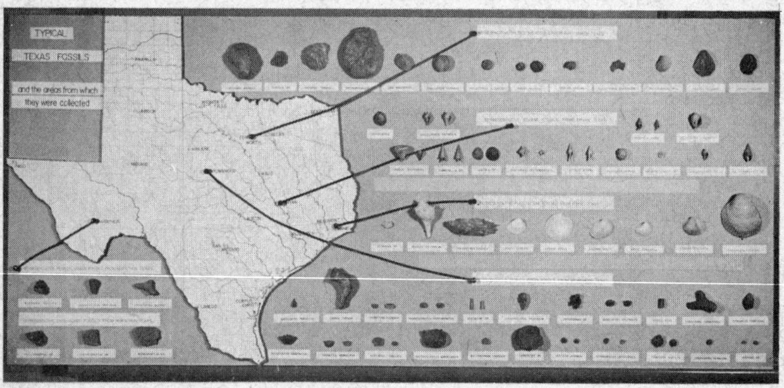

FIG. 33.—Regional display of fossils. Representative fossils from selected areas in Texas are illustrated here.

available, it is possible to include fossils from a larger number of collecting localities. A spot of glue is used to attach one end of the string to the fossil, and another dab of glue will attach the opposite end of the string to the map.

Formational Display. Some collectors prefer to display the fauna of certain geologic formations as individual exhibits or displays. If the specimens are small they may be glued to cards which have been ruled into squares. The name of the formation can be written at the top of the card, and the name of each fossil in the square directly beneath the specimen. The card can be cut to fit the bottom of small cardboard cartons or cigar boxes, and the name of the formation can be placed on one end and on the top of the box. If it is not desirable to mount the fossils permanently, you can make cardboard partitions for the box and place a specimen, with a label, in each partitioned space.

Whatever display method is decided upon, the material should be displayed in such a way that it will tell a story or, at least, be self-explanatory. For this reason, the layout should be carefully planned, and each specimen should be clearly and neatly labeled. It is important to arrange the material in such a way that the viewer can easily follow the theme of the story that is being told.

SPECIAL TECHNIQUES

Many collectors like to make plaster models of their fossils and to use these in their displays. Others have experimented with embedding fossils in clear plastic or partially embedding them in plaster of Paris mounts. Some like to photograph their specimens.

Making Plaster Models. Plaster casts of rare or unusual fossils are often made. Liquid rubber, also called "liquid latex," is probably the most widely used material for making molds from which to cast plaster models. This material is easy to apply, dries quickly, and can be obtained from most art, hobby, or handicraft shops.

The steps for making a rubber mold are as follows:

1. Be sure that the fossil is clean and dry.

2. Using a soft brush, apply liquid rubber to the surface of the fossil with smooth, even strokes. The rubber should be carefully worked into surface irregularities such as ribs, spines, or nodes, and air bubbles should be avoided.

3. After the first coat has dried (this usually takes about fifteen minutes), apply another coat and add subsequent coats until the rubber covering is about ½-inch thick. When you have finished, wash the brush thoroughly in warm soapy water.

4. When the mold is completely dry, remove it carefully from the original fossil.

5. After the original has been removed, carefully wash and dry the interior of the mold to remove any foreign material that may be present. The mold is then ready to be used to make a plaster cast.

Although several types of casting materials are available, plaster of Paris is most commonly used in making models of fossils; it is easily obtained from most drug, paint, or hardware stores. The procedure for making a plaster cast of a fossil, using the rubber mold described above, is as follows:

1. Fill a plastic or pottery bowl with the correct amount of water (experimentation is the best way to determine the correct amount).

2. Next, add plaster of Paris slowly until the plaster is slightly above the surface of the water. It is best to use a generous amount of plaster to make sure that there will be enough of the mixture to fill the mold completely.

3. Thoroughly mix the plaster and water with a stick or spatula until the mixture has the consistency of thick cream.

4. Pour this mixture into the rubber mold. Make certain that the plaster reaches all parts of the mold and that all air bubbles have been blown away or have been punctured with a pin.

5. After allowing the plaster to harden (this usually takes forty-five minutes to one hour), remove the cast carefully from the mold and allow it to dry.

FIG. 34.—Plaster cast of a trilobite. A latex mold was used to cast this specimen.

6. Wash and dry the mold after each cast to remove any pieces of plaster that may have adhered to the inside of the mold.

The completed cast may be painted with water colors to approximate the coloration of the original specimen (Fig. 34). If you like, powdered or liquid tempera paint may be added to the plaster of Paris or water to give a uniform color to the casting mixture.

Embedding Fossils in Bio-Plastic. Liquid casting plastic, commonly called Bio-Plastic, is a synthetic resin in the form of a syrupy liquid. With the addition of a catalytic agent and the application of gentle heat, Bio-Plastic hardens into a crystal-clear solid (Fig. 35).

Bio-Plastic may be used to embed rare, delicate, or other highly prized specimens that the collector wishes to show to best advantage. Not only does the plastic provide an attractive mount, but it provides ample protection while still leaving the fossil available for close examination.

A discussion of plastic-casting techniques is beyond the scope of this book; those desiring additional information about this type of mounting should send for a copy of *How to Embed in Ward's Bio-Plastic*. (This free publication is available from Ward's Natural Science Establishment, P. O. Box 1712, Rochester 3, New York.)

Partially Embedding Fossils in Plaster of Paris. Fossils may also be mounted on plaster of Paris blocks (Fig. 36). After mixing the plaster as described above, pour the mixture into a shallow tray or dish (such as a coaster or ash tray) that has previously been

Courtesy of Ward's Natural Science Establishment

Fig. 35.—Ammonite mounted in Bio-Plastic.

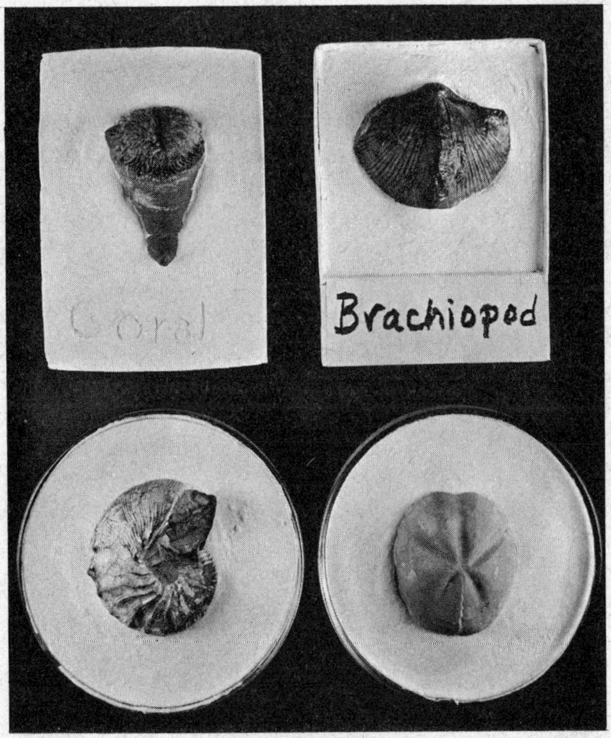

Fig. 36.—Fossils mounted in plaster of Paris. From left to right: Paleozoic coral; Paleozoic brachiopods; Cretaceous ammonite; Cretaceous "heart urchin" (echinoid).

lightly oiled. After the plaster has hardened slightly, the fossil should be gently, but firmly, pressed into the top of the plaster. When the plaster is completely set, the block may be removed by tapping the bottom and sides of the mold. A colored base is easily obtained by adding tempera or water-soluble paint to the plaster mixture before pouring it into the mold. If desired, the name of the specimen may be inscribed on the block before the plaster has thoroughly hardened.

PHOTOGRAPHING FOSSILS

Some collectors have combined the hobbies of fossil-collecting and photography and have made excellent photographs of their specimens. Much of this type of photography is close-up work, as many of the specimens are relatively small. Close-up lenses or attachments can be added to most cameras, and some of the medium-priced cameras will focus as close as two to three feet. More expensive models will focus to within a few inches of the specimen.

Photographs may be taken on black-and-white or color film and in daylight or under artificial lighting. Exposures are best determined by a photoelectric exposure meter, but the settings given on the exposure-data sheet that accompanies the film may be used as a general guide.

Lighting is most important, and photoflood lamps are recommended as they give the photographer excellent control of the lighting situation. The main light (a No. 2 photoflood in a 10-inch reflector is recommended) should come from the upper left side and should be so adjusted as to bring out the more important surface features of the specimen. A smaller bulb in a smaller reflector may be used as a fill-in light and should be positioned at right angles to the main light. If enlargements are to be made, it is best to use one of the slower fine-grained films, and the exposed film should be processed in one of the fine-grain developers. This procedure will eliminate or minimize objectionable graininess in the final print.

Some paleontologists coat fossils with ammonium chloride before taking the photographs. This gives the specimen a uniform coating of white which brings out the surface features and shows them to best advantage.

Chapter VIII

A GLIMPSE INTO THE PAST

Our discussion of fossils, thus far, has clearly shown that plants and animals have not always been as they appear today. The earth's physical features have also changed.

At various times in earth history the seas have risen and the continents have been flooded by the encroaching waters. Thus, areas which we now know as continents have formerly been the sites of ancient seas and waterways. During later periods of geologic time these seas retreated, draining the water from the lands and leaving a record of the geological history of the area. This history is recorded in the sediments which were later consolidated to form the rocks as we know them today. The geologist, applying the stratigraphic principles discussed in Chapter III, carefully studies these ancient sediments and their enclosed fossils in an attempt to unravel the physical and biological history of the area.

Earth scientists are continually piecing together the record of great changes in climate, geography, and life that have taken place in prehistoric times. These changes are the clues by which they can reconstruct the more important events in the history of the earth.

This chapter is concerned with those changes, both physical and biological, which have played an important part in earth history. It should contribute to a better understanding of fossils and the rocks in which they are found. (Before reading further, the reader may find it helpful to review briefly the Geologic Time Scale on p. xii.)

THE ARCHEOZOIC ERA

During this portion of geologic time the earth was devoid of life so far as can be determined by direct fossil evidence. However, the occurrence of supposed organic limestones and carbon-bearing deposits strongly indicates the presence of organisms. It is believed that most of these early organisms had not yet developed hard parts and were, therefore, incapable of being preserved.

Archeozoic rocks are composed primarily of highly *metamorphosed* sedimentary and igneous rock and give evidence of much volcanic activity.

THE PROTEROZOIC ERA

During this era, often referred to as late Precambrian time, primitive life was present, as indicated by the fragments and impressions of soft-bodied plants and animals. These fossils consist primarily of the remains of radiolarians, worm burrows, a few primitive brachiopods, and calcareous algae. The algae built large masses of organic limestone and are the most abundant fossils of this time. These ancient plants (Fig. 80), are sometimes called "stone cabbages." They formed thick reeflike deposits in certain areas.

Proterozoic rocks are composed of igneous, sedimentary, and metamorphic types. Sedimentary rocks are predominant and consist of shales and sandstones, plus some *tillite* (rock formed from material deposited by glaciers). There are also numerous lava flows and other evidence of volcanic activity.

The end of Precambrian time was marked by extensive *orogeny* (mountain-building) on the continents. These orogenic movements resulted in fracturing, folding, and other great changes in the rocks; and the lands were elevated well above sea level. This great disturbance, called the *Killarney Revolution,* was followed by extensive erosion which probably lasted for millions of years. During this portion of geologic time the Precambrian mountains were worn away, and the rock fragments derived from the erosive processes were deposited elsewhere.

This period of erosion is marked by a great unconformity (see p. 36). There is no way of knowing the amount of geologic history that is lost in this great erosional break in the record. We do know, however, that it was long enough for the primitive life of the Precambrian to develop into the relatively complex invertebrate animals which appear in the Cambrian.

THE PALEOZOIC ERA

Numerous fossils remain from the Paleozoic era, for Paleozoic rocks have not been subjected to such great physical change as have those of the Precambrian. With the beginning of the Paleozoic era, therefore, we can more accurately interpret the various physical and biological events of earth history.

The Paleozoic era has been divided into seven periods of geologic time. These periods were of varying duration and are separated on the basis of relatively brief periods of broad continental uplift. The uplifts were followed by advances of the seas, which again submerged the continents and brought with them the sediments that would be the evidence of the next geologic period.

The Cambrian Period. The oldest period of the Paleozoic has been named the Cambrian. The period derived its name from *Cambria,* the Roman name for Wales. It was here that the rocks were first studied and described.

PHYSICAL HISTORY. In Cambrian time sedimentary rocks were deposited in great troughs on the east and west coasts of North America. Large thicknesses of shales, sandstones, and limestones accumulated in these ancient seas, which at one time covered as much as 30 per cent of the North American continent. These sediments were derived from the weathering of Precambrian igneous, metamorphic, and sedimentary rocks.

At the end of the Cambrian, the continents were raised and the seas retreated. There is little evidence of Cambrian mountain-building with the exception of the *Green Mountain,* or *Vermontian, Disturbance*. This orogeny was confined to New England and the east coast of Canada.

The climate of this period is rather difficult to infer. In general, however, the presence of limestone deposits and typical marine organisms suggests a rather warm, mild climate.

CAMBRIAN LIFE. Because Precambrian rocks contain few and poorly preserved fossils, we must look to the Cambrian rocks for the first reliable record of former life. This record indicates that land masses were still barren and devoid of life but that in the warm, shallow seas large numbers of marine plants and invertebrates were thriving. The majority of invertebrate phyla and classes are represented by Cambrian fossils, but the vertebrates are notably absent.

Although Cambrian life was unlike that of the present (Fig. 37), it was not as totally primitive as one might suppose, and it ranged from simple spongelike creatures to complex arthropods.

The dominant animals of Cambrian seas were the *trilobites* (Fig. 128) and *brachiopods* (Fig. 105). Together these make up 80 to 90

Fig. 37.—Reconstruction of Middle Cambrian sea floor. This restoration, representing an area in British Columbia, shows swimming jellyfishes (*4*), large arthropods (*3* and *5*), branching sponges, (*2*), trilobites (*1* and *8*), sea cucumbers (*7*) and seaweed (*6*). (Diorama by George Marchand, courtesy of the University of Michigan Museum of Paleontology.)

per cent of known Cambrian fossils. Most trilobites ranged from one to four inches in length, but certain giant forms grew to be as much as eighteen inches long. Brachiopods were predominantly small inarticulate forms with phosphatic shells.

Present also, but in smaller number, were *sponges* and *spongelike animals, worms, cystoids, snails,* and *cephalopods.*

Cambrian rocks, in general, may be expected to yield mostly trilobites and brachiopods. A few localities, however, have provided the paleontologist with varied and numerous well-preserved speci-

Courtesy of U. S. National Museum

FIG. 38.—Trails of extinct invertebrates on ripple-marked Cambrian sandstone.

mens (Fig. 9). The best-known and most important locality of this type is that of the Burgess Shale in Canada (see p. 17).

The Ordovician Period. The Ordovician period was named for the Ordovices, an ancient tribe of North Wales.

PHYSICAL HISTORY. The physical appearance of North America during Ordovician time was much different from the one we know today. The continents were lowered even more than in Cambrian time, allowing widespread invasion of the seas. At the height of this great inundation, as much as 70 per cent of the North American continent was under water.

As these great seas spread over the continent, they deposited thick beds of shales and limestones. These limestones and the multitudes of fossil marine invertebrates of Ordovician age suggest warm, uniform temperatures and an absence of climatic barriers.

Throughout Cambrian and Ordovician time, vast deposits of marine sediments had been accumulating from eastern Canada, through western New England, New York, and Pennsylvania to Virginia. In late Ordovician time these sediments were uplifted and folded into the *Taconian Mountains,* which attained their maximum development in western New England and eastern New York. This orogeny, called the *Taconian Disturbance,* was accompanied by considerable volcanic activity.

The end of the period was further marked by a general retreat of the widespread seas that had long dominated the Ordovician scene.

ORDOVICIAN LIFE. The warm Ordovician seas were inhabited by large numbers of marine invertebrates (Figs. 39 and 40), and their remains have provided fossil-collectors with some of the world's finest specimens. There are especially fossiliferous outcrops of Upper Ordovician rocks in Ohio and Indiana.

Ordovician life was more complex and more varied than that of the Cambrian. The dominant Cambrian forms, the trilobites and brachiopods, were even more abundant than before and were joined by several other important fossil-forming groups.

Plant life consisted almost wholly of seaweed and algae.

Corals made their first appearance early in the Ordovician; they were represented by both solitary and colonial types.

Bryozoans first appear in Lower Ordovician rocks, although questionable bryozoans have been reported from Upper Cambrian rocks. During this portion of geologic time, they underwent rapid and extensive development. These tiny animals built branching calcareous colonies which added much to the limestone-building process of that time.

Brachiopods developed more durable shells of calcium carbonate, permitting adaptation to a wider range of environments.

Gastropods, while abundant and varied, are usually found in a very poor state of preservation.

Pelecypods, usually found as internal or external molds, became increasingly abundant in the latter part of the period. The clams, like the snails, are usually poorly preserved and difficult to identify.

Cephalopods were the giants of the Ordovician. One straight-shelled form, *Endoceras* (Fig. 39), grew to be as much as fifteen feet long. It had a maximum diameter of almost one foot and was

Courtesy of Chicago Natural History Museum *C. R. Knight*

FIG. 39.—An Ordovician seashore. The giant cephalopod *Endoceras* (*1*), which grew to be as much as fifteen feet long, is shown here with flat coiled cephalopods (*2*) and trilobites (*3*). All have been washed ashore after a storm.

FIG. 40.—Life of an Ordovician sea floor. This reconstruction, representing an area near Chicago, shows straight-shelled swimming nautiloid cephalopods (*1*); tabulate "honeycomb" corals (*2*); trilobites: *Calymene* (*4*), and *Isotelus* (*5*); solitary corals tentacles extended (*6*); a snail (*7*); and a large straight-shelled nautiloid (*8*) resting on the bottom. Seaweeds, brachiopods, coiled cephalopods, and several different types of corals are also shown. (Restoration by George Marchand, courtesy of Chicago Natural History Museum.)

the largest animal of the time. Most Ordovician cephalopods are characterized by straight shells, but some species developed curved, loosely coiled, or tightly coiled shells.

Ostracodes, tiny bivalved crustaceans, first occur in the Lower Ordovician. Large numbers of these may be collected in certain Ordovician shales and limestones.

Trilobites apparently reached the peak of their development during this period. Some species assumed unusual shapes, and one type reached a length of almost thirty inches.

Echinoderms were predominantly the attached types. Typical representatives were the *cystoids,* primitive *blastoids,* and numerous *crinoids.* A few free-moving echinoderms, including the first *starfishes,* were also present.

Graptolites were among the most distinctive and common animals of the Ordovician seas. These floating colonial animals, which attained world-wide distribution by drifting with the ocean currents, have proved extremely valuable in intercontinental correlation.

Vertebrates, consisting of small, primitive, armored fishes with backbones, made their first appearance in the Ordovician period. The introduction of these animals marks one of the most important events in the development of animal life. Their skeletal remains consist of fragmental bony plates and scales, found primarily in the Rocky Mountain area. These early fishes are known as *ostracoderms* ("armored skin") (Figs. 47–*3* and 47–*5*) and are believed to be related to the modern hagfish or lamprey (see p. 254).

The Silurian Period. The Silurian, like the Ordovician, was first studied in Wales, the name being derived from an ancient Welsh tribe, the Silures.

Physical History. At the beginning, and also during the middle, of Silurian time, oceanic waters again covered North America.

Lower Silurian rocks consist primarily of thick beds of conglomerates and sandstones which were deposited from western New York to Alabama. This distribution indicates that the land along the east coast was still quite high in the Early Silurian.

Middle Silurian deposits are characterized by shales, limestones, and dolomites. Considerable Middle Silurian volcanic activity is indicated by thick lava flows and beds of volcanic ash in New Brunswick and Maine.

Late Silurian time found the seas more restricted; desert conditions must have predominated across New York, northern Pennsylvania, southern Ontario, and southern Michigan. An isolated sea in this area underwent excessive evaporation, resulting in great salt deposits. These layers of salt and gypsum were deposited over an area of 100,000 square miles, and in places reach a maximum thickness of 1,800 feet. Silurian deposits are thin and relatively scarce in the western United States.

The end of Silurian time on this continent was marked by a regression of the continental seas. There is no evidence of mountain-building or extensive uplift in North America. But in western Europe the *Caledonian Disturbance* resulted in the uplift of lofty mountain ranges extending about 4,000 miles across several countries.

SILURIAN LIFE. Silurian seas were warm and temperate. Such conditions were most favorable for supporting the marine life of the time (Figs. 41 and 42). This was particularly a time of coral-reef building, and the widespread distribution of these reefs points to an absence of restricted climatic zones.

In general, Silurian invertebrates showed marked similarity to those of the Ordovician. Some groups, however, underwent considerable expansion, while others diminished in numbers and variety.

Plant life made a decided advance with the development of the earliest known land plants. Their remains, unfortunately, are poorly preserved and do not provide much information as to their nature.

Corals, particularly reef-building types, became far more numerous. *Halysites,* the chain coral (Fig. 100–*3*), and *Favosites* (Fig. 100–2), the honey-comb coral, are typical of this period.

Bryozoans were still abundant and important as rock-builders in certain regions.

Brachiopods developed even more than in earlier periods, resulting in many new types. Silurian brachiopods indicate a trend to relatively smoother, globular, short-hinged shells.

Mollusks were represented by *gastropods, pelecypods,* and *cephalopods.* But none of these were an important part of the fauna.

Ostracodes, some attaining a length of an inch, were abundant and flourished in the warm Silurian seas.

Eurypterids (Figs. 42 and 129) though appearing first in the Ordovician, reached the height of their development in the Silurian. These scorpionlike arthropods usually ranged from a few inches to a foot in length, but a few species were as much as seven to nine

Courtesy of Buffalo Museum of Science

FIG. 41.—Restoration of Silurian sea bottom in vicinity of Buffalo, New York. Crinoids (*1*) and cystoids (*7*) are shown along with straight-shelled cephalopods (*2*), trilobites (*3*, *4*, and *5*), bryozoans (*6*), and corals (*8*). In addition, clams, brachiopods, and several small trilobites may be seen on the sea floor.

feet long. The first known land animals appear in the Silurian. They were similar to the present-day scorpions and were probably descended from the eurypterids.

Trilobites, which had been so typical of the Cambrian and Ordovician faunas, were declining in numbers. Many Silurian trilobites underwent a remarkable degree of specialization, resulting in long spines and in bodies with peculiar shapes.

Echinoderms were represented by *cystoids, blastoids, crinoids,* and an occasional *echinoid*. The *crinoids,* or sea lilies, were the predominant echinoderms. Their remains are so numerous in certain limestones that these rocks are called "crinoid hash."

Graptolites, rare in Silurian rocks, appear to have been much less abundant than in the Ordovician.

Vertebrates of the Silurian consisted of primitive fishes of the ostracoderm type. But their remains are exceedingly rare.

Courtesy of Rochester Museum of Arts and Sciences

FIG. 42.—Silurian *Eurypterus* feeding on worm. These extinct scorpionlike arthropods appear to have lived in waters of relatively low salinity, as their remains are not usually found in association with typical marine forms.

The Devonian Period. The Devonian system derives its name from Devonshire, England, where it was first studied.

PHYSICAL HISTORY. In early Devonian time the sea advanced along the old Appalachian trough which paralleled the east coast of North America. But very little of the North American continent was submerged at this time.

Throughout the Middle Devonian a long seaway extended from Alaska across the Mississippi Valley. This body of water connected with a more narrow sea which reached from southern California across Nevada and Utah. During this part of the Devonian, as much as 40 per cent of the continent was submerged. The presence of reef-building corals and thick limestone deposits is indicative of warm, temperate climates.

Upper Devonian rocks in North America are characterized by thick shales and sandstones. The seas gradually withdrew in Late Devonian time so that by the end of the period most of the continent was virtually devoid of water.

Early in Middle Devonian time, parts of New England and the

Acadian region in Canada were subjected to gradual uplift. These orogenic movements, continuing until the end of the Devonian, terminated in the building of the *Acadian Mountains.*

DEVONIAN LIFE. Life in the Devonian was varied and profuse. Marine invertebrates continued to dominate the scene (Figs. 43, 44, and 45). Devonian outcrops in western New York, Iowa, Indiana, and northern Michigan afford excellent collecting for both amateurs and professionals.

Land plants were plentiful, and their remains are the earliest that can be studied in detail. These include many types, ranging from small leafless plants a few inches in height to giant tree ferns forty feet tall (Fig. 43). The addition of these land plants to the continent must have done much to improve the appearance of Middle and Late Paleozoic landscapes. Plant spores, useful as microfossils, appeared first during this period and became increasingly abundant in later geologic periods.

Sponges, particularly those with siliceous skeletons, underwent marked expansion. Especially typical of the time were *Hydnoceras* and *Prismodictya* (Fig. 91–*1*).

Corals were very numerous, attained large sizes, and built extensive reefs (Fig. 44).

Bryozoans flourished among the coral reefs and were of many different types.

Brachiopods reached their peak; in certain Devonian shales and limestones their remains were both abundant and varied. *Chonetes* and *Spirifer* were particularly numerous in Devonian seas.

Mollusks continued to develop and invade new environments (Fig. 45). *Gastropods* are usually not well preserved, but loosely coiled forms such as *Platyceras* (Fig. 46) are typical. *Pelecypods* and *cephalopods* were of many types. Cephalopods were characterized by the goniatite suture pattern, rounded saddles and angular lobes, (Fig. 121-*b*). This marked the first departure from the nautiloid-type suture of earlier periods.

Trilobites were still declining, but a few types were abundant in limited areas. Some of these were very large, and one species of *Dalmanites* attained a maximum length of twenty-nine inches.

Echinoderms, with the exception of the *sea lilies,* were less abundant than any of the groups discussed above.

Vertebrates apparently underwent rapid evolution during the Devonian, and most groups of modern fishes had developed by the

Courtesy of Chicago Natural History Museum *C. R. Knight*

FIG. 43.—Early land plants. This scene reconstructs an area in western New York in Middle Devonian time. Shown here are one of the early tree ferns (*1*), horsetail rushes (*2*), a "scale tree" one of the early lycopods (*3*), and *Psilophyton* (*4*) a primitive plant with no leaves.

Courtesy of Rochester Museum of Arts and Sciences

FIG. 44.—Restoration of part of a sea floor in western New York at the beginning of Middle Devonian time. Corals, both solitary and colonial (*1–5*), are the dominant animals in this scene. However, crinoids, or "sea lilies," (*6*), *Gyroceras* (*7*), a coiled frilled cephalopod (capturing a trilobite), and a large uncoiled nautiloid cephalopod (*8*) are at rest on the bottom. Present also are several trilobites (*9–11*). The large spiny trilobite *Terataspis grandis* (*10*) attained a length of almost two feet.

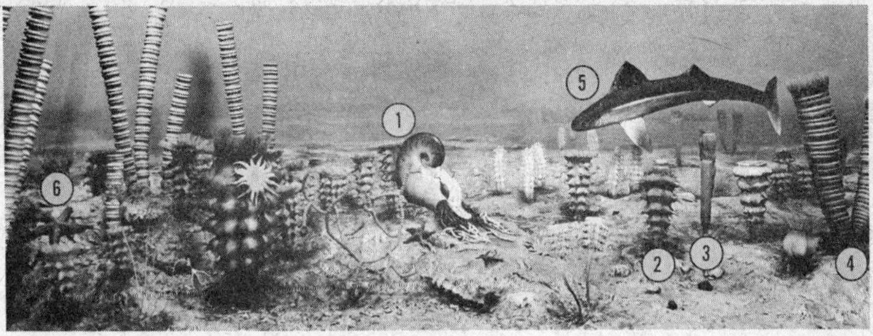

Courtesy of Rochester Museum of Arts and Sciences

FIG. 45.—Reconstruction of Late Devonian sea bottom in western New York. A large coiled cephalopod (*1*) crawls along the bottom among several types of sponges (*2* and *3*), and large solitary corals (*4*). The sharklike *Cladoselache* swims overhead (*5*) and a large starfish (*6*) is on the extreme left.

end of the period. Because of this rapid expansion and the occurrence of numerous well-preserved fish remains, the Devonian has been called the "Age of Fishes" (Fig. 47). Still present were the primitive ostracoderms, but they were joined by the *placoderms,* the first fishes with jaws (see p. 254).

The earliest true *sharks* (those with cartilaginous skeletons) first appear in the Devonian. Also present were a group of sharklike fish called *arthrodires* (see p. 255). These peculiar animals were heavily armored and attained a length of as much as thirty feet (Fig. 147).

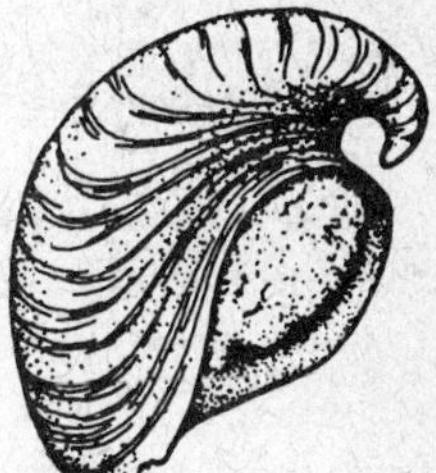

FIG. 46.—*Platyceras,* a loosely coiled Devonian gastropod (about actual size).

Present for the first time were the *lungfishes.* This primitive group possessed gills but had developed lungs as accessory breathing organs. Representatives of this group are still living today, forming an important link between the gill-breathing fishes and air-breathing amphibians. Not only was the swim bladder modified to serve as a primitive lung, but some of these fishes developed paired flipper-like fins; they were therefore able to live, for a short period, out of water and to have a limited degree of mobility on the land.

Amphibians made their appearance in the Devonian, marking another milestone in vertebrate development. Like modern amphibians, these early forms could live on the land in the adult stage but had to go back to the water to lay their eggs.

FIG. 47.—Devonian fishes. In the foreground are two ostracoderms (*3* and *5*), and more advanced fishes (*2* and *4*) are in the background. There are solitary corals (*1*), siliceous sponges (*6*), and brachiopods (*7*) living on the bottom. (From a painting by John Pemberton Cowan, courtesy of Hughes Tool Company.)

The Mississippian Period. This period derives its name from the upper Mississippi Valley, where there are extensive exposures of thick fossiliferous limestones. In Europe the Mississipian is not recognized as a separate system, but is referred to as the Lower Carboniferous. (The Pennsylvanian period recognized by American geologists is roughly equivalent to the Upper Carboniferous in Europe.)

PHYSICAL HISTORY. Mississippian seas covered most of what is now known as the Mississippi Valley, and great thicknesses of limestones were deposited in this area. In eastern North America Mississipian deposits are principally continental in origin and consist of conglomerates and sandstone.

Climatic conditions of this time were probably warm and temperate, as evidenced by thick deposits of crinoidal limestones. The presence of salt and gypsum in Newfoundland and Michigan indicates fairly arid conditions in these areas. Moderately humid conditions can be inferred from the occurrence of coal in parts of Pennsylvania and West Virginia.

There is no evidence of large-scale mountain-building at the end of the Mississippian. But in Europe the *Variscan Mountains* were uplifted and formed an arc across England, France, and Germany. Numerous local uplifts occurred in North America, resulting in emergence of the continents, which marked the end of the period.

Mississippian Life. The plants and animals of the Mississippian appear to be closely related to the Devonian forms preceding them (Fig. 48).

Plants were locally numerous and in some areas formed coal deposits. Although most Mississippian plant remains are found in a poor state of preservation, it is assumed that they were quite similar to those of the Pennsylvanian.

Foraminifers made their first real contribution as rock-builders during this period. The genus *Endothyra,* for example, is a major constituent of the Salem limestone of Indiana.

Corals of the reef-building variety were unexplainably absent in the warm, clear Mississippian seas, but certain solitary and colonial forms were common.

Bryozoans were characterized by lacy or latticelike structures (Fig. 101) which were used to support the colony. *Archimedes* is a typical Mississippian bryozoan in which the colony is spirally coiled. Hence this form is called the "corkscrew" bryozoan (Fig. 101–2).

Brachiopods of Mississippian time developed varieties with long spines on their shells.

Mollusks were represented by numerous and varied *gastropods* and *pelecypods.* Among the *cephalopods,* the goniatite was still the dominant form.

Trilobites were few in number, rapidly approaching extinction. The forms that survived were small individuals with very simple ornamentation.

Echinoderms underwent their greatest expansion since their appearance in the Cambrian. During the Mississippian the *blastoids* and *crinoids* reached the peak of their development. Crinoidal limestones are particularly abundant in Iowa and Indiana. *Pentremites,* a typical bud-shaped blastoid (Figs. 49 and 137-*b*) was especially numerous during Mississippian time.

Vertebrates are well known from the remains of both fishes and amphibians. The *sharks* were very numerous, represented by about three hundred species. They may be easily identified by their flat "pavement" teeth, which were well adapted for crushing the shells

Fig. 48.—Restoration of a "garden" of "sea lilies" (crinoids) of Mississippian time. Crinoids grew in great profusion in this portion of geologic time and were of many different types. Another echinoderm, a brittle star, is on the bottom in lower foreground. (Restoration by George Marchand, courtesy of Chicago Natural History Museum.)

Fig. 49.—Calyx of *Pentremites,* a Mississippian blastoid (about actual size). (Photograph courtesy of Dr. G. A. Cooper, U. S. National Museum.)

of mollusks, brachiopods, and arthropods. Some paleontologists believe that the sharp reduction of trilobites during this time is associated with the great increase in the number of shell-crushing sharks.

Amphibians, though rare, are known from footprints and a few skeletons.

The Pennsylvanian Period. The Pennsylvanian (the Upper Carboniferous in Europe) is famous for its great deposits of coal. The name of the period was derived from the state of Pennsylvania, where the system was first studied in detail.

PHYSICAL HISTORY. During the Pennsylvanian there was considerable restriction of the seas, bringing about an increase in continental deposits. In the eastern half of the United States, the lands were very low and were subjected to frequent inundations by the sea. These fluctuating periods of shallow seas and low, swampy coastlands were responsible for the accumulation of thick deposits of plant remains. During later geologic time this plant material was converted into coal.

Terrestrial sandstones were deposited throughout the central and eastern United States, and marine sandstones, shales, and limestones were deposited in some parts of western North America.

Pennsylvanian sediments indicate warm, humid climatic conditions. The abundant tropical and semitropical plants were widely distributed over the Northern Hemisphere. This climatic interpretation is further supported by the kinds of marine invertebrates, and land animals that lived during Pennsylvanian time.

In North America the Pennsylvanian period closed quietly, with a general uplift of the continents. There is no evidence of widespread crustal deformation, but there were local mountain-building disturbances in western Texas and southern Oklahoma.

PENNSYLVANIAN LIFE. The Pennsylvanian period was most favorable to the development of life. On land there was an unprecedented expansion of plant and animal life, and the seas contained an abundant and varied fauna.

Plants of the Pennsylvanian have left an exceptionally fine fossil record. They flourished in the warm, humid lowlands and were of many different types (Fig. 50). *Calamites* (Fig. 50–*5*), the giant scouring rush, grew as high as thirty feet. *Lepidodendron* (Figs. 50–*2* and 50–*6*), and *Sigillaria* (Fig. 50–*1*), the scale trees, were abundant and often reached a height of one hundred feet. True ferns and seed ferns developed rapidly, and were much larger than similar forms living today.

Fusulinids (Fig. 87) were the most typical protozoans of the Pennsylvanian period. These small spindle-shaped foraminifers look like little grains of wheat. They are so numerous in certain limestones that they comprise the bulk of the rock. Fusulinid limestones

Courtesy of Chicago Natural History Museum

FIG. 50.—Reconstruction of Pennsylvanian coal forest. Here are shown the typical swamplike vegetation and large insects of the Pennsylvanian period. *Sigillaria* (*1*), ferns (*3*), and *Calamites* (*5*) are shown as they might have grown. Logs of the large scale tree *Lepidodendron* (2 and *6*) may be seen in the foreground. A large cockroach is on the trunk of the *Sigillaria* (*1*), a beetle is on one of the *Lepidodendron* logs (2), and a giant dragonfly (*4*) hovers above.

are common in certain parts of northern and western Texas and in Kansas. These tiny protozoans have proved to be important guide fossils for the petroleum geologist.

Corals, greatly reduced in kinds and numbers, were restricted in occurrence.

Bryozoans of the delicate, lacy types were common. They are especially abundant in Kansas.

Brachiopods with spiny shells were abundant, as were many other forms.

Mollusks continued to flourish; many Pennsylvanian limestones yield large numbers of fossil *gastropods* and *pelecypods*. The *goniatites* were beginning to develop more complicated suture patterns. They, along with certain nautiloids, were the major *cephalopods* of this time.

Insects were present in such amazing numbers and varieties that the Pennsylvanian has been called the "Age of Insects." Some forms of these early insects closely resemble species that are living today, but they are noted for their large size. Dragonflies with a wingspread of almost thirty inches were not uncommon, and some Pennsylvanian cockroaches attained a length of four inches.

Echinoderms are known from abundant *crinoid* remains and from the fragmental plates and spines of *sea urchins*.

Vertebrates continued their steady expansion with further development of the *fishes* and *amphibians*. A most important event was the introduction of the first reptiles. It is probable that these early forms, which were quite small, closely resembled amphibians. Their fossil remains are rare and very poorly preserved.

The Permian Period. The Permian, which is the last period of the Paleozoic era, derives its name from the province of Perm in eastern Russia. Although the system was first studied and described in Russia, the thickest and most fossiliferous section of Permian rocks is found in western Texas and southeastern New Mexico.

PHYSICAL HISTORY. In the Permian, the changing conditions that started in the Pennsylvanian came to the dramatic climax. Permian seas in North America were quite restricted, and the western seas were apparently closely related to the seas of Late Pennsylvanian time. The Upper Pennsylvanian deposits grade transitionally into basal Permian deposits, so that it is difficult to locate the exact boundary between the two systems.

In northwestern West Virginia and adjoining areas of Ohio and Pennsylvania there are widespread continental deposits known as the *Dunkard group*. The presence of brachiopods and sharks' teeth in certain of the Dunkard beds indicates oscillations of the sea similar to those of the Pennsylvanian.

Thick beds of red shale, salt, and gypsum were deposited in Kansas, Oklahoma, and southeastern New Mexico. Deposits of this nature point to increasingly arid climatic conditions in Permian time.

Massive, fossiliferous reef-like limestones are common in western Texas and southeastern New Mexico. Many interesting and unusual silicified fossils have been recovered from certain of these Permian formations (see Figs. 10 and 51).

Permian rocks have played an important part in the formation of many of the scenic areas of the western United States. In New

Mexico the famous Carlsbad Caverns were dissolved out of soluble Permian limestones; and the white sand of the White Sands National Monument area was formed from the erosion of nearby gypsum beds. The rocks of Colorado's Garden of the Gods are partly Permian in age, as are the red sandstones of Monument

FIG. 51.—Permian sea bottom diorama. This reconstruction, representing an area in western Texas, shows a varied and profuse group of marine invertebrates. Shown are a pelecypod (*1*), three types of coiled cephalopods (*2, 9,* and *11*), a cylindrical sponge (*4*), and beadlike sponge (*3*), a coiled gastropod (*5*), two types of brachiopods (*6, 7,* and *8*), and solitary corals (*10*). (Diorama by George Marchand, courtesy of University of Michigan Museum of Paleontology.)

Valley in northeastern Arizona. An excellent section of Permian rocks, exposed in the rim of the Grand Canyon in Arizona, adds much to the color of the canyon.

Tillites (consolidated deposits of sediments deposited by glaciers) in South America, Africa, India, and Australia indicate the presence of great continental glaciers.

Permian climates varied from a desertlike aridity to warm, humid conditions. Variations in temperature ranged from glacial cold to tropical heat.

The close of the Permian was accompanied by widespread mountain-building disturbances. There were great uplifts in Colorado, New Mexico, and Texas; this orogeny formed what is referred to as the ancestral Rocky Mountains.

In the eastern United States, sediments that had accumulated in the old Appalachian seaway were folded and faulted by the great *Appalachian Revolution*. This orogenic disturbance resulted in the building of the *Appalachian Mountain* system and marked the end of the Paleozoic era.

PERMIAN LIFE. The widespread climatic and geographic changes that occurred near the end of the Permian resulted in trying times for many plants and animals. These organisms were forced to adapt themselves to new and changing environments or face extinction. Some of them, such as the once-numerous trilobites and blastoids, were unable to meet the challenge and made their last appearance in geologic history.

Plants of the Permian were similar to those of the Pennsylvanian. However, the introduction of cooler and more diverse climatic conditions brought about a sharp reduction in the numbers of coal-forming plants.

Fusulinids were still abundant and important rock-building forms. Although some of them became relatively large during the Permian, they had completely disappeared by the end of the period.

Corals were rare. Certain specialized forms, among them the honey-comb corals, became extinct.

Brachiopods, particularly the spiny types, were still common (Figs. 10 and 51).

Mollusks, in general, resembled those of the Pennsylvanian. *Cephalopods,* however, showed marked advances and developed increasingly complex suture patterns.

Trilobites had virtually disappeared from the seas, becoming extinct with the close of the Permian.

Echinoderms were scarce. The *blastoids* became extinct, while the *crinoids* greatly diminished in numbers.

Vertebrates made rapid and significant advances during this portion of geologic time. *Fishes* continued to develop in the seas, and *amphibians* were thriving in and near the rivers. The *reptiles,* holding undisputed control of the lands, underwent a remarkable degree of specialization. Both herbivorous and carnivorous types were numerous.

Among the more specialized Permian reptiles were the *pelyco-*

saurs (fin-backed lizards) (Figs. 52 and 154). This group was characterized by long, bony spines growing out of their backs; the spines were joined together by skin which made the animals appear as if they had sails on their backs. Other forms more closely resembled the large lizards of today. These reptiles were the forerunners of the great dinosaurs of the Mesozoic era.

Courtesy of Chicago Natural History Museum *C. R. Knight*

FIG. 52.—Permian reptiles and amphibians. Characteristic reptiles of this period were *Casea* (*1*), the fin- or sail-back lizards *Edaphosaurus* (*2*) plant-eater and *Dimetrodon* (*3*) a carnivore. *Diplocaulus* (*4*), an amphibian with a broad skull shaped like an arrowhead, is in the pool at the lower right.

Important, though few in numbers, were a group of reptiles with tooth and skull structure somewhat similar to that of a mammal. It is believed that these small reptiles were probably the ancestors of the mammals.

THE MESOZOIC ERA

Mesozoic ("middle life") is the name applied to the era that includes the Triassic, Jurassic, and Cretaceous periods. This portion of geologic time was so named because early researchers believed that Mesozoic life forms were midway between the primitive forms of the Paleozoic and the more advanced Cenozoic types. It has been called the "Age of Reptiles" because of the large numbers of reptiles that ruled land, sea, and sky.

The Triassic Period. The name Triassic (Latin *trias,* three) originated from the three distinct divisions of this system exposed in northern Germany. In North America, Triassic exposures are much less numerous and more poorly developed than are those of Europe.

Physical History. At the beginning of Triassic time the lofty Appalachian peaks underwent great erosion and by the end of the period had undergone considerable reduction in height.

In late Triassic time a series of long troughs developed along the Atlantic border of North America. This downwarped area received thick deposits of conglomerates, sandstones, and shales. These sediments, known as the *Newark group,* are interbedded with lava flows; the entire section was tilted in the latter part of the period.

In the western part of the continent, shallow seas deposited shales and limestones. In the Grand Canyon region of Arizona there was considerable deposition of shales and terrestrial sandstones.

Triassic formations in the southwestern region of the United States are responsible for some remarkable scenery. The Painted Desert and Petrified Forest of Arizona and Zion Canyon in southern Utah are all associated with rocks of Triassic age.

The presence of thick deposits of salt and gypsum in many parts of the world indicates extensive aridity. The widespread occurrence of reptile and amphibian remains suggests warm, temperate climates over great areas of the earth. The remains of these animals, plus the nature of Late Triassic vegetation, are indicative of a subtropical condition for certain areas.

The Triassic closed with the *Palisades Disturbance,* which resulted in the uplift and faulting of the sediments of the Newark group along the Atlantic Coast. In the western part of the United States the period closed quietly, with no evidence of extensive mountain-building.

Triassic Life. Triassic plants and animals show marked advance over the preceding Paleozoic forms. However, because of unfavorable conditions of preservation, the record of Triassic life in North America is not very extensive.

Plants of the coal-forming type have been found in outcrops of the Newark group in Virginia and the Carolinas. The *coniferous trees* became abundant, and their remains are found in large numbers in the Petrified Forest of Arizona. *Cycads,* a group of plants with palm-like leaves, were also abundant at this time (see p. 194 and Fig. 54).

Corals built reefs in many parts of the world. These animals, which were very similar to modern reef-building forms, built thick calcareous deposits now raised high in the Alps and Himalayas.

Brachiopods appear to be closely related to Permian species, but were greatly restricted in numbers and distribution.

Mollusks were becoming more common, particularly *pelecypods* and *cephalopods*. The latter were well represented by the *ammonites*, which underwent rapid development and filled the seas in vast numbers. Triassic ammonites developed very complex suture patterns and displayed a wide variety of shapes and sizes. Regarded as the most distinctive invertebrates of the Triassic period, they are valuable guide fossils for rocks of this age.

Vertebrates were by far the most outstanding animals of the Triassic. *Fishes* and *amphibians*, though common, were outnumbered by the *reptiles*, which were not only numerous but also had developed many unusual forms. The *phytosaurs* (Fig. 158), semiaquatic crocodilelike reptiles, were characteristic of this time (see p. 265).

The earliest known land dinosaurs appeared in this period, but most of them were quite small compared with the giant reptiles of later Mesozoic periods. These Triassic forms walked on their hind legs and are known from their skeletons and their three-toed birdlike tracks, which are abundant in certain Triassic shales in the Connecticut Valley.

Marine reptiles were represented by two major groups: the *ichthyosaurs* (Figs. 53 and 155), streamlined fishlike reptiles, and the *plesiosaurs*, with clumsy, flattened turtlelike bodies, and long necks (Figs. 53 and 156). Both of these forms appear to have descended from land reptiles and represent a secondary adaptation to marine life (see p. 261).

Mammals have been reported from the Triassic, but there is some argument as to whether these are true mammals or a continuation of the mammal-like reptiles which appeared in the Permian. Much of this confusion arises because of the fragmental nature of the fossil remains. There was probably mammalian development during the Triassic, but it was held to a minimum by the large number of reptiles which continued to dominate the earth.

The Jurassic Period. The rocks of the Jurassic system were named for the Jura Mountains situated between France and Switzerland. Thick layers of sandstones, shales, and limestones are exposed in these mountains.

Physical History. Jurassic seas in North America were limited in extent. There is no evidence of Jurassic deposition in the eastern United States; this area probably underwent erosion during Jurassic time. In the western portion of the United States great thicknesses of shales and sandstones were deposited in the Grand Canyon region. The deposits of sandstone represent Jurassic sand dunes deposited under desertlike conditions. This sand, known as the *Navajo sandstone,* has been eroded into some spectacular scenery in Zion Canyon National Park and Rainbow Bridge National Monument in Utah.

Courtesy of Chicago Natural History Museum *C. R. Knight*

Fig. 53.—Marine reptiles. Among the reptiles that invaded the sea were the plesiosaurs (*1*), long-necked fish-eaters, and the porpoiselike ichthyosaurs (*2*).

The *Morrison formation,* consisting primarily of sandstones and shales, is another well-known Jurassic deposit. This formation covers a large portion of the Rocky Mountain region and is famous for its dinosaur remains. Its beds contain large numbers of fresh-water invertebrates, reptiles, primitive mammals, and land plants. This material was deposited in swampy, humid lowlands which offered an ideal environment for the huge cold-blooded dinosaurs.

Jurassic climates were mild and equable, with local conditions of aridity in at least part of the period.

Near the end of Jurassic time the Pacific border of North America was subjected to strong movements of folding and uplift known as the *Nevadian Disturbance.* This orogeny was accompanied by considerable volcanic activity; it produced the Sierra Nevada ranges which extend from Mexico to northwestern Alaska.

Jurassic Life. Most Jurassic life seems to be a continuation of Triassic forms.

Plants of the Jurassic closely paralleled those of the Triassic, with the notable exception of an increase of the *conifers* and the *cycads.* The latter were so numerous in the Triassic and Jurassic that this portion of the Mesozoic has been called the "Age of Cycads." The *Ginkgo,* or maidenhair tree (Fig. 86), which had appeared during late Permian time, became increasingly abundant. The ginkgos were abundant and world-wide during the Jurassic but today are represented by a single living species. Modern flowering plants and hardwood trees had not yet appeared.

Corals of the reef-building type were more numerous and closely related to modern forms.

Mollusks continued to undergo marked and rapid expansion. *Gastropods* were especially numerous. *Pelecypods* of a type related to the modern oysters appeared for the first time. The oysterlike forms *Gryphaea* (Fig. 112–*3*) and Exogyra (Fig. 112–5) were locally abundant. *Cephalopods* were well represented by many complexly sutured ammonites. The *belemnoids* (Fig. 124), primtive squidlike creatures, were widespread; their fossilized cigar-shaped internal skeletons are abundant in many Jurassic rocks.

Arthropods are known from the remains of lobsters, crabs, ostracodes, and insects.

Echinoderms were represented by relatively modern *crinoids* and the increasingly abundant *sea urchins.*

Vertebrates were predominantly reptilian, including many strange and unusual forms. *Reptiles* of all shapes and sizes successfully occupied a variety of environments on the land, in the sea, and in the air. Some typical Jurassic forms were *Brontosaurus* (Fig. 166–*1*) and *Diplodocus,* huge quadrupedal plant-eaters. Some of these great creatures were as much as eighty-five feet long and weighed thirty-five or forty tons. *Stegosaurus* (Fig. 169) was another quadrupedal herbivorous dinosaur; it had a double row of large, bony, triangular plates along its back, which served as protection from large carnivorous dinosaurs. For additional protection *Stegosaurus* had a long, flexible tail bearing four long, sharp-pointed spikes. Though this animal weighed as much as ten tons and reached a length of fifteen to twenty-five feet, its ridiculously small head contained a brain about the size of a walnut. An early paleontologist has called the skeleton of this grotesque creature a "monument to stupidity."

Allosaurus (Fig. 164) was the largest of the Jurassic carnivorous dinosaurs. This great beast was thirty-five feet long. It walked on its hind legs, its powerful jaws armed with large, sharp teeth. The tail was long and heavy, undoubtedly serving to balance its body. The forelimbs were relatively small with sharp claws which were used in tearing its prey.

Marine reptiles continued to expand; *ichthyosaurs* and *plesiosaurs* abounded in the Jurassic seas.

A remarkable branch of reptiles were the flying forms known as *pterosaurs* ("wing-lizards") (Figs. 54, 160, 161). These unusual reptiles had hollow bones (as birds do) and relatively small bodies, and some Cretaceous forms had wingspreads of as much as twenty-five feet (see p. 267). The wing of these creatures consisted of a thin, leathery membrane stretched between the limbs. Gliding was probably the principal mode of flight among this group. These flying beasts, known also as *pterodactyls,* may have possessed a higher degree of intelligence than their marine and terrestrial counterparts. This is indicated by their relatively large brain case. It has also been suggested that the pterosaurs might have been warm-blooded.

One of the most important events of the Jurassic was the appearance of the first birds (Figs. 54 and 171). They are known from the skeletons of two specimens, and the single feather and a few fragments of a third. Given the name *Archaeopteryx,* these primitive birds had teeth, claws on their wings, and other distinct reptilian characteristics. Indeed, only the presence of feathers distinguishes their fossils from the remains of certain of the smaller dinosaurs. All of the *Archaeopteryx* remains were found in fine-grained limestone at Solnhofen, Bavaria (see p. 9).

Mammals, although small and primtive, were definitely present during the Jurassic. They are known from fragmental tooth and jaw remains which indicate that they ranged from the size of a rat to that of a small dog. Their teeth suggest that one group was adapted to plant-eating, while another, more sharp-toothed group, was apparently carnivorous. Since the scarcity of Jurassic mammalian remains makes it difficult to compare these early forms with the typical forms of today, their geologic history is imperfectly known.

The Cretaceous Period. The rocks of the Cretaceous were first studied in the White Cliffs of Dover along the English Channel. The name of the period is derived from the Latin word *creta* meaning "chalk," which characterizes the calcareous Cretaceous rocks all over the world.

Physical History. At the beginning of the Cretaceous, marine waters overlapped the Atlantic and Gulf coastal plains of North America. This sea deposited great thicknesses of sands, shales, and chalky limestones. On the west coast another sea extended eastward

Courtesy of Chicago Natural History Museum *C. R. Knight*

Fig. 54.—Jurassic birds and some reptilian relatives. *Archaeopteryx* (*2*), the earliest known bird, had teeth, claws on its wings, and a long jointed tail. The two small bipedal dinosaurs (*1*) are investigating the remains of a large arthropod. *Rhamphorhynchus* (*3*), a flying reptile, flies overhead while two more are at rest on a tree. The plants (*4*) are cycadeoids—a typical Mesozoic gymnosperm.

to the foot of the Sierra Nevada range in California. In the west central part of the continent a great depression, the Rocky Mountain trough, was developed. The depression was filled with a large sea which extended from the Gulf of Mexico across the Great Plains and Rocky Mountain area, through parts of Canada, and into the Arctic ocean. This sea represents the last great submergence of the North American continent, and in it were deposited great thicknesses of sandstones, shales, and limestones. Many of these formations are extremely fossiliferous, yielding large numbers of vertebrate and invertebrate fossils.

Cretaceous climates were probably mild and temperate, though somewhat cooler than they had been in the Jurassic. There is also evidence of climatic differentiation, particularly in the early part of the period. In Late Cretaceous time, when widespread seas covered western North America, climates were probably more mild and equable than today.

The Cretaceous period (and with it the Mesozoic era) was brought to a close by the *Laramide Revolution*. During this period of crustal deformation the sediments of the Rocky Mountain trough were folded, faulted, and uplifted to form the great *Rocky Mountain System*. This great mountain-building revolution was accompanied by much volcanic activity in the western part of the United States. Hence volcanic materials, such as lava and ash, are common in many areas of this region.

CRETACEOUS LIFE. The Cretaceous period witnessed several major advancements in the development of plants and animals. Plant life moved forward with the introduction of the flowering plants and most of our modern trees. These types made up the bulk of the Cretaceous flora. In the animal world, reptiles reached their climax, while the great dinosaurs became extinct at the end of the period. Most of the major groups of invertebrates, having completed their development, were represented by many species (Fig. 55). Cephalopods, on the other hand, were on the decline.

Plants of the Cretaceous took on a decidedly modern appearance. Flowering plants appeared in great profusion in early Cretaceous time. By the middle of the Cretaceous, such familiar trees as walnut, elm, oak, magnolia, and maple were well represented. The grains and grasses also went through a period of rapid expansion. These plants, as well as the more advanced forms of trees, flowers, and shrubs, provided food and protection for the birds and mammals of the Cenozoic, and thus probably aided greatly in their expansion.

Foraminifera were extremely abundant, and their calcareous shells make up a large part of many Cretaceous formations.

Brachiopods were present in about the same numbers as in modern seas.

Mollusks continued to flourish and undergo unprecedented development. *Pelecypods* of many types, including thick-shelled oysters and thin-shelled clams, were plentiful; numerous species developed. Certain of them were attached reef-building forms known as *chamids* or *rudistids* (Fig. 56). Some reached a great degree of

FIG. 55.—Reconstruction of a Late Cretaceous sea floor. *Baculites,* an uncoiled ammonite (*1*), *Placenticeras,* a flat coiled ammonite (*5*), and belemnoids (*6*) dominate this scene. A variety of clams (*4*) and gastropods (*2* and *3*) may be seen on the ocean floor. (Restoration by George Marchand, courtesy of University of Michigan Museum of Paleontology.)

specialization, producing a variety of unusual shell forms; their massive shell deposits are common in certain Cretaceous formations. Other typical Cretaceous pelecypods were *Gryphaea, Exogyra, Pecten* and *Inoceramus* (Fig. 57). *Gastropods* were common and resembled modern forms but are usually found poorly fossilized. *Cephalopods* were in their last stages of development. The abundant complexly sutured *ammonites* were present in many shapes and sizes (Figs. 55 and 123). Most of the shells were in the form of the typical flat coil, but some were straight, loosely coiled, or coiled in a high spiral. Many of these were covered with ornate spines, ribs, and nodes, while others were perfectly smooth. This extreme degree of specialization foreshadowed the extinction of the group at the end of the Cretaceous. *Belemnoids* were still plentiful but less so than during Jurassic time. .

Echinoderms, particularly the characteristic Cretaceous *heart urchins* such as *Hemiaster* (Fig. 143–*3*) were most numerous. They may be found in great profusion in certain Lower Cretaceous limestones and marls of Texas.

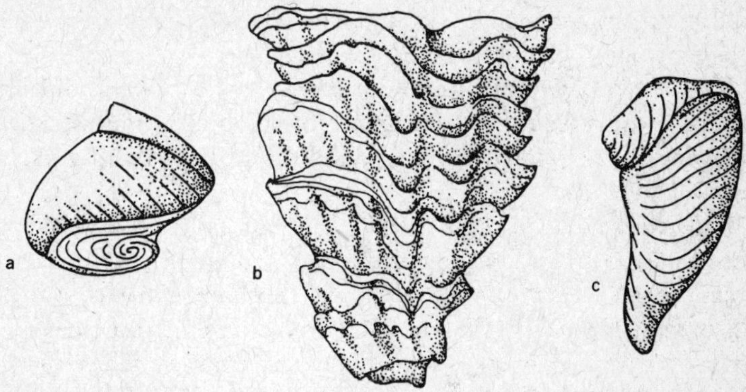

FIG. 56.—Unusual Cretaceous pelecypods. (*a*) *Toucasia* (reduced one half). (*b*) *Radiolites,* and (*c*) *Monopleura* both about natural size). All from the Edwards limestone (Lower Cretaceous) of Texas.

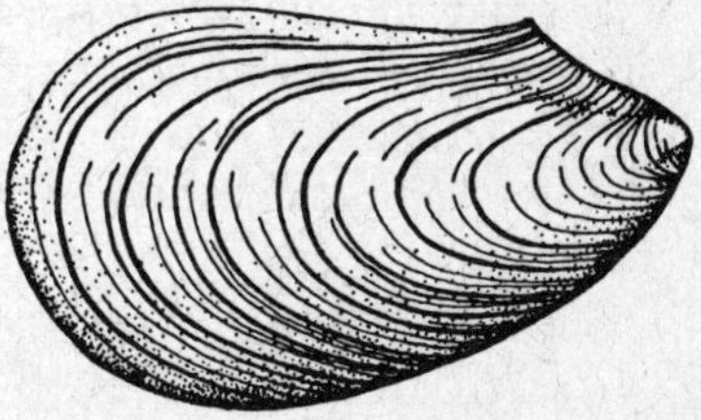

FIG. 57.—*Inoceramus,* a Cretaceous pelecypod (about one half actual size). Some individuals grew to be as much as five feet long and several feet wide.

Vertebrate fossils are well represented by fish, reptiles, birds, and primitive mammals.

Fishes of this period were quite similar to modern forms. The remains of their teeth and bones may be collected in many Cretaceous shales and limestones.

Reptiles, numerous and varied, still comprised the dominant vertebrates. Probably the most famous dinosaur of the "Age of Reptiles" was *Tyrannosaurus rex* ("tyrant lizard king") (Figs. 162

and 165). This mighty Cretaceous flesh-eater was forty to fifty feet long, and when standing on its hind legs was almost twenty feet tall. Its small hands were armed with sharp, powerful claws. The twenty-foot tail was used as a balance and also as a club for fighting. The skull was almost four feet long and three feet wide; it had many sharp-pointed, double-edged teeth, some of them six inches long. The widely gaping jaws could open until there was a four-foot space between top and bottom. The skeleton of this carnivorous creature is called "King of the Dinosaurs."

Herbivorous dinosaurs were well represented by several different groups, among them the *trachodonts,* or duck-billed dinosaurs, the *ankylosaurs,* or armored dinosaurs, and the *ceratopsians,* a group of horned dinosaurs.

Trachodon (known also as *Anatosaurus*) (Figs. 162 and 168), one of the more typical duck-billed forms, had the front of its mouth expanded into a broad, flat bill closely resembling that of a duck. There were no teeth in the front of the bill, but on either side of his jaws there were two rows of five hundred teeth each. The structure of the teeth shows that *Trachodon* was a vegetarian. The bill was not the only ducklike feature of this strange reptile, for the toes of its front feet were webbed and served as paddles when it was swimming. There were several other types of duck-billed dinosaurs, all of which had peculiarly shaped skulls. Judging from the number of trachodont skeletons that have been found, it appears that this was the most abundant group among the larger dinosaurs.

Although *Stegosaurus,* the Jurassic armored dinosaur, was now extinct, it had its counterparts in the Cretaceous. Two such forms were *Ankylosaurus* and *Palaeoscincus. Ankylosaurus* (Fig. 162) was about twenty feet long, its low, squat body entirely protected by heavy plates of bone. Long, bony spikes protruded from the sides, and the end of its heavy tail was enlarged to form a bony mass that must have served as a very effective club. *Palaeoscincus* (Fig. 58) was similar to the form described above, with the exception of a more extensive development of the protective spikes along the sides of the body.

The Cretaceous also marks the appearance of the *ceratopsians,* or horn-faced dinosaurs. These are among the last and most highly specialized groups of Mesozoic reptiles. One of the better-known forms, *Triceratops* (Figs. 162 and 165) developed a bony frilled shield to protect its head and neck. It had a large horn over each

Courtesy of Chicago Natural History Museum *C. R. Knight*

FIG. 58.—Dinosaurs of the Late Cretaceous. The development of the dinosaurs reached its peak near the end of the Cretaceous period. Some of the more interesting forms were the hooded *Corythosaurus* (*1*), *Parasaurolophus* (*2*) with its characteristic crest, and the ostrichlike *Struthiomimus* (*3*). Armored dinosaurs such as *Palaeoscincus* (*4*) and duck-billed forms such as *Edmontosaurus* (*5*) were prevalent.

eye and a small nose horn on top of a sharp parrotlike beak. Some of these animals grew to be as much as thirty feet long and eight feet high. The skull, from the front of the beak to the back of the shield, sometimes reached a length of seven feet. Strange as it may seem, these ferocious-looking monsters were vegetarians. The heavy, ornate armor developed by them and by the dinosaurs described above was a means of protection from the great hunters such as *Tyrannosaurus* and his flesh-eating kin. Another ceratopsian, *Proto-*

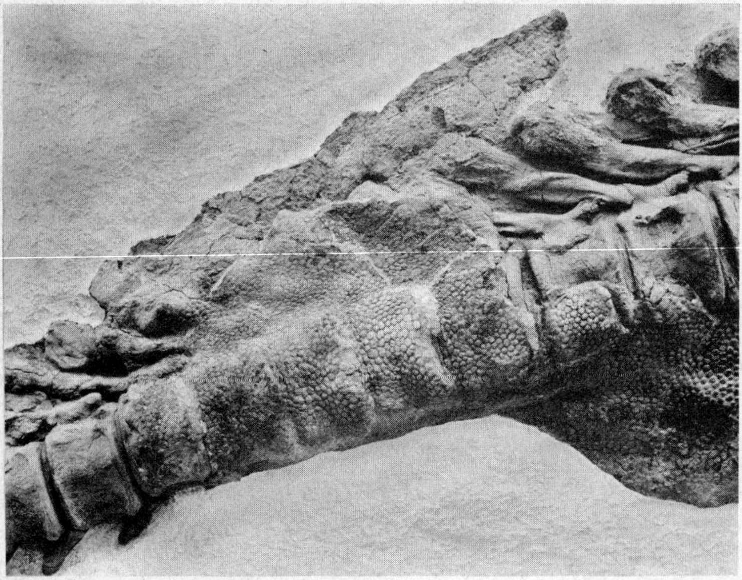

Courtesy of U. S. National Museum

FIG. 59.—Portion of the tail of *Corythosaurus* (see Fig. 58), a Late Cretaceous dinosaur, with part of the skin preserved.

ceratops, furnished scientists with conclusive proof that these primitive reptiles laid eggs. The first such eggs, some up to eight inches long, were discovered in the Gobi Desert of Asia in 1923 (Fig. 60). The eggs, two of which contained skeletons of unhatched baby dinosaurs, were collected by members of an expedition of the American Museum of Natural History.

In the seas *ichthyosaurs* and *plesiosaurs* were still present, though less numerous than during the Jurassic. In late Cretaceous time these swimming forms were joined by a group of large, highly specialized marine reptiles called *mosasaurs. Tylosaurus* (Figs. 61 and

157) typifies this group, which was structurally quite similar to modern lizards. Its limbs, however, had been modified into flipperlike paddles that aided in swimming, and the flexible, powerful thirty-foot body was well adapted for rapid movement through the sea. Its long head and gaping mouth filled with numerous sharp, re-

Courtesy of American Museum of Natural History

FIG. 60.—Dinosaur eggs. This nest, containing an even dozen dinosaur eggs, was discovered in Lower Cretaceous sandstones in the Gobi Desert of Mongolia. They were laid by *Protoceratops,* an early horned dinosaur, and range from five to eight inches n length. Some eggs found in this area contained the bones of unhatched dinosaurs.

curved teeth established *Tylosaurus* as undisputed ruler of the Cretaceous seas.

Present also was the giant marine turtle *Archelon.* This great creature was almost twelve feet long and had a comparatively light, soft shell. Reptiles of this type (such as *Protostega,* Fig. 61–*3*) were the forerunners of the modern turtle.

Flying reptiles were highly advanced, though less numerous and varied. *Pteranodon* (Figs. 61 and 160) was a typical pterosaur that might have been seen in Cretaceous skies. This giant winged reptile had a wingspread of as much as twenty-five feet; yet its light,

Courtesy of Chicago Natural History Museum *C. R. Knight*

FIG. 61.—Giant sea-lizard, turtle, and flying reptiles of the Cretaceous. The pterosaur *Pteranodon* (*1*) had a wingspread in excess of twenty feet and the huge fish-eating *Tylosaurus* (*2*) grew to a length of thirty feet. *Protestega* (*3*) a giant sea-turtle, had a shell as much as six feet long.

fragile body was probably less than two feet long. The head of *Pteranodon* had a long, sharp-pointed, toothless beak in front. On the back of its head was a long triangular extension of the skull. *Pteranodon,* like its Jurassic ancestors, was probably better adapted for gliding than for active flight.

Before leaving our discussion of this fantastic and successful group of animals, we should briefly consider one of the most perplexing problems that paleontologists have ever encountered: Why did the dinosaurs become extinct? This group of animals ruled the earth for over a hundred million years—a hundred times as long as man has dominated it! They had successfully invaded land, sea, and air; attained the greatest size of all animals; and were still numerous and varied at the end of the Mesozoic. Yet, suddenly (geologically speaking), the dinosaurs vanished from the face of the earth!

Scientists have long pondered this baffling mystery and are still not agreed as to what may have brought about the extinction of this successful tribe. It seems that no single factor was responsible for their disappearance. Rather, there were several combinations of circumstances that contributed to their downfall. Some of the major "extinction theories" arc as follows:

1. Drastic changes in climate and geography probably played an important part in the extinction of this group. Cretaceous mountain-building resulted in the drainage of the lush swamps and produced much cooler and more arid climates. As the swamps disappeared, the plant food of the great herbivorous dinosaurs vanished. The resulting extinction of the herbivorous dinosaurs removed the food supply of the carnivorous forms. The dinosaurs were apparently unable to adapt themselves to the drastic changes in environmental conditions that marked the end of the Mesozoic.

2. The small mammals that were becoming increasingly abundant may have eaten the dinosaurs' eggs. This does not, of course, account for the disappearance of the marine reptiles. These lived in the water and their young were probably born alive.

3. It has also been suggested that "racial old age" may have been partially responsible. The reptiles were an ancient race, and, as is typical of many old races, their "old age". was marked by overspecialization. Most forms were greatly restricted in environment and diet. Others developed large and useless body structures, and were of titanic proportions. Such drastic types of specialization resulted in

the inability to meet the changing conditions outlined in the first theory.

4. Another theory is that some widespread epidemic may have wiped out the dinosaurs. But this is largely speculation, as the remains show no particular evidence of disease.

5. Some scientists have postulated the occurrence of glandular disorders which were associated with the large size of the dinosaurs. But this does not account for the disappearance of the smaller types.

These are primarily speculations, but it is very probable that one of these factors or a combination of several of them led to the extinction of the dinosaurs.

Birds were more specialized and more abundant than they had been in Jurassic time, and many interesting Cretaceous fossil birds (Fig. 172) have been described (see p. 276).

Mammals of the Cretaceous were small, primitive types. They were probably much more numerous than is indicated by their scattered fossil remains—mainly teeth and skulls. They probably resembled the modern hedgehogs or shrews.

The domination of the reptiles during Mesozoic time held the development of mammalian life to a minimum. But with the end of the Mesozoic, the reptile hordes decreased sharply in number and kind. The mammals seemed waiting for the opportunity to occupy the place of supremacy soon to be vacated by the dwindling reptile tribe. This great change of fauna marked the approach of the Cenozoic era, the "Age of Mammals."

THE CENOZOIC ERA

The Cenozoic era, which began 70 million years ago, is the shortest of the geological eras. It is divided into two periods: the Tertiary and the Quaternary.

The era derives its name from the Greek words *kainos,* "recent," and *zoikos,* "pertaining to life." This name is most fitting, since the Cenozoic witnessed the development of most species of modern invertebrate life.

The Tertiary Period. The name *Tertiary,* derived from an early, but now outdated, rock classification, means "containing a third part." This name has become so firmly entrenched in geologic literature that it is still in use today, though not recognized by some geologists.

The period has been divided into five distinct epochs; these are, in ascending order, the Paleocene, Eocene, Oligocene, Miocene, and Pliocene. (The meaning and derivation of these terms have been discussed in Chapter III.)

The development of most of the earth's familiar features took place in the Tertiary.

The Atlantic and Gulf coastal plains and the west coast of North America were covered by marginal seas during the early part of the period. Great accumulations of marine sediments were deposited in these areas; some of the formations have yielded large numbers of well-preserved invertebrate fossils.

In the Great Plains and western United States thick deposits of continental rocks were being derived from the erosion of the Rocky Mountains. These sediments have been a most valuable source of Tertiary mammal remains. They have also produced some of the most striking scenery in the West.

Near the middle of the period there began a widespread series of mountain-building movements. These disturbances resulted in the formation of the Alps and Caucasus Mountains in Europe and the Himalayas in Asia. North American ranges elevated near the close of the Tertiary include the Coast Ranges of California and Oregon and the Cascade Mountains in Oregon and Washington.

The Tertiary was also a period of extensive volcanic activity. The western part of the continent was subjected to one of the longest and most severe periods of vulcanism in earth history. This activity, which began with the *Laramide Revolution,* has continued sporadically until the present. We owe some of our magnificent Western scenery to the activity of these volcanoes. Mt. Shasta and Mt. Lassen of California, Mt. Hood in northwestern Oregon, and Mt. Ranier in southwestern Washington are all volcanic peaks of majestic beauty. There were many great lava flows associated with these volcanoes. In southern Idaho the Craters of the Moon National Monument portrays strikingly a typical Tertiary lava field. One of the world's greatest lava fields was formed on the Columbia Plateau in the northwestern part of the United States. Here a great field of volcanic material covers approximately 200,000 square miles to depths of as much as several thousand feet.

Tertiary climates in North America were in general warmer, more humid, and more equable than our climate of today. In Early Tertiary time tropical and subtropical climates extended as far north as the Canadian border. Arid conditions are indicated for the Great Plains area in the latter part of the period. Near the end of the Tertiary the climate grew steadily colder, heralding the coming of the first Pleistocene Ice Age. (For an account of Tertiary plant and animal life, see p. 135.)

The Quaternary Period. The name *Quaternary,* derived from an early, outmoded classification, means "consisting of four each." This is a relatively short geologic period. It includes the Pleistocene, or "most recent" epoch and the Recent epoch, which extends to the present time.

Late Tertiary mountain-building caused great elevation of the continents and withdrawal of the seas. These physical changes resulted in colder climates and the development of great ice sheets in northern Europe, Siberia, and North America. On the North American continent glaciers covered almost all of Canada and extended southward into southern Illinois. This was truly the "Age of Ice."

The introduction of colder climates in North America brought about the extinction of many Tertiary forms. Following them came the development of new types (such as the *woolly mammoth* and *woolly rhinoceros;* see p. 281). *Marine invertebrates* and *plants* of the Pleistocene were essentially like those of today. The major differences of the flora and fauna are probably the result of migrations brought about by changing climates. (For a more detailed discussion of Pleistocene plants and animals, see "Cenozoic Life," below.)

Geologists recognize four major glacial periods and three intervening warmer periods during which the glaciers melted and retreated. The presence of these great masses of ice on the continents caused depression of the land, fluctuation of the sea level, and considerable change in the drainage pattern of many streams.

The last great ice sheet retreated from Europe and North America between 12,000 and 15,000 years ago.

Cenozoic Life. The close similarity between Tertiary and Quaternary organisms makes it desirable to discuss them under the general heading of "Cenozoic Life." The most noteworthy biologic event of the Cenozoic was the rapid rise of the mammals. Their development, which had been retarded by the hordes of Mesozoic reptiles, was so complete that this era has been called the "Age of Mammals."

The mammals, supplemented by the modern plants which had appeared in the Cretaceous, provide us with a complete and accurate record of Cenozoic life. Tertiary and Quaternary invertebrates, though obviously descended from Cretaceous stocks, were essentially modern in aspect.

The plants of the beginning of this era were basically modern in appearance. The great hardwood forests and grassy plains bore striking similarities to those of today. They furnished an ideal setting in which the remarkable mammalian development was to take place.

Foraminifers of many types were present in astronomical numbers. The remains of these protozoans are a major constituent of many Tertiary rocks; they are valuable index fossils in the Tertiary formations of Pacific and Gulf Coast oil fields (see p. 49).

Corals of this time were plentiful and varied, but were restricted to the warmer parts of the world.

Bryozoans, very common in Tertiary rocks, are particularly numerous in certain shale formations.

Brachiopods, which had passed their peak of development in the Paleozoic, made up a very small portion of Cenozoic life.

Echinoderms were well represented by *crinoids, echinoids,* and *starfishes.* The crinoids were predominantly stemless free-swimming forms. The echinoids were of all types, apparently nearing their maximum stage of development.

Mollusks were the dominant marine invertebrates of the Cenozoic. *Gastropods* and *pelecypods,* most of them similar to living types, were common in fresh and salt water, while the *pulmonate* (air-breathing) snails were abundant on the lands. *Cephalopods* were represented by a few species of *nautiloids,* but the vast numbers of ammonites which had ranged the Mesozoic seas were conspicuously absent, having become extinct at the end of Cretaceous time.

Vertebrates—fishes, amphibians, reptiles, birds, and mammals—were firmly established in great numbers.

Fishes were characterized by the expanded development of the bony fishes, or *teleosts. Sharks* were plentiful. Some of them were sixty to eighty feet long and had six-inch teeth. Probably the best-known fossil-fish fauna is that of the Eocene Green River beds of southern Wyoming and northwestern Colorado. These strata contain large numbers of well-preserved bony fishes (Figs. 8 and 62).

Amphibians included *salamanders, frogs,* and *toads,* all of them closely related to the forms living today.

Reptiles were greatly diminished in numbers and kinds. *Snakes, lizards, crocodiles,* and *turtles* were probably present in about the same numbers as today.

Birds had lost their teeth, and they closely resembled modern types. Because of their fragile skeletons they are quite rare as fossils. A few of them grew to be very large, but their wings were so small that they were unable to fly. The bone structure of their legs indicates that they must have been very powerful runners. *Diatryma,*

Courtesy of Ward's Natural Science Establishment

FIG. 62.—*Diplomystis humilis,* a well-preserved Eocene fish from the Green River beds of Wyoming.

an ostrichlike bird from the Eocene of Wyoming, grew to be as much as seven feet tall (Fig. 173).

Mammals underwent a tremendous development during this era. After their first appearance in the Triassic as simple shrewlike forms, their development progressed slowly. Paleocene mammals were primitive, but by Eocene time they had become larger, more intelligent, and better adapted to different environments.

Mammals of the early Tertiary were ancient forms that have few direct descendents living today. There were several distinct stocks among these archaic mammals; some of the more important or unusual forms will be mentioned here.

Ground sloths were common in the southern United States in Pliocene and Pleistocene time. *Megatherium,* the largest of this group, weighed many tons and stood twenty feet tall (Fig. 64). These strange animals were the forerunners of the modern tree sloths of South America.

Glyptodonts, the ancestral armadillos, developed at about the same time as the ground sloths. They were present in the southern United States in Pliocene and Pleistocene times. One of this group,

FIG. 63.—Restoration of a large flightless bird that inhabited South America during Pliocene time. This form was about five feet tall. (From a painting by J. C. Hansen, courtesy of American Museum of Natural History.)

Courtesy of Chicago Natural History Museum *C. R. Knight*

FIG. 64.—The giant ground sloth *Megatherium* (at left), a Pleistocene inhabitant of North America was almost as large as a modern elephant. On the right are two armadillolike mammals known as glyptodonts. Some of these primitive armored creatures attained a length of ten feet.

Glyptodon (Figs. 64 and 174), had a solid turtlelike shell almost five feet high. From the front of the bone-capped head to the tip of the tail, a large individual might be fifteen feet long. The heavy, thick tail was protected by a series of bony rings, and the end was developed into a bony, heavily spiked club.

Carnivores are first represented by an archaic group known as the *creodonts* (Greek *kreas,* flesh, + *odontos,* tooth). These were present in the Paleocene and ranged from the size of a weasel to that of a large bear. Their claws were sharp and well developed, but their teeth were not as specialized as those of modern carnivores. They had relatively small brains, indicating a very low order of intelligence, and they became extinct at the end of the Eocene. These early meat-eaters were followed by more specialized carnivores which developed throughout the Cenozoic. Although they must have been very numerous, they have left a rather meager fossil record. The saber-toothed cat (or "tiger") *Smilodon* (Fig. 65) is well known from Pleistocene deposits, as is *Canis dirus,* "the dire wolf." Both of these forms, representing the cat and dog families, have been found in large numbers at the Rancho La Brea tar pits, Los Angeles, California (see p. 9 and Figs. 3 and 65).

The *pantodonts,* also called *amblypods,* were primitive, hoofed, herbivorous animals. *Coryphodon,* a typical pantodont, was about three feet tall and had a stout, heavy body.

The largest of the Eocene animals were the *uintatheres,* or *Dinocerta. Uintatherium* (Fig. 175) had three pairs of blunt horns; the males had daggerlike upper tusks. Some of the uintatheres were as much as seven feet tall at the shoulders and as large as a small elephant. The small size of the brain in relation to the body size suggests that these animals were less intelligent than most mammals of that time.

The *elephants,* first appearing in the Late Eocene, seem to have developed along the same lines as the horse. Early elephantlike animals were about the size of a small modern elephant but had longer heads and shorter trunks. As the development of the group continued there resulted an increase in size, a change in skull and tooth structure, and an elongation of the trunk. The *mammoth* (Figs. 65, 66, and 176) and the *mastodon* (Fig. 67) are well-known fossil forms. The latter resembled the modern elephants, but the structure of their teeth was quite different (Fig. 177-*a*). In addition, the mastodon skull (Fig. 67) was lower than that of an elephant and

FIG. 65.—Reconstruction of a scene at a Pleistocene water hole near Los Angeles. About 100,000 years ago at Rancho La Brea in Los Angeles, animals which gathered to drink from certain water pools were sometimes trapped in underlying tar seeps. In the above scene a young mammoth, *Archidiskodon* (*1*), has become mired in the asphalt. *Smilodon* (*2*), the saber-toothed cat, attempting to prey on the unfortunate elephant has become trapped himself. Several giant vultures (*Teratornis, 3*) are waiting to feed upon the carcasses of the trapped animals. The large number of well-preserved bones (see Fig. 3, p. 10) recovered from the La Brea tar pits suggests that the above situation must have occurred many times. (By permission from *Prehistoric Animals* by J. Augusta and Z. Burian, Spring Books, London.)

the tusks were exceptionally large, some reaching a length of nine feet.

The true elephants, or mammoths, had several North American representatives, of which the *woolly mammoth* (Figs. 66 and 176) is probably the best-known. This animal lived until the end of the Pleistocene; like the woolly rhinoceros described below, it is known from ancient cave paintings and frozen remains. Evidence from

Courtesy of Chicago Natural History Museum *C. R. Knight*

FIG. 66.—Woolly mammoth and woolly rhinoceros. The above might have been a scene during the last Ice Age some 25,000 years ago. Remains of the woolly mammoth (*1*) have been found in a state of excellent preservation (see Fig. 4, p. 13) in the frozen tundra of northern Siberia and Alaska. Their bones are commonly found in many parts of the United States. The woolly rhinoceros (*2*) attained a length of twelve feet and stood six feet high. Cave drawings of both of the above animals (see Fig. 78, p. 176) indicate that they were known by prehistoric man.

these sources shows that this great beast had a coat of long black hair, with a wool covering beneath it.

During Pleistocene time mammoths were widespread over the United States. Their remains are abundant in many stream deposits of this age.

The *perissodactyls,* or "odd-toed" hoofed animals, include such living forms as the horse and rhinoceros. Extinct representatives of the group include the *titanotheres, chalicotheres,* and *baluchitheres.* These animals grew to tremendous size and took on many unusual body forms.

One of the first perissodactyls was *Hyracotherium* (also called *Eohippus*), which is the earliest known horse (Figs. 68 and 19). This small animals was about a foot high, and its teeth indicate a diet of

Courtesy of New York State Museum

FIG. 67.–Restoration of the Cohoes mastodon. The remains of this great animal were discovered in 1866 in Pleistocene deposits of New York state. The restoration of this life-size model was executed under the direction of Dr. John M. Clarke at the New York State Museum.

FIG. 68.—Cenozoic horses. (*a*) *Hyracotherium* (also called *Eohippus*), which lived during Eocene time, was little more than a foot tall. (*b*) *Pliohippus,* a Pliocene horse about the size of a pony, was the first single-toed horse. See also Fig. 19, p. 43. (By permission from *Texas Fossils* by W. H. Matthews III, Bureau of Economic Geology, University of Texas, Austin.)

soft food. Following the first horse, there is a complete series of fossil horses (Fig. 19), providing an excellent record of the development of this important animal group (see p. 43).

The *titanotheres* appeared in the Eocene, at which time they were about the size of a sheep. By Middle Oligocene time they had increased to gigantic proportions but still had very small and primitive brains. *Brontotherium* (Figs. 69 and 178) was somewhat rhinoceros-like in appearance, standing eight feet tall at the shoulders. A large bony growth from the skull was extended into a flattened horn divided at the top. Despite rapid development during the Tertiary,

Courtesy of Chicago Natural History Museum *C. R. Knight*

FIG. 69.—An Oligocene landscape. The giant titanothere *Brontotherium* (2) stood eight feet tall at the shoulders and was among the largest of the early North American mammals (see also Fig. 175, p. 282). Their skeletons, along with those of the tortoise, *Stylemys* (*1*) and *Hyaenodon* (*3*), a primitive carnivore, are found in the badlands of South Dakota.

these queer beasts became extinct in Middle Oligocene time. *Brontotherium* is the largest land mammal ever discovered in North America.

Chalicotheres, though in some ways like titanotheres, exhibited many peculiarities of their own. The head and neck of *Moropus,* a typical chalicothere, was much like that of a horse. His front legs were longer than his hind legs, and his feet similiar to those of a rhinoceros except that they bore long claws instead of hoofs. This grotesque creature lived from the Eocene epoch into the Pleistocene.

Rhinoceroses are also "odd-toed" hoofed animals; there are many interesting and well-known fossils in this group. *Baluchitherium,* the largest land mammal known to science, was a hornless rhinoceros that lived in late Oligocene and early Miocene time. This immense beast measured about thirty-four feet from head to tail and stood almost eighteen feet high at the shoulder. He must have weighed many tons. Baluchitheres have not been discovered in North America and appear to have been restricted to Central Asia.

The *woolly rhinoçeros* (Fig. 66) was a Pleistocene two-horned form that ranged from southern France to northeastern Siberia. These animals are well known from complete carcasses recovered from the frozen tundra of Siberia and remains that were found preserved in an oil seep in Poland. These unusual specimens, as well as cave paintings made by early man, have given us a complete and accurate picture of this creature.

Near the end of the Pleistocene the earliest species of modern man appeared (see Chapter XI).

Chapter IX

A BRIEF HISTORY OF PALEONTOLOGY

Although, as pointed out in Chapter I, fossil remains have long been of interest to man, the term *paleontology* was probably introduced simultaneously in France and Russia about 1834. But long before this, some of the early Greek and Roman scholars speculated on the origin and meaning of fossils, and a few of them correctly concluded that they represented the remains of ancient organisms.

The development of paleontology was impeded during the Middle Ages, but progress was made during the Renaissance. The eighteenth and nineteenth centuries witnessed significant advances in paleontology; near the end of this period it attained the status of a science.

PALEONTOLOGY IN THE ANCIENT HISTORIC WORLD

The occurrence of marine shells far from the sea caused considerable speculation among early Greek and Roman thinkers.

The Greek Philosophers. Many Greek philosophers were puzzled by the presence of typical marine shells, enclosed in rocks far removed from any body of salt water. Some were of the opinion that the sea may have originally occupied these areas. More often, however, the presence of these fossils was explained as the results of supernatural agents.

Anaximander of Miletus (611–547 B.C.) was possibly the first person to consider seriously the real meaning of fossils, but it is doubtful that he fully realized their significance. Observing the remains of fossil fish high above sea level, he concluded that they had been the forerunners of all living forms. Anaximander has, in fact, been called the first evolutionist because he suggested that man had evolved from fish. It has been suggested, however, that he may have been repeating the ideas of early Egyptian scholars. Another early Greek was Xenophones of Colophon (576–480 B.C.), who noticed the fossil remains of large numbers of shells, fish, and other marine organisms at points far inland and inferred that the seas had formerly covered the earth. Many scientists believe that Xenophones was the first to recognize fossils as the remains of once-living organisms entombed in the rocks; he has therefore been called the first paleontologist.

About a hundred years later, Herodotus of Halicarnassos (*ca.* 484–*ca.* 426 B.C.), reported the presence of nummulites (a large foraminifer) in Egyptian limestones. He assumed that these objects were petrified lentils left over from the food supplies of the slaves who had built the pyramids. Later, however, noting the presence of fossil fish and shells, he concluded that the sea had once covered the area. Another early philosopher, Empedocles of Agrigentum, who flourished about 440 B.C., noticed an abundance of fossil shells and bones in Sicily and concluded that they had originally been animal forms. Empedocles' studies of these fossils led him to postulate that plants had appeared before animals and that all animals had undergone four stages of development. He apparently believed that plants, animals, and man appeared in this order because each is dependent upon its predecessors for survival. His writings lead us to believe that he was probably the first to arrive at the concept of the struggle for existence and the survival of the fittest in the animal kingdom.

Aristotle (384–322 B.C.), the greatest Greek naturalist, recognized fish remains as fossils but apparently believed that the fish had originated in the rocks. One of Aristotle's students, Theophrastus (*ca.* 371–*ca.* 287 B.C.), further expounded Aristotle's theory of the earth's crust. He speculated that either the fish had wandered in from the sea via underground rivers or the fish eggs had been left behind in the earth to hatch at a later time. Theophrastus believed that these fish were later changed into stone in some way. There is evidence to indicate that Theophrastus himself had observed fossil bones and believed them to be the products of certain "plastic forces" at work within the earth. Strabo (*ca.* 63 B.C.–*ca.* A.D. 21), an eminent Greek geographer, noted the remains of marine organisms at altitudes well above sea level and inferred that these lands had once been under the sea but had later been elevated above sea level.

The Roman Philosophers. The Romans did little to further the early ideas of geology in general, and even less in the field of paleontology. Two Roman writers, however, made contributions worthy of note. The first was Titus Lucretius Carus (*ca.* 99–*ca.* 55 B.C.), who set forth his ideas of the universe in his great poem, *De rerum natura* ("On the Nature of Things"). He wrote of many geological phenomena, including weathering, earthquakes, and the origin of springs, displaying an unusual amount of knowledge about the earth and the forces affecting it. Lucretius has also been credited with advancing ideas about the struggle for existence and the survival of the fittest. The second Roman writer, the biographer and historian Caius Suetonius Tranquillus (*ca.* 72–*ca.* 123), in one of his books mentions a collection of bones at the villa of Emperor Augustus. These bones, which were quite large, were believed to be the remains of an extinct race of human giants—a belief commonly associated with such fossils as late as the eighteenth century.

PALEONTOLOGY IN THE MIDDLE AGES

Little progress was made in the development of paleontology in the Middle Ages. Fossils attracted scant attention from Christian theologians; during this period the Arabs were responsible for the advances in geology. One notable Arab scholar was Avicenna (979–1037), a Persian physician and great Islamic philosopher. He observed that banks of soft mud turned to stone and that there was some relation between mountain-building and earthquakes. With respect to fossils, however, Avicenna was of the opinion that "plastic forces" within the earth's crust were capable of modeling all types of plants and animals. This was actually an extension of the ideas of Aristotle and Theophrastus which had been put forth some seven hundred years earlier.

During this period fossils were usually referred to as "figured stones" (Fig. 70). Some churchmen believed fossils to be the work of the devil, placed in the rocks to confuse or mislead men. The starlike shape of certain crinoid stems led others to believe that the stars were responsible for the origin of these forms. Still others argued that fossils were "jokes" or "freaks of nature," or that they were types of life discarded by the Creator during experimental attempts. The old idea of "plastic forces" was revived and supported by the theory that vapors from within the earth produced all fossils.

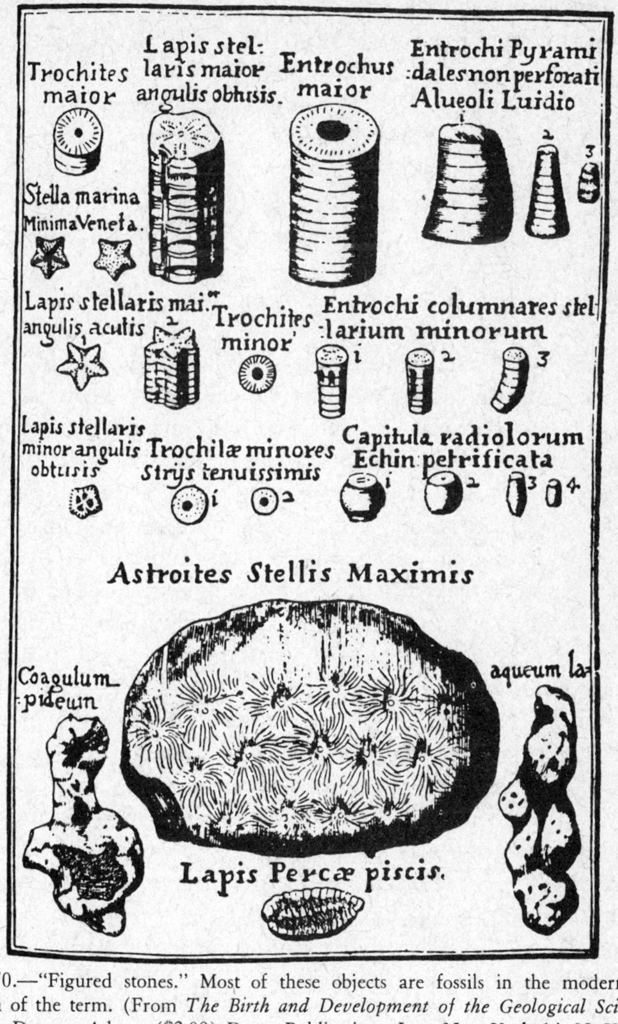

FIG. 70.—"Figured stones." Most of these objects are fossils in the modern acceptation of the term. (From *The Birth and Development of the Geological Sciences* by Frank Dawson Adams ($2.00) Dover Publications, Inc., New York 14, N. Y.)

PALEONTOLOGY DURING THE RENAISSANCE

Prior to the fifteenth century the ideas of early naturalists such as Aristotle, Lucretius, and Avicenna on the origin of fossils had been accepted. However, starting about 1500, there was considerable progress in paleontological thought; and the term *fossil,* which had once been applied to all objects dug out of the ground, gradually came to be applied exclusively to organic remains. Although some of the scientists of this period were correct in their conclusions about fossils, their ideas were not accepted by most people. It was customary during this period, for example, to explain fossils as remnants of the great Flood recorded in the Scriptures. This difference of opinion as to the origin of fossils created a controversy between scientists and theologians that lasted about three hundred years. Various nonscientific interpretations explained fossils as the remains of dragons, giants, and monsters.

During the Renaissance the following early naturalists concerned themselves with fossils. Leonardo da Vinci (1452–1519), great Italian artist, naturalist, and engineer, noted well-preserved fossil shells in the mountains of Italy. He reaffirmed the theory that fossils were evidence of past marine life and that they proved that the present relations between lands and seas have not always existed. He asserted, moreover, that the Flood could not possibly be responsible for producing all fossils, nor for their occurrence in the highest mountains. He also took to task the earlier theories that fossils could have originated in the rocks by such means as "plastic forces."

Girolamo Fracastoro (1483–1553), Italian physician and poet, published a book in which he expressed the opinion that fossils could not have been the result of the Biblical Flood—a dangerous opinion even during the Renaissance. Indeed, many scientists holding this belief were persecuted and a few were burned at the stake.

Bernard Palissy (*ca.* 1510–1589), French potter and naturalist, recognized fossils for what they are now known to be. Some writers believe that Palissy was probably the first person in France to discern that fossil fishes and shells are the remains of prehistoric marine animals.

Georg Bauer (under the pseudonym of Georgius Agricola) (1494–1555) wrote *De re metallica,* published in 1556, which classified rocks and minerals along with a few "fossils"—most of which were actually minerals.

A Swiss scholar, Konrad von Gesner (1516–1565), was the author of the first illustrated and descriptive work dealing with fossils. The illustrations were prepared from crude woodcuts, but even so the general nature of some of these fossils is easily seen. Unfortunately, however, Gesner, like others before him, believed that these objects were imitations of organisms rather than actual organic remains. In addition, like the "fossils" of Agricola, many of the specimens described in Gesner's work were inorganic in origin.

PALEONTOLOGY IN THE SEVENTEENTH CENTURY

The seventeenth century brought an increased interest in fossils and their origin, and a more scientific approach was made to the solution of this age-old problem.

One of the earlier genuinely scientific workers in the field was Nicolaus Steno (1638–1687), Danish bishop, physician, and professor of anatomy. In 1669 he published a book describing the occurrence of marine and fresh-water rocks and mentioning the presence of fossils in these deposits. Steno also dissected sharks and compared their teeth to the "tongue-stones" which were believed to have fallen from heaven during the dark of the moon. He proved that the "tongue-stones" were actually the teeth of fossil sharks. Steno was also one of the first to realize that rock strata were deposited in a normal succession—younger rocks overlying older rocks.

Martin Lister (1638–1712), famous English physician, is not usually associated with paleontology. He was, however, the author of several important publications dealing with both fossil and recent shells. Lister did not, unfortunately, believe that fossils had ever been part of any animal but preferred to consider them as "cockle-like stones."

Robert Plot (1640–1696), the first keeper of the Ashmolean Museum at Oxford, was another of England's pioneer naturalists. In 1677 Plot published *The Natural History of Oxfordshire* in which he illustrated some three hundred fossils. Plot agreed with Lister that these fossils did not represent the remains of former organisms but had been formed by "plastic forces" within the earth. He was also of the opinion that fossils may have been created as "ornaments" for the interior of the earth, and that they had no other significance.

Edward Lhuyd (also spelled Llwyd) (1660–1709) was Plot's successor in the Ashmolean Museum and the author of a large illustrated catalogue of English fossils. Noting that certain fossils occurred in particular strata, he concluded that these fossils may have originated from spore-bearing vapors which were derived from the sea. He thought that these vapors carried with them the seeds of animal life and that when they later condensed and fell to the earth's crust, the seeds, or spores, developed in the earth to form fossils.

Benoit de Maillet (1656–1738), a French consul in Egypt, is thought to have been the first to recognize that older rocks contain fewer fossils of existing species than do younger rocks. He published this idea, along with several others of geological importance, in his *Telliamed* (de Maillet spelled backwards) which appeared in 1748.

PALEONTOLOGY IN THE EIGHTEENTH AND NINETEENTH CENTURIES

In the late eighteenth and early nineteenth centuries paleontology became firmly established as a science. The organic origin of fossils was generally accepted, while the basic principles of the science were developed by a large number of natural scientists.

One of the most important of these was Carl von Linné (1707–1778), the famous Swedish botanist. Linné, better known as Linnaeus (the Latinized version of his name), was the author of the *Systema naturae,* the first edition of which was published in 1735. Modern paleontological, botanical, and zoological nomenclature is based on his early writings; and the importance of his work in the field of natural science can scarcely be overemphasized. In the tenth edition of his *Systema naturae,* published in 1758, Linné announced the principles for the definition of genera and species. It was also in this work that he established his now universally used system of binomial nomenclature which is based on morphologic similarity among organisms (see p. 68). In addition, Linnaeus named and described many fossils, particularly those from Silurian rocks in Sweden.

Jean Étienne Guettard (1715–1786), French physician and naturalist, was another to offer further proof that fossils are not inorganic freaks but the remains of former living organisms. He is also credited with what may have been the earliest *paleoecologic* studies. That is, he attempted to study fossils in relation to their past physical and biological environments and to draw some conclusions as to life conditions during the time the fossils were living. Guettard noted, for example, that certain types of fossil organisms were always attached to other fossils and that many fossil shells have undergone the same type of abrasion and wear that recent shells are now being subjected to. He inferred from these data that the fossil shells and the recent shells had occupied similar habitats and lived in similar faunal association and hence that ancient ecology could be interpreted by studying the ecology of similar recent forms.

James Hutton (1726–1797), a wealthy Scot, was educated as a physician but did not practice medicine. His activities as a "gentleman farmer" apparently led him to become interested in soils and ultimately in geology. He was one of the first to recognize that the earth had undergone great changes and that these changes were evident in the rocks of the earth's crust. These ideas, presented before the Royal Society of Edinburgh in 1785 and published in the two-volume *Theory of the Earth* in 1795, were based on data derived from observations in the field. Hutton considered all past events of earth history to be somehow connected and continuous with present occurrences. This idea is embodied in the very important principle of *uniformitarianism,* which states that the present is the key to the past and that existing processes could in sufficient time have accounted for all the earth's geologic features. Hutton's ideas have prompted many writers to call him the founder of modern geology.

Georges Léopold Chrétien Frédéric Dagobert Cuvier (1769–1832) was another noted biologist and paleontologist. He was a capable naturalist and was a professor of natural history and anatomy in Paris. A skilled comparative anatomist, Cuvier has been called the "father of vertebrate paleontology" because of his studies of fossil vertebrates. Baron Cuvier did much to further the study of Tertiary mammals, being particularly successful in reconstructing these forms from relatively few bones, jaws, and teeth. He noted, moreover, that certain species were restricted to the same strata and that many of these species are now extinct. He concluded, also, that these ancient animals had lived in the area where their remains are now found and that their characteristics provide evidence of climatic variations of the past. An ardent "anti-evolutionist," Cuvier believed that the characteristics of each species were immutable (incapable of change) and that all organisms were the products of special creation. He proposed the theory of *catastrophism,* which explained the differences in faunas in successive strata by assuming a series of catastrophes or cataclysms, each of which was followed by a special creation of new organisms. Cuvier's ideas dominated paleontologic thought until 1859, at which time Charles Darwin published his *Origin of Species* (see p. 160).

Alexandre Brongniart (1770–1847), a French mineralogist and

zoologist, joined Cuvier in stratigraphic and paleontologic studies of the Tertiary strata in the Paris Basin. These early investigators noted the presence of marine and fresh-water deposits, each with its own characteristic fauna. They demonstrated further that certain strata always contained the same fossils and could therefore be grouped together into units designated as *formations*. Their geologic maps of this area are among the earliest published, and the principles that they developed were to serve as a guide in working out the geologic history of other areas all over the world.

Jean Baptiste Pierre Antoine de Monet, better known as Chevalier de Lamarck (1744–1829), was a well-known French scientist who achieved fame, first as a botanist and later as a zoologist. Some of his publications were pioneering works on invertebrate animals, embodying many of the fundamental principles used in modern classification. Lamarck related his study of living animals to extinct forms that he found in the rocks and arrived at conclusions which made him one of the earliest and most important figures in the development of evolutionary thought. He argued, in brief, that changes developed or acquired during the lifetime of an individual are transmitted to the offspring. This theory, now termed *Lamarckism,* is no longer accepted by most scientists (see p. 160), but they do acknowledge that Lamarck laid the foundation for many of the basic principles of the theory of organic evolution. Lamarck's contributions were so important that he has been called the "father of invertebrate paleontology."

One of the greatest advances in the history of paleontology was made in the early nineteenth century by William "Strata" Smith (1769–1839), an English surveyor and engineer. Smith, in his work in coal-mining and canal construction, observed that each layer of rock contained fossils characteristic of that particular stratum and that such strata might be identified by their fossils and thereby correlated over wide areas. Through practice he was soon enabled to correlate stratigraphic units merely by looking at the fossils they contained. He did much work on the Jurassic system of England and published the first geologic map of that country. Smith's work formed the basis for stratigraphic paleontology as we know it today and stimulated the use of fossils in geologic mapping and correlation. It is little wonder that he is known as "the father of stratigraphy" as well as the "father of English geology."

C. G. Ehrenberg (1795–1876) was one of the earliest investigators of microscopic organisms. He proposed the term *microgeology* for the study of rock-forming microorganisms; and he published works on foraminifers, ostracodes, and diatoms. Another early student of microfossils was Alcide d'Orbigny (1802–1857), a French professor of paleontology, who published an eight-volume work on the paleontology of France. He also published numerous papers on foraminifers (which he erroneously classified as cephalopods). He has been called "the father of micropaleontology."

Charles Darwin (1809–1882) is best known for his demonstration of the principles of organic evolution. His book on the *Origin of Species,* published in 1859, has had a profound effect on biologic thought during the past century (see p. 160), and his theory of coral-reef formation has been utilized by zoologists and paleontologists alike.

In the United States notable paleontological contributions were made by several early scientists. It is to James Hall (1811–1898), however, that we must give major credit for furthering stratigraphy and paleontology in nineteenth-century America. Hall (Fig. 71) was one of the earliest directors of the State Geological Survey of New York and, later, state geologist of Iowa and of Wisconsin. A prodigious collector of fossils, and the author of a large number of scientific papers and books, he made numerous noteworthy contributions to paleontology. Among his more important publications were *Geology of New York,* published in 1843; and *Paleontology of New York,* an eight-volume classic published during the years 1847 to 1894. The latter work contained descriptions of the Paleozoic invertebrates of the state.

While Hall concentrated on invertebrate fossils, two other pioneer paleontologists were furthering the cause of vertebrate paleontology.

One of these men was Professor Edward D. Cope (1840–1897). Cope studied at the University of Pennsylvania and the Smithsonian Institution in Washington, D.C. He taught at Haverford College and the University of Pennsylvania and was curator at the Philadelphia Academy of Sciences. He published over six hundred papers dealing with recent and fossil vertebrates; and he accumulated a large collection of fossil mammals that is now housed in the American Museum of Natural History in New York. Although beset by such hardships as hostile Indians and rugged terrain, Cope collected widely throughout the western United States and made many important paleontological discoveries.

Cope's contemporary O. C. Marsh also did much to lay the foundations of American vertebrate paleontology. Marsh studied at Yale and abroad and later taught at Yale. He was a wealthy man and financially able to devote a great deal of time to fossil-collecting; he has been credited with many original paleontological finds in North

Fig. 71.—James Hall, pioneer American paleontologist. (Courtesy of American Museum of Natural History.)

America. Among Marsh's more famous discoveries were pterodactyls, mosasaurs, toothed birds, *Brontosaurus,* and *Uintatherium* (see Appendix A). He is also well known for his work on fossil horses.

Cope and Marsh were originally friends, but because of quarrels over collecting localities they became bitter enemies. Their feud rapidly developed into a collecting and fossil-naming contest unprecedented in the history of paleontology. Although this rivalry grew to rather ridiculous proportions, it did result in greatly accelerating the study of vertebrate paleontology in North America.

TWENTIETH-CENTURY PALEONTOLOGY

Paleontology in the present century has been characterized by a more intense application of paleontological principles to systematic, stratigraphic, and evolutionary studies. The expansion of the petroleum industry has brought about an increase in the industrial application of paleontology, particularly in the field of micropaleontology (see p. 49). The research work of paleontologists retained by national and state geological surveys, and museums, and their service as teachers of paleontology, have considerably advanced the science of paleontology in the past fifty years. In addition, the general public has shown an increased interest in all forms of prehistoric life and there has been a marked trend toward fossil-collecting as a hobby. Many amateur earth scientists have made outstanding collections of fossils.

CHAPTER X

FOSSILS AND EVOLUTION

Organic evolution may be defined as a process of cumulative change characterized by the progressive development of plants and animals from more primitive ancestors. A study of evolutionary processes indicates that the plants and animals of today have reached their present state of development as a result of gradual, orderly changes which have taken place in the geologic past.

EVIDENCE OF ORGANIC EVOLUTION

Most of the evidence of evolution, though indirect, clearly indicates that all organisms developed from a few simple ancestors to the multitude of diverse and complex organisms that inhabit our earth today. This evidence, complex and varied, is supported by both geologic and biologic studies. The major kinds of evidence that support the theory of evolution are discussed below.

Evidence from Comparative Anatomy. Anatomical studies of certain organisms indicate similar structural developments in different types of plants and animals. These organs of similar structure often show relationships between apparently unrelated plants and animals. For example, the leg of a horse, the flipper of a whale, the wing of a bat, and the wing of a bird all have the same type of skeletal structure and all are organs of locomotion. Furthermore, many of the bones of one animal (except for some that have been lost) correspond directly to those of another (Fig. 72). Organs which bear such fundamental structural resemblances are said to be *homologous structures*.

Likewise, there are similarities in the spinal column, digestive system, and central nervous system of the vertebrates. There is, for example, a marked likeness in the structure of the backbone of all mammals. These similarities between various vertebrate structures indicate kinship and descent, with modification, from a common ancestor.

There are some useless structures in organisms which can be recognized as once useful parts that have lost their function. These *vestigial structures* offer additional proof of evolution. Typical of such structures is the human vermiform appendix. In man the appendix is now only a source of trouble; but in certain of the lower animals (for example, the rabbit) this organ is an essential part of the digestive system. Its presence in man is best explained as a relic

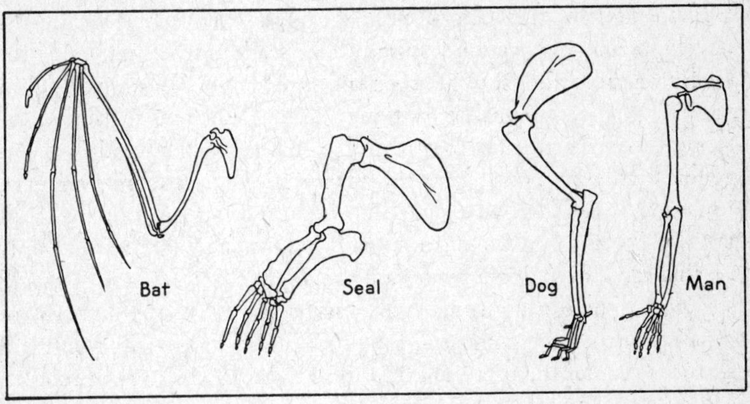

FIG. 72.—Comparison of skeletal elements in mammals. The limbs shown above contain the same skeletal elements. It is easy, however, to see how each bone and assemblage of bones has been adapted, or has evolved, to meet a given task in a special environment. (By permission from *Introduction to Geology* by H. E. Brown, V. E. Monnett, and J. W. Stovall, Ginn and Company, 1958.)

of a once useful part of the digestive system of a remote ancestor.

Other vestigial structures in man are the useless ear-moving muscles (homologous to those of lower mammals); the pineal body in the skull (remnant of a third eye which is still well developed in certain lizards); and the caudal vertebrae or coccyx (rudimentary vestiges of a tail). Comparative anatomists have recognized about 180 vestigial structures in the human body, each of which has apparently become useless as a result of evolutionary change. Vestigial structures are considered to be illustrative proof of evolution because they indicate that animals possessing them have descended from ancestors in which these structures were once useful parts.

Evidence from Comparative Physiology or Biochemistry. Organisms not only possess certain structural similarities but also show marked resemblances in their physiological processes and products. Certain chemical tests show close similarity between the body fluids of various animals; for example, blood analyses indicate a closer chemical relationship between man and ape than between man and pig. There is also considerable uniformity in the proportion of constituent salts between sea water and the blood of a vertebrate. This biochemical relationship has been offered as evidence that the ancestors of all vertebrates were once inhabitants of the sea and, through evolutionary processes, later became adapted to their diverse habitats of today.

Evidence from Embryology. A study of the early stages in the development of plants and animals offers additional support of the evolutionary relationship between the simple and the complex forms of life. It is an established fact that animal embryos in their early stages possess structures that resemble structures of the adult forms of less highly developed animals. For instance, all vertebrate embryos undergo an early growth stage in which gill slits are present. Gills are present and functional in adult fishes, but they are present only in the early or tadpole stages of the higher amphibians. Yet gill structures, though nonfunctional, always appear in the embryos of reptiles, birds, and mammals. Evolutionists see these embryonic gill slits as a relic of the past—an indication that the ancestors of reptiles, birds, and mammals were aquatic animals.

These and other embryological observations have given rise to the *biogenetic law* or the *law of recapitulation*. This law states that *ontogeny recapitulates phylogeny*—that is, that the development of the individual (ontogeny) recapitulates, or repeats, the development of the race (phylogeny). The biogenetic law appears to agree with studies on the nature of successive growth stages in plants and animals, and it thereby lends support to the theory of organic evolution.

Evidence from Taxonomy, or Classification. The Linnaean system of classification of plants and animals (see Chapter VI) is based upon structural resemblances between living forms and upon fossil evidence from extinct forms. Indeed, the fundamental units of classification (phyla, classes, orders, etc.) are based on varying degrees of similarity of structure within each group of organisms. This grouping of plants and animals according to fundamental similarities places them in an ascending series of increasing complexity. Taxonomy (the science of biological classification), then, assumes that the closest similarities are to be found among closely related organisms and that the greatest variation will be found among those forms that are either totally unrelated or distantly related. The structural relationships on which this system of classification is based indicate a line of common descent which can best be attributed to, and explained by, the processes of organic evolution.

Evidence from Geographic Distribution. Biologists have learned that plants and animals inhabiting closely situated islands are much more alike than are organisms living on more distantly separated islands. Moreover, in areas isolated by barriers such as mountain ranges or large bodies of water, there are often found species peculiar to these isolated areas, but related to species from adjacent regions. Apparently isolation leads to the development of new species; there are numerous instances of this particular evidence for organic evolution. For example, the fauna of Australia, long separated from the rest of the world, has remained very primitive and quite different from that of other continents. Also, the African and Eurasian camels resemble each other much more closely than they resemble the llamas of South America, which descended from the same ancestor. Distributional relationships of this type are considered to be the natural result of descent with change.

Evidence from Genetics and Controlled Breeding. Man has been able, in a limited way, to bring about evolution by means of the controlled selective breeding of plants and animals, retaining desired characteristics and eliminating undersirable ones. For example by breeding and selection man has developed various forms of dogs, such as the greyhound, Chihuahua, and dachshund. Yet all breeds of modern dogs can be traced back to a single species of wild dog. By the same methods, horse-breeders have developed such diverse forms of horses as the Shetland pony, Arabian race horse, and the Percheron (a heavy draft horse). In much the same manner, students of *genetics* (the science of heredity) have been able to obtain further evidence of evolution by means of controlled laboratory experiments.*

Evidence from Fossils. Paleontological studies offer undeniable proof of organic evolution (see p. 47). Investigation of the fossil record indicates that the simplest forms of life are to be found in

* A. M. Winchester, *Heredity: An Introduction to Genetics* (New York: Barnes and Noble, Inc., 1961). This easy-to-read book will provide the reader with a basic understanding of genetics and heredity.

the lower (older) strata of the earth and that organisms gradually changed into the more complex forms which are found as fossils in the younger rocks of the earth's crust. Thus, when fossils are arranged in chronological order they commonly show a series of changes that are readily explainable as the products of organic evolution.

THEORIES OF EVOLUTION

The earliest ideas concerning evolution and the history of life can be found in the writings of some of the early Greek philosophers (see p. 144). However, the foundation for modern evolutionary thought was laid down during the nineteenth century.

There have been three basic theories which have attempted to explain organic evolution, and each of these has been modified in the light of modern knowledge of evolutionary processes.

Lamarck's Theory of Inheritance of Acquired Characteristics (1809). As noted in the preceding chapter, this theory, also known as the *theory of use and disuse*, was proposed by Jean Baptiste de Monet, Chevalier de Lamarck, an early French biologist (see p. 152). Lamarck believed that structural variations or new organs are acquired—in the course of generations—as a result of need and that characteristics acquired during its lifetime by an organism are transmitted to some slight extent to its offspring. For example, the child of a man who had by years of training become a champion runner would be able to run a little faster than he could if his father had never practiced running. Or the son of a blacksmith would, by virtue of his father's physical condition, be born with larger biceps than would the son of an accountant. Modern biology has produced no evidence to support Lamarckism, as this school of thought is sometimes called, and the theory is of little importance today. It is interesting to note, however, that Lamarckism was for a while the officially "correct" doctrine of Communist geneticists. This theory has recently been—and still is—of some importance in the cultural conflict between Communism and the "West."

Darwin's Theory of Natural Selection (1859). As already mentioned (p. 153), Charles Darwin, by far the most important figure in the history of the theory of evolution, proposed this theory in his classic book *The Origin of Species*. Darwin's theory assumes that organisms produce far more offspring than can be expected to survive. These large numbers of offspring (no two of which are identical—the factor of *variation*) are in continual competition for food and other necessities. This *struggle for existence* leads to the *survival of the fittest.* The offspring of organisms best fitted for survival will inherit the favorable characteristics of their parents. In the struggle for existence not only the less fit individuals but less fit species are at a disadvantage and are eventually eliminated.

Modern biologists and paleontologists believe that much of Darwin's theory is correct, but have raised serious objections to some of his ideas. These objections have resulted in the modification of some parts of the original Darwinian theory.

De Vries's Mutation Theory (1901). Proposed by the Dutch botanist Hugo De Vries, this theory is based on the belief that all inherited variations from the species type are produced by changes in the germ plasm of organisms. De Vries believed that these changes, called *mutations,* are the chief method by which species change and new species appear. Mutations—which may be either quite pronounced or hardly noticeable—are known to occur in many types of organisms (and may be produced in the laboratory). This theory postulates that new species may appear suddenly instead of resulting from a series of minute changes through many generations.

THE MECHANICS OF EVOLUTION

All organisms are subject to change, which may be brought about in a variety of ways. The principal methods by which evolutionary changes occur are variation, mutation, struggle for existence, natural selection, heredity, and isolation.

Variation. Although it is a well-known fact that like begets like, offspring are never identical to their parents or to their brothers or sisters. The science of genetics has shown that variation and mutation arise through changes in the germ plasm and that they can be transmitted from one generation to another.

Struggle for Existence. As mentioned earlier, all plants and animals produce far more offspring than can possibly survive. This overpopulation brings about fierce competition for food, space, air, light, and water. The struggle for existence also involves a continual battle against natural enemies, parasites, and disease. Competition of this sort is particularly hard on the young, most of which do not survive. For example, many of the lower animals produce thousands or millions of eggs each year, and many trees produce countless numbers of seeds. Although the majority of these organisms fail to reach maturity, their parents must produce these great numbers of offspring if any are to be successful in the struggle for existence.

Natural Selection. In the struggle for existence even the smallest advantage may be decisive, for nature appears to favor those organisms which are well adapted to their environments and which can best compete with their neighbors. At the same time those that are weak find themselves at a disadvantage and will ultimately be exterminated. Natural selection, then, is the tendency for species to survive according to their ability to adapt to natural conditions. Nature uses natural selection in much the same manner that the stock-breeder uses artificial selection; since the unfit are eliminated, only the fit remain to perpetuate the race.

Heredity. Heredity, the transmission of characteristics from parent to offspring, is an important mechanism of evolution. Organisms possessing hereditary characteristics that are helpful, either in the animal's native environment or in some other environment that is open to it, are favored in the struggle for existence. Consequently, the offspring are able to benefit from the advantageous characteristics of their parents.

Isolation. Isolation appears to play a very important part in the development of new forms. Isolation may be brought about by a physical factor, such as a mountain range or an ocean, or by a biological factor, such as change in the food supply. The presence of such barriers within the geographic range of a species prevents interbreeding with organisms from other localities, thus causing greater differentiation in these populations than in freely interbreeding populations (see p. 159). If such species are isolated for sufficiently long periods, they form new species and lose their capacity for breeding with the parent species.

PRESENT VIEWS ON EVOLUTION

Virtually all students of the life sciences now agree that organic evolution is an established fact, and they seek to interpret and explain its processes and results in the observable aspects of nature.

Current evolutionary thought assumes that portions of both Darwin's and De Vries's theories are correct and that they are complementary to each other. The mutation theory shows that variations (either sudden and striking or gradual and cumulative) may occur, and Darwin's theory of the survival of the fittest shows how these variants can be preserved.

Much of today's research is directed toward learning more about the relation between genetics and evolution; great strides have been made in the attempt to better understand the mechanisms of heredity and the causes and effects of mutational change. Considerable attention has also been given to the evolutionary effect of isolation as brought about by such factors as environmental, reproductive, or geographical barriers.

Chapter XI

HUMAN FOSSILS

The story of fossils would not be complete without some mention of fossil man. Although it is essentially true that the study of mankind falls more properly within the realm of anthropology,* man's early history is more easily interpreted in the light of geological findings. Geology, by means of studies of fossil plant and animal associations and the rocks which contain them, provides information as to the approximate age and time sequence of prehistoric men and their primitive cultures.

Man is a mammal and a member of the order Primates (Latin *primus,* first). Other primates are the lemurs, tarsiers, monkeys, and apes. Primates are characterized by elongated limbs and enlarged hands and feet, each having five digits with cupped or flattened nails. The thumb and first toe are normally set apart from the other digits, a structural form which aids in the grasping and manipulation of objects. The brain is large, the eyes highly specialized. Man, along with the monkeys and apes, has been placed in the suborder Anthropoidea (Greek *anthropos,* man + *eidos,* resemblance). Anthropoids possess large eyes that face forward, relatively specialized teeth, and large brains. Most are able to sit in an upright position, leaving the hands free for manipulation of objects.

Unfortunately, the fossil record of the primates is scant; it is somewhat ironic that man knows more of the early history and development of certain other organisms than he does of his own. However, continued exploration and research have led to the discovery of an increasingly large number of fossilized human remains. These discoveries, many of which are found in association with various extinct Pleistocene animals, clearly indicate that man lived on earth during the Ice Age.

* Melville Jacobs and B. J. Stern, *General Anthropology* (New York: Barnes and Noble, Inc., 2nd ed., 1955), pp. 8–32. A good introduction to the field of anthropology.

Although a detailed account of fossil man is not within the scope of this book, this chapter will provide a brief introduction to the development of man in terms of his fossil record.

THE EARLIEST PRIMATES

In spite of the scarcity of primate fossils and the numerous breaks in the fossil record, it is now known that the primates originated in the Early Tertiary (see the Geologic Time Scale, p. xii). The earliest known primate, a small lemurlike animal, was found in Paleocene deposits in Wyoming. However, intervening evolutionary forms between this early primate and man have not been found in the New World; hence these later primates appear to have originated in the Old World.

The primates expanded during Eocene time and several Eocene lemurs have been described. The remains of *Notharctus,* a primitive lemur, are fairly common in certain Eocene strata of North America. *Notharctus* (Fig. 73), like present-day lemurs, was small, primarily arboreal (tree-dwelling), and had a long tail and small face. Modern lemurs are confined mainly to Madagascar, but some are found in Africa and Indonesia.

Another group of primates, the tarsiers, also appeared during Eocene time. These rat-sized, fragile, wide-eyed creatures were apparently widespread during the past but are now restricted to the jungles of Indonesia and the Philippines. Although rare as fossils, tarsier remains have been reported from the Eocene of Europe and North America.

The monkeys appear to have developed during middle Tertiary time, and can be traced from the Oligocene to the present. The oldest known monkey is *Parapithecus,* which was collected from Lower Oligocene rocks in Egypt.

The earliest ape, *Propliopithecus,* was also discovered in Egypt from rocks of Early Oligocene age. The original find was followed by later discoveries of well-preserved apes in Miocene deposits of Africa. One of these, *Proconsul,* may have been ancestral to the chimpanzee, gorilla, and man. Since no fossil brain cases of *Proconsul* have been found, there has been no adequate basis for estimating its brain size or intelligence. However, the arm, leg, and foot bones suggest that *Proconsul* walked on hind legs without need

FIG. 73.—*Notharctus,* a primitive lemur from Eocene deposits of North America. This early primate may have been an early ancestor to man. (From a painting by F. R. Jaques under the direction of William Gregory, courtesy of American Museum of Natural History.)

for support from the arms. Furthermore, its teeth and jaws were more nearly human in shape than are those of any modern or extinct apes. These remains suggest a creature that was not arboreal but, because of its erect posture and bipedal locomotion, was well adapted to life on the ground.

THE AUSTRALOPITHECINES OR MANLIKE APES

Fossil skeletons of the australopithecines, also called the southern apes, have been found in Pleistocene cave deposits of South Africa. The earliest known southern ape, *Australopithecus africanus,* was discovered in 1925. These remains consisted of the incomplete skull of a child about five years old. The structure of the skull, teeth, and certain other features strongly suggest its relationship to early man. Later discoveries consisted of humanlike jaws and skulls, in addition to arm, leg, and toe fragments.

Although the remains of many of these creatures have been found, each is incomplete and difficult to compare with the others. For this reason the exact evolutionary position of the australopithecines is not known. Some scientists are of the opinion that they represent the earliest men. Other authorities state that they are a terminal group of manlike apes and as such are not ancestral to man. Irrespective of their evolutionary position, these are important fossils, and their remains have provided us with a rather clear picture of the characteristics of the group. *Australopithecus* was bipedal, probably less than five feet tall, and had a roughly upright posture. He had an apelike head, powerful jaws, and teeth closely resembling our own (Fig. 74). His most primitive feature is the relatively small brain capacity which is somewhat less than that of the largest modern gorillas.

EARLY FOSSIL MEN

The earliest known fossil man has been found in rocks of Early Pleistocene age. This early human (or near-human) being is followed by a succession of Middle and Late Pleistocene men which are known both from their skeletal remains and from their *artifacts* (implements or weapons of prehistoric age).

East Africa Man. The bones of what appear to be the oldest known member of the human race were found in East Africa in late 1960.

These bones (a lower jaw, two skull bones, the foot bones, some of the hand bones, and a collarbone) were found in Lower Pleistocene deposits in Olduvai (Oldway) Gorge in Tanganyika. They are believed to be the remains of an eleven or twelve year-old child. The discoverer, Dr. Louis S. B. Leakey, curator of the Coryndon

Fig. 74.—Skulls of apes and men. In considering apes and men as a group, it is useful to recognize two sets of skull features: one set (technically called paleanthropic) characterizes apes and early men; the other set (called neanthropic) characterizes modern men. A comparison between these two groups may be seen at right. (By permission from *Life: An Introduction to Biology* by G. G. Simpson, C. S. Pittendrigh, and L. H. Tiffany, © 1957, by Harcourt, Brace, and World, Inc. Redrawn from figures in Romer, *Vertebrate Paleontology,* University of Chicago Press.)

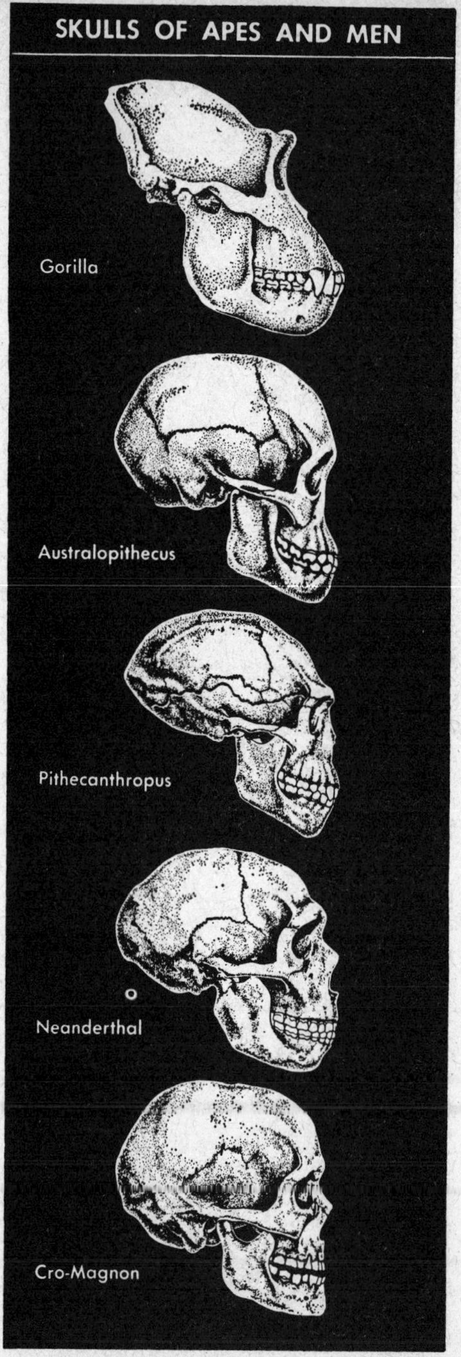

Museum, Nairobi, Kenya, is of the opinion that the child had been murdered. This is indicated by a nick in the skull that apparently came from a sharp blow and by radiating fractures from the point of impact in the skull.

The bones of another person, thought to be an adult, were found with the bones of the child; the sex of these individuals has yet to be determined. It is hoped that further study of the bones and the collecting site will yield additional information about these very important fossils.

Estimated to be greater than 1.75 million years old, the bones of these two individuals are considerably older than *Zinjanthropus boisei* or ("East Africa Man"), who was discovered by Dr. Leakey in 1959. (The more recent finds were obtained from a lower [therefore older] layer of rocks.) *Zinjanthropus* was also collected at Olduvai Gorge. This primeval human, called the "Nutcracker man" because of the unusually large jaw teeth, had sufficient intelligence to make and use a variety of pebble tools. Found with these crude implements were a hammer stone and numerous waste flakes from the manufacture of the tools.

These remains, consisting of a complete skull (minus the lower jaw) are believed to be those of a boy about eighteen years of age. He had a long face with a very low forehead, and the base of the skull indicates that he stood erect. His teeth appear to be definitely human and the molars are exceptionally large.

The skull of *Zinjanthropus* was associated with the bones of frogs, rats, mice, and young pigs and antelopes. The remains of these small animals suggests that East Africa man could kill only the smallest animals and must have been largely vegetarian. This assumption is further supported by the structure of his teeth which indicate that he must have fed primarily on coarse vegetation.

According to data derived by the latest methods of radioactive dating, the age of *Zinjanthropus* has been placed at 1.75 million years. This means that man has been on earth more than twice as long as scientists had previously thought possible.*

Java Ape Man. The remains of the Java ape man, *Pithecanthropus erectus* ("erect ape man"), were first noted in 1891 on the banks of the Solo River, near the village of Trinil in Java. During the period between 1891 and 1940, parts of five different skulls, a

*In 1962 Dr. Leakey reported the discovery of skull fragments believed to be more than 14 million years old. Collected in Kenya, South Africa, they appear to represent an evolutionary position midway between *Proconsul* and *Zinjanthropus*.

half-dozen femurs (thigh bones), and a number of teeth were found. Some of these bones were found in conjunction with the remains of Pleistocene elephants, rhinoceroses, tapirs, and other extinct mammals.

Pithecanthropus apparently lived 400,000 to 500,000 years ago and, although primitive, possessed many human characteristics. The skull is apelike, the forehead sloping or flat, and the lower jaw lacks a chin (Figs. 75 and 77). But the teeth are near-human and the brain

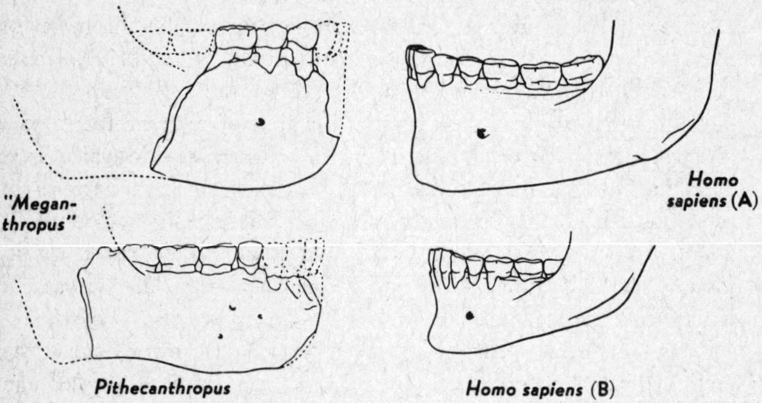

FIG. 75.—The mandibles (reconstructed) of *"Meganthropus palaeojavanicus"* and *Pithecanthropus,* compared with two mandibles of *Homo sapiens.* (*A*) the mandible of an Australian aboriginal, and (*B*) the mandible of a European. Approximately one half size. (By permission from *The Fossil Evidence for Human Evolution* by W. E. L. Clark. Copyright, 1955, by the University of Chicago.)

size begins to approach modern human brain capacities. In addition, a cast of the inside of the skullcap provides evidence of a near-human level of brain development, especially in relation to its speech area. Muscle attachments on the femurs indicate that Java man probably had an upright posture.

Peking Man. Between 1927 and 1937 scientists recovered fossilized remains of more than forty individuals of prehistoric men who had lived in the vicinity of Peking, China. These fossils of primitive men, named *Sinanthropus pekingensis* ("China man of Peking"), were collected from cave deposits which also contained the remains of extinct Middle Pleistocene mammals.

The brain case and certain other skeletal parts of *Sinanthropus* closely resemble similar parts of *Pithecanthropus.* This fact has led many anthropologists and paleontologists to conclude that Java man and Peking man are members of the same race. Indeed, some recent classifications classify Peking man as *Pithecanthropus pekingensis.* It has been pointed out, however, that the Chinese skulls have a larger brain capacity, and some investigators claim that unlike Java man, Peking man apparently possessed cutting tools of stone and knew how to use and control fire. The Chinese ape men were probably cannibals, as indicated by the fact that the basal parts of most of the skulls had been broken open so that the brains could be removed. Furthermore, most of the long bones had been split so as to expose the marrow.

Giant Primates. Among the more unusual and interesting primate remains are those of the so-called Javan and South Chinese giants. These fossils consist primarily of massive jaw fragments and exceptionally large teeth which are believed to have belonged to gigantic apes or men. One such form is *Gigantopithecus blacki* ("Black's giant ape"), whose teeth are twice as large as the corresponding teeth in a gorilla and six times larger than modern man. The teeth of this primate, along with the teeth of other Pleistocene mammals, were found in a Chinese chemist's shop in Hong Kong. Chinese druggists commonly pulverize fossil teeth for use in certain medications, and paleontologists have found many interesting fossils on "field trips" to their shops.

Part of another exceptionaly large primate jaw containing two teeth was found in Java in 1941. This jaw (Fig. 75) is considerably larger than that of any known anthropoid ape or man, but the teeth, despite their great size, appear to be unquestionably human in form. This specimen was appropriately named *Meganthropus paleojavanicus* ("great man of ancient Java"). It has been suggested that *Meganthropus* was ancestral to *Pithecanthropus* and later normal-sized men. However, many authorities believe that *Meganthropus* lived at the same time as earlier species of *Pithecanthropus* and was a special form of Java man. Because of the fragmentary nature of their fossil record, it is impossible to determine whether these great creatures are in the direct line of human ancestry or constitute a separate branch of primates.

Heidelberg Man. The oldest human fossil found in Europe consists of a pair of almost complete lower jaws containing sixteen well-preserved teeth. This valuable find was made near Heidelberg,

Germany, in 1907. These teeth and jaws possess definite human characters, although the receding chin suggests relationships with the apes. This Early Pleistocene form, named *Homo heidelbergensis,* may possibly represent an intermediate stage between ape and man. There is also some indication that Heidelberg man may have been a close ancestor of Neanderthal man (see below). The Heidelberg jaw was found in association with the remains of Pleistocene elephants, horses, rhinoceroses, and other mammals. The age of these remains have been placed at about 450,000 years, making Heidelberg man a contemporary of Peking man.

Neanderthal Man. *Homo neanderthalensis,* probably the best-known of all fossil men, was described from a skullcap and some leg bones dug up from the floor of a limestone cave in the Neanderthal (also spelled Neandertal) Valley near Dusseldorf, Germany. These fossils were discovered in 1856, but were not recognized as a distinct human species until 1864. In the meantime, the bones were variously regarded as a pathologically deformed specimen, as the skull of an idiot, or as belonging to primitive savages.

Another skull, that of a young female, had been found in a quarry on the Rock of Gibraltar as early as 1848. However, it was not recognized as a Neanderthal until 1906. Since the original 1848 discovery, several complete skeletons, in addition to many incomplete skeletons of men, women, and children, have been collected. These abundant remains suggest that Neanderthal man was widespread and prolific during Late Pleistocene time. His skeletal remains have been found in many parts of Europe and in Iran and Iraq.

The neaderthaloids were apparently cave-dwellers and hunters; their skeletons are often accompanied by stone implements such as scrapers, spearheads, and axes. Neanderthal remains are also found associated with the bones of the animals that they hunted. These include the woolly mammoth, giant cave bear, bison, horse, and woolly rhinoceros.

Because of the large number of Neanderthal remains that have been found, we have obtained a rather clear picture of the physical characteristics of these early people. They were short, stocky individuals, typically about five feet in height. The head was thrust forward and the shoulders were stooped; this gave the body a slouched appearance (Fig. 76). The hands and feet were large and the knees were slightly bent. The head of Neanderthal man was large and marked by a low forehead, flat nose, receding chin, and

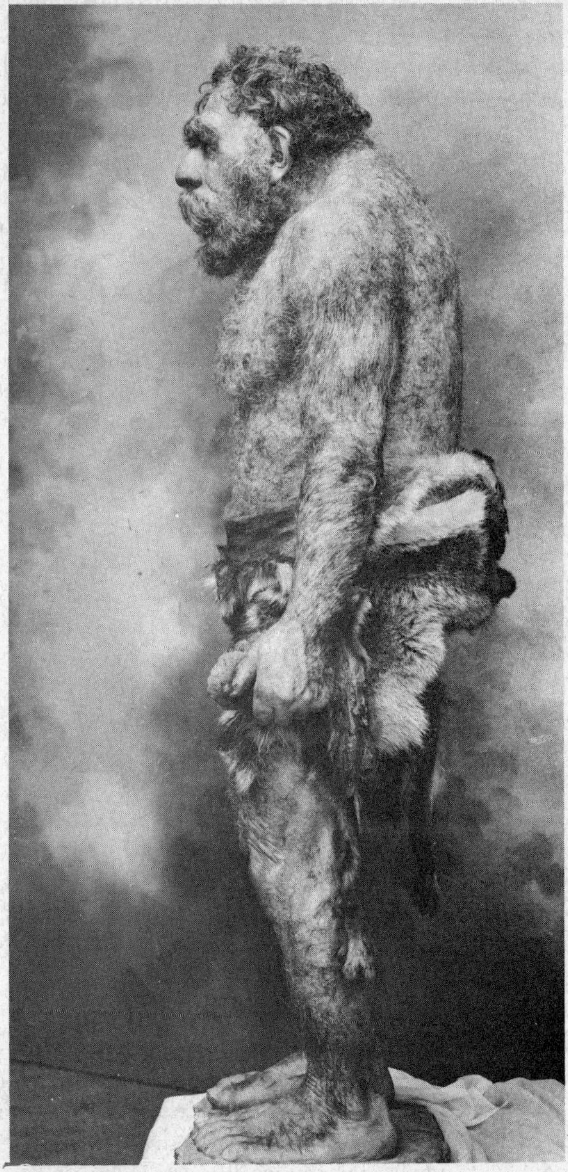

Fig. 76.—Neanderthal man. Restoration of male neanderthaloid as seen from the left side. (Frederick Blaschke, sculptor; photograph courtesy of Chicago Natural History Museum.)

heavy brow ridges; his face was coarse-featured and brutish (Fig. 77).

In spite of his primitive appearance, Neanderthal man had a brain capacity which was approximately equal to that of modern man. As noted above, he had also developed a primitive culture and is known to have used fire. Furthermore, the manner in which certain Neanderthal skeletons were arranged indicates that he buried his dead. Food, stone implements, and other artifacts were found in the graves of some of the skeletons. Such objects strongly suggest that the Neanderthals had some type of religion or burial ritual.

It was originally believed that Neanderthal man was directly ancestral to *Homo sapiens,* or modern man. However, specimens have been found which combine the characteristics of both Neanderthal and modern man. Even more important is the discovery of fossil remains of modern man that are as old or older than Neanderthal man.

HOMO SAPIENS

The first true man, or *Homo sapiens* (Latin *homo,* man +*sapiens,* wise) appeared during the last glacial stage approximately 35,000 years ago.

Cro-Magnon Man. The earliest recorded discovery of prehistoric *Homo sapiens* was made in 1868 at the rock shelter of Cro-Magnon, near the village of Eyzies in the Dordogne Valley of France. The Cro-Magnons, as these early people are called, are well known from a large number of skeletons which have been collected in western and central Europe.

Cro-Magnon man appears to be modern in all respects and is far advanced over Neanderthal man. He was tall (many skeletons exceed six feet in height), walked erect, and had relatively long legs with straight thigh bones. The head was long with a high forehead, long nose, and pointed chin (Fig. 77). The Cro-Magnon was as highly developed mentally as he was physically. His brain capacity was equal to that of present-day men, and he fashioned many well-formed tools from flint and bone. He also possessed considerable artistic ability as evidenced by the large numbers of paintings and sculptured bones which have been found in many of his caves (Fig. 78).

Prehistoric Man in America. The early development of man took place in the Old World, and he was relatively late in arriving

Fig. 77.—Restorations of fossil men. *Pithecanthropus erectus* (left), *Homo neanderthalensis* (center), and *Homo sapiens* (Cro-Magnon man) (right). (Restorations by J. H. McGregor; photographs courtesy of American Museum of Natural History.)

Courtesy of Chicago Natural History Museum

FIG. 78.—Restoration of Cro-Magnon man drawing on wall of a cave. Previously completed drawings may be seen on the wall above the man.

in the Western Hemisphere. It is now generally agreed that the early inhabitants of both North and South America belong to the Mongoloid division of *Homo sapiens*. The ancestors of these early Americans apparently migrated from northeastern Asia (Siberia) and moved into Alaska by way of the Bering Strait area. There were probably many such migrations, the first of which occurred after the last Pleistocene glaciation more than 10,000 years ago.

It is now evident that the first men reached the New World before the extinction of such typical Pleistocene mammals as the mammoth, mastodon, ground sloth, and various extinct horses and bison. However, all human fossils found thus far in America belong to *Homo sapiens,* the species of modern man. Important discoveries of American prehistoric men are discussed below.

FOLSOM REMAINS. Some of the oldest known American stone implements were found near Folsom, New Mexico in 1926. More of these chipped stone arrowheads, called Folsom points, were later discovered in Colorado, Texas, Arizona, and many other states.

It now appears certain that the Folsom culture was widespread in North America. The points found in the northern foothills of the Brookes Range in Alaska lend support to the theory that man migrated to North America via the Bering Strait. Folsom points have been found in close association with the remains of extinct species of bison and camels, but so far there has been no evidence of Folsom man himself.

MINNESOTA MAN. One of the more controversial North American human fossils is a skeleton discovered near Pelican Rapids, Minnesota in 1931. Minnesota "man" (actually the skeleton of a young girl) was found in glacial lake-bed deposits which have been estimated to be as much as 20,000 years old. However, many authorities believe that this estimate is excessive and that these remains are less than 10,000 years old. Still others argue that this well-preserved skeleton is not prehistoric but has been buried recently.

TEPEXPAN MAN. Another discovery of great importance was made near the village of Tepexpan in Mexico in 1947. Here, in Upper Pleistocene deposits generally accepted to be as much as 10,000 years old, were found much of the skeleton and the almost complete skull of a man. The remains were found in association with the bones of the imperial mammoth, a well-known Pleistocene elephant. The same rock layer that yielded the skeleton of Tepexpan man also contained several stone artifacts and the bones of extinct bison, horses, and glyptodonts (see p. 137).

Midland Man. The remains of Midland "man" (in reality the skeletal fragments of a female) were found north of Midland, Texas, in 1953. The remains were exposed by wind erosion and were accompanied by a variety of stone points and fragmental animal bones. Some of the latter had been burned, and radiocarbon dating indicates that they may be as much as 12,000 years old.

THE PILTDOWN HOAX

Any discussion of prehistoric man must necessarily include some mention of *Eoanthropus dawsoni* ("Dawson's dawn man"). These remains, commonly called Piltdown man, were found by an amateur anthropologist in 1912. They were collected from Pleistocene river gravels near Piltdown in Sussex, England, and consisted of pieces of a human skull and the right half of a lower jaw. The skull fragments are essentially those of *Homo sapiens,* but the jaw, which contained two molar teeth, is massive and chinless and definitely apelike in character.

These remains were immediately regarded with suspicion by some paleontologists and anthropologists who could not reconcile the great differences between the jaw and the skull. The skeletal fragments generated intense interest among scientists for some forty years and were also a source of great controversy. Then, in 1953, these specimens were finally exposed as a modern human skull and the lower jaw of an orangutan (an anthropoid ape). These conclusions were reached after careful investigation revealed that the bones and teeth had been artificially stained to look like authentic fossils. In addition, the teeth had been artificially abraded, and the ivory composing them was found to be identical to that in modern teeth. Equally conclusive were the results of fluorine analyses and other chemical tests to which the bones were subjected. The results of these tests indicate that the Piltdown fragments are not prehistoric, but of Recent age.

In short, this specimen, after more than forty controversial years, was exposed as one of the most successful and carefully perpetrated hoaxes in the history of science. Thus, through the combined use of painstaking research and the most modern scientific techniques, Piltdown man has finally been removed from the list of human fossils.

Appendix A

MAIN DIVISIONS OF THE ORGANIC WORLD

The beginning fossil-collector is usually amazed at the many different plants and animals which have left some record of their existence. In order that we may more fully understand these different types of prehistoric life, it is necessary to know something about the organisms that are living today.

In this section of the book we will discuss the more important groups of plants and animals which have left some sort of paleontological record. For each of these groups we will begin with a discussion of the more simple organisms and proceed to the more advanced forms in the approximate order of their appearance in geologic time. Because scientific workers do not always agree on the same classification, the system adopted in this book contains the latest ideas of several authorities. It is simple enough to understand, yet complete enough to help the collector to know and classify his fossils. It should be noted that this classification differs in some respects from that of certain older paleontological publications. Therefore, it has seemed advisable to list alternative taxonomic names for some of the groups that are discussed.

In some instances the brief descriptions and illustrations of each group will enable the collector to make a preliminary identification of his fossils. For more detailed information about each group, the reader should refer to "Publications about Fossils" (p. 303), and more especially to those titles listed under "Reference Works."

This part of the book presents a synopsis of the plant and animal kingdoms. After this there is a brief summary of the major groups of the plant kingdom. Attention is directed to those plants which have left some sort of fossil record. This is followed by a discussion of the general characteristics and relative paleontological importance of the various invertebrate animals. Emphasis is placed on the invertebrates because this type of fossil is most commonly collected

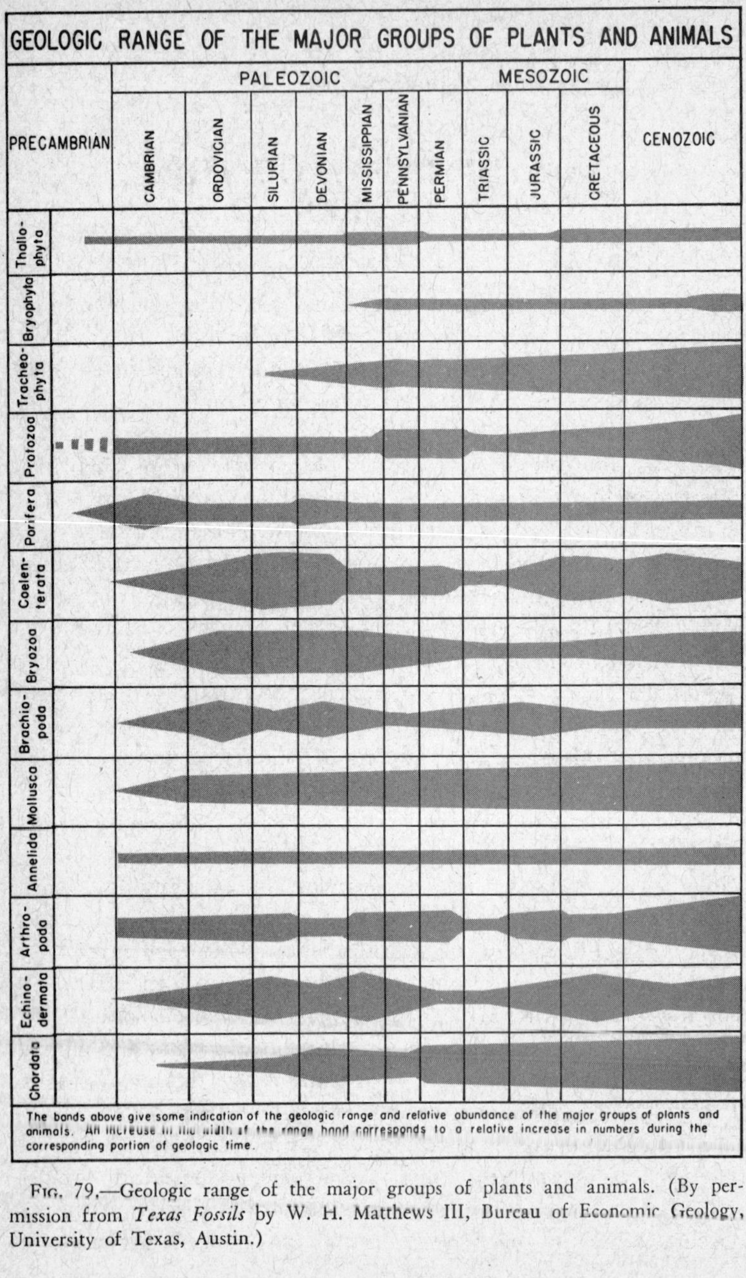

FIG. 79.—Geologic range of the major groups of plants and animals. (By permission from *Texas Fossils* by W. H. Matthews III, Bureau of Economic Geology, University of Texas, Austin.)

by the amateur. Finally, there is a general, but less detailed, review of the vertebrates.

As each group of organisms is discussed, reference is made to the portions of geologic time of which they are most characteristic. The reader may find it helpful to refer frequently to the Geologic Time Scale (p. xii) in order to properly place the organisms in geologic history. Figure 79 shows the distribution of the major groups of plants and animals throughout geologic time.

Not all scientists agree as to the names and ranks of the various organisms or the order of their development. This is especially true of plant classification. The following classification is therefore based upon the work of several authorities and includes, primarily, those groups that are of some importance as fossils.

The synopsis below provides a general perspective of the plant and animal kingdoms, and lists a few of the distinguishing characteristics of each group. There are, in addition, examples of each group (usually listed by common name but some genera are given in italics), some statement as to their relative importance as fossils, and their *geologic range* (that is, the duration of the group through geologic time). This synopsis thus provides the reader with a brief review of the various kinds of plants and animals and gives some indication of the order in which they have developed. Those groups marked with a dagger (†) are extinct.

KINGDOM PLANTAE (PLANTS)

Subkingdom Thallophyta (thallus plants; body undifferentiated without roots, stems, or leaves; relatively unimportant as fossils; Precambrian to Recent)

Division * Algae (diatoms, algae, and seaweeds; diatoms of some value as fossils; algae have very long geologic history; Precambrian to Recent)

Division Fungi (bacteria and fungi; have long geologic history but unimportant as fossils; Middle Devonian to Recent)

Subkingdom Embryophyta (plants forming an embryo; Silurian to Recent)

Division Bryophyta (mosses and liverworts; plants without vascular tissues or roots; rare as fossils; Mississippian to Recent)

Division Tracheophyta (plants with vascular tissue; most fossil plants in this division; Silurian to Recent)

* The term division has equal taxonomic rank with the term phylum as used in the animal kingdom (see p. 70).

Subdivision Psilopsida (roots absent, leaves absent or simple; known mostly as fossils; Silurian to Recent)

Subdivision Lycopsida (club mosses, scale trees, etc.; leaves simple, usually small, stems not joined; club mosses found fossil; Silurian to Recent)

Subdivision Sphenopsida (horsetails; plants with small, wedge-shaped leaves, stems joined; known mostly as fossils; Devonian to Recent)

Subdivision Pteropsida (ferns, cycads, conifers, flowering plants, etc.; leaves usually large and complex; many important as fossils; Devonian to Recent)

CLASS FILICINEAE (ferns; many found fossil; Devonian to Recent)

CLASS GYMNOSPERMAE (seed-ferns, cycads, ginkgos, conifers, etc.; cone-bearing plants, chiefly evergreens; many found fossil; Devonian to Recent)

†*Order Pteridospermales* (Pteridospermae) (seed-ferns such as *Neuropteris;* many found fossil; Mississippian to Jurassic)

†*Order Cycadeoidales* (cycadeoids; resemble cycads; extinct; Triassic to Cretaceous)

Order Cycadales (cycads; plants resembling palms; important as fossils; Late Permian, or Triassic to Recent)

†*Order Cordaitales* (the early conifers; known only as fossils; Mississippian to Permian)

Order Ginkgoales (ginkgos or maidenhair trees; primitive plant, most species extinct; Permian to Recent)

Order Coniferales (pines, junipers, and firs; cone-bearing softwoods or evergreens; many fossil species; Pennsylvanian to Recent)

CLASS ANGIOSPERMAE (flowering plants and hardwoods; many fossil species; Triassic to Recent)

SUBCLASS DICOTYLEDONEAE (oaks, roses, maples, etc.; plants with two seed leaves in the embryo; herbs and woody plants; Jurassic to Recent)

SUBCLASS MONOCOTYLEDONEAE (grasses, lilies, palms, etc.; plants with one seed leaf in the embryo; mostly herbs, some trees; Jurassic to Recent)

KINGDOM ANIMALIA (ANIMALS)

Phylum Protozoa (foraminifers, radiolarians, etc.; one-celled animals, typically microscopic; important as fossils; Cambrian to Recent)

CLASS SARCODINA (unicellular animals with pseudopodia; many fossil species; Cambrian to Recent)

Order Foraminifera (foraminifers or "forams"; unicellular animals with many-chambered shells; very important as fossils; (?) Cambrian, Ordovician to Recent)

Order Radiolaria (radiolarians; unicellular animals with siliceous unchambered shells; many fossil species known; Cambrian to Recent)

Phylum Porifera (sponges; most primitive of all multicellular organisms; relatively unimportant as fossils; Precambrian to Recent)

Phylum Coelenterata (corals, jellyfishes, hydroids, etc.; multicellular animals with definite body cavity; corals important as fossils; Cambrian to Recent)

CLASS HYDROZOA (hydroids; unimportant as fossils; Cambrian to Recent)

†*Order Stromatoporoidea* (extinct, colonial, encrusting forms which build dense, calcareous, laminated deposits; important fossils and rock-builders in Silurian and Devonian; Cambrian to Cretaceous)

CLASS SCYPHOZOA (jellyfishes and conulariids; not important as fossils; Cambrian to Recent)

†SUBCLASS CONULATA (four-sided pyramidal fossils bearing transverse markings; their zoological affinities are doubtful but, on basis of their fourfold symmetry, they are assigned to the coelenterates; some species useful as Paleozoic guide fossils; Cambrian to Early Triassic)

CLASS ANTHOZOA (corals and sea anemones; body cavity divided by radial vertical partitions called septa; both individual, or solitary, and colonial, or compound types common; exclusively marine in habitat; many species important as fossils—especially in Paleozoic; Ordovician to Recent)

SUBCLASS ALCYONARIA (Octocorallia) ("sea pens," "sea whips," horny corals; exclusively colonial, having eight pinnately branched tentacles and eight mesenteries; not extensively known as fossils; (?) Silurian, or Permian to Recent)

SUBCLASS ZOANTHARIA (most corals and all sea anemones; solitary or colonial; usually possess hard exoskeleton; important as fossils; Ordovician to Recent)

†*Order Rugosa* (Tetracoralla) (extinct colonial or solitary corals; septa arranged in quadrants; important as fossils; Ordovician to Permian)

Order Scleractinia (Hexacoralla) (solitary or colonial corals with septa in multiples of six; most modern corals in this order; some forms important reef-builders; important as Mesozoic and Cenozoic fossils; Triassic to Recent)

†*Order Tabulata* (extinct, exclusively colonial, corals characterized by tabulae; septa absent or weak; important as fossils; Ordovician to Permian, or (?) Eocene)

Phylum Platyhelminthes (flukes, tapeworms, etc.; flatworms; not known as fossils)

Phylum Nemathelminthes (*Trichina* or pork worm; roundworms; not definitely known as fossils)

Phylum Trochelminthes (rotifers—the "wheel animals"; not known as fossils)

Phylum Bryozoa ("moss-animals" or "sea mats"; colonial encrusting animals; important as fossils in Paleozoic rocks; (?) Cambrian, or Ordovician to Recent)

Phylum Brachiopoda ("lamp shells" or brachiopods; bivalved attached forms; (?) Precambrian, or Cambrian to Recent)

Class Inarticulata (brachiopods with unhinged valves, without teeth or sockets; common in rocks of Lower Paleozoic age; important as fossils; (?) Precambrian, or Cambrian to Recent)

Class Articulata (brachiopods with hinged valves, possessing teeth and sockets; most modern species in this class; important as fossils; Early Cambrian to Recent)

Phylum Mollusca (mollusks: clams, snails, squids, etc.; soft-bodied animals, most with external hard parts; important as fossils; Cambrian to Recent)

Class Amphineura (chitons, "sea-mice," or "coat-of-mail" shells; shell composed of eight valves or plates; not common as fossils; Ordovician to Recent)

Class Scaphopoda ("tusk-shells"; shell composed of a single tusklike valve; generally not a common fossil but locally abundant in certain Cenozoic formations; (?) Ordovician, Devonian to Recent)

Class Pelecypoda (clams, mussels, oysters, scallops; shells composed of two valves, usually, but not always, of equal size; common fossils, especially in Mesozoic and Cenozoic rocks; Ordovician to Recent)

Class Gastropoda (snails, slugs, conchs; slugs are without shells, snails and conchs—marine snails—have a single-valved shell which is typically coiled; common fossils in Paleozoic, Mesozoic, and Cenozoic rocks; Early Cambrian to Recent)

Class Cephalopoda (squids, octopuses, the pearly nautilus, and the extinct ammonoids; shell composed of one valve usually coiled and partitioned by septa; valuable fossils, especially in Paleozoic and Mesozoic rocks; Cambrian to Recent)

subclass nautiloidea (nautiloids; cephalopods with external chambered shells containing simple septa or dividing partitions; only genus extant is *Nautilus;* useful fossils in Lower Paleozoic rocks; Early Cambrian to Recent)

†SUBCLASS AMMONOIDEA (ammonites; extinct cephalopods with external single-valved shells; septa more complex than in nautiloids; especially important as Mesozoic guide fossils; Devonian to Cretaceous)

SUBCLASS COLEOIDEA (Dibranchia) (squids, octopuses, cuttlefish, and the extinct belemnoids; squidlike cephalopods with shell internal or lacking; not usually found as fossils; Late Mississipian to Recent)

†*Order Belemnoidea* (Belemnitida) (belemnites; extinct squidlike animals with internal skeleton; some species valuable Mesozoic guide fossils; Late Mississippian to Cretaceous)

Phylum Annelida (earthworms, leeches, etc.; segmented worms; fossil record in form of jaws, teeth, and tubes; (?) Precambrian, or Cambrian to Recent)

Phylum Arthropoda (crabs, shrimps, insects, spiders, ostracodes, and the extinct trilobites and eurypterids; segmented animals with jointed appendages; most of little paleontological importance; Cambrian to Recent)

†**Subphylum Trilobitomorpha** * (trilobites and related forms; Cambrian to Permian)

†CLASS TRILOBITA (trilobites; extinct three-lobed arthropods; important as Paleozoic guide fossils; Cambrian to Permian)

Subphylum Chelicerata (scorpions, spiders, mites, "horseshoe" or "king crabs," and the extinct eurypterids; relatively unimportant as fossils; Cambrian to Recent)

CLASS MEROSTOMATA (king crabs and eurypterids; the latter are of some importance as fossils; Cambrian to Recent)

†*Order Eurypterida* (eurypterids; extinct, aquatic, scorpionlike arthropods; relatively unimportant as fossils; Ordovician to Permian)

CLASS ARACHNIDA (scorpions, spiders, and ticks; rare as fossils; Silurian to Recent)

Subphylum Crustacea (crayfish, crabs, lobsters, etc.; mostly aquatic arthropods; generally of little paleontological importance; Cambrian to Recent)

CLASS OSTRACODA (ostracodes; small bivalved crustaceans; valuable microfossils; Ordovician to Recent)

CLASS CIRRIPEDIA (barnacles; mostly unimportant as fossils; Pennsylvanian to Recent)

* The subphyla of Arthropoda are considered to be classes by some authorities.

Class Malacostraca (lobsters, crabs, shrimps, sow bugs, crayfishes; not important as fossils; (?) Cambrian, or Ordovician to Recent)

Subphylum Insecta (insects; not important as fossils; Middle Devonian to Recent)

Phylum Echinodermata ("sea lilies," sea cucumbers, starfishes, sea urchins, etc.; typically possessing spiny skins; exclusively marine in habitat; important as fossils; Cambrian to Recent)

Subphylum Pelmatozoa (cystoids, blastoids, crinoids; attached, stemmed echinoderms; Cambrian to Recent)

†Class Cystoidea (cystoids; extinct bladderlike echinoderms; Cambrian to Devonian)

†Class Blastoidea (blastoids or "sea buds"; extinct budlike echinoderms; of some importance as Mississippian fossils; Ordovician to Permian)

Class Crinoidea ("sea lilies" and "feather stars"; abundant in Upper Paleozoic rocks; Ordovician to Recent)

Subphylum Eleutherozoa (sea cucumbers, starfishes, sea urchins, etc.; free-moving, stemless echinoderms; class Echinoidea of importance paleontologically; (?) Middle Cambrian, or Ordovician to Recent)

Class Stelleroidea (starfishes and "brittle stars"; not important as fossils; Ordovician to Recent)

subclass asteroidea (starfishes; not important as fossils; Ordovician to Recent)

subclass ophiuroidea ("brittle stars" and "serpent stars"; possess slender, whiplike arms; not important as fossils; Ordovician to Recent)

Class Echinoidea (sea urchins, heart urchins, and sand dollars; spiny, unattached echinoderms; body composed of numerous calcareous plates; important as fossils, especially in Mesozoic strata; Ordovician to Recent)

Class Holothuroidea (sea cucumbers; saclike sausage-shaped echinoderms; relatively unimportant as fossils; (?) Middle Cambrian, or Mississippian to Recent)

Phylum Chordata (graptolites, fish, amphibians, reptiles, birds, and mammals; have a dorsal nerve cord; Cambrian to Recent)

Subphylum Hemichordata (chordates with preoral notochord; class Graptolithina important as fossils; Cambrian to Recent)

†Class Graptolithina (Graptozoa) (graptolites; extinct colonial animals with chitinous exoskeletons; Cambrian to Mississippian)

Subphylum Vertebrata (vertebrates; animals with a vertebral column; Ordovician to Recent)

SUPERCLASS PISCES (fishes; aquatic, gill-breathing; Ordovician to Recent)

CLASS AGNATHA (lampreys, hagfishes; primitive fishes without jaws; Ordovician to Recent)

†CLASS PLACODERMI (placoderms; extinct primitive, armor-plated fishes with jaws; Silurian to Permian)

CLASS CHONDRICHTHYES (sharks, rays, skates; jawed fishes with cartilaginous skeletons; Devonian to Recent)

CLASS OSTEICHTHYES (perch, catfish, trout, eel; bony fishes with jaws; Middle Devonian to Recent)

SUPERCLASS TETRAPODA (amphibians, reptiles, birds, mammals; vertebrates with paired appendages; Late Devonian to Recent)

CLASS AMPHIBIA (salamanders, frogs, toads, etc.; spend early developmental stages in water; Late Devonian to Recent)

CLASS REPTILIA (lizards, snakes, turtles, crocodiles, dinosaurs, plesiosaurs, ichthyosaurs, mosasaurs, pterosaurs, etc.; cold-blooded tetrapods, breathe by lungs; Pennsylvanian to Recent)

†*Order Cotylosauria* (cotylosaurs; extinct primitive, amphibian-like reptiles; ancestors of reptiles; Pennsylvanian to Triassic)

Order Chelonia (turtles and tortoises; tetrapods with bony exoskeleton; unimportant as fossils; (?) Permian, or Traissic to Recent)

†*Order Pelycosauria* (extinct fin- or sail-back reptiles like *Dimetrodon;* relatively common during Permian; Late Pennsylvanian to Permian)

†*Order Therapsida* (therapsids, or theromorphs; extinct mammal-like reptiles; probably ancestral to the mammals; Permian to Triassic)

†*Order Ichthyosauria* (ichthyosaurs; extinct fishlike, swimming reptiles; common during Mesozoic; Triassic to Cretaceous)

†*Order Sauropterygia* (extinct marine reptiles with paddlelike flippers; Triassic to Cretaceous)

†*Suborder Plesiosauria* (plesiosaurs; extinct marine reptiles with turtlelike bodies; common during Mesozoic; Triassic to Cretaceous)

Order Rhynchocephalia ("beak-headed" reptiles like *Sphenodon;* primitive lizardlike form; Triassic to Recent)

Order Squamata (lizards and snakes; most diverse and abundant of living reptiles; Traissic to Recent)

†*Order Thecodontia* (thecodonts; extinct relatively rare rep-

tiles believed to be ancestral to crocodiles and dinosaurs; Triassic only)

†*Suborder Phytosauria* (phytosaurs; crocodilelike reptiles; Triassic only)

Order Crocodilia (crocodiles, alligators and gavials; largest living reptiles, closely related to dinosaurs; Triassic to Recent)

†*Order Pterosauria* (pterosaurs; extinct flying reptiles; common during Middle and Late Mesozoic; Jurassic to Cretaceous)

†*Order Saurischia* (theropods and sauropods, etc.; have hip bones similar to modern lizards; Triassic to Cretaceous)

†*Suborder Theropoda* (*Tyrannosaurus, Allosaurus,* etc.; bipedal carnivorous saurischians; Triassic to Cretaceous)

†*Suborder Sauropoda* (*Brontosaurus, Diplodocus,* etc.; quadrupedal, primarily herbivorous, large saurischians; Triassic to Cretaceous)

†*Order Ornithischia* (ornithopods, stegosaurs, ankylosaurs, ceratopsians, etc.; herbivorous dinosaurs with hip bones similar to birds; Jurassic to Cretaceous)

†*Suborder Ornithopoda* (duck-billed dinosaurs like *Trachodon;* semiaquatic, typically bipedal; Jurassic to Cretaceous)

†*Suborder Stegosauria* (plated dinosaurs like *Stegosaurus;* herbivorous, quadrupedal; Jurassic to Cretaceous)

†*Suborder Ankylosauria* (armored dinosaurs like *Palaeoscincus;* four-footed, herbivorous, armored forms; restricted to Cretaceous rocks)

†*Suborder Ceratopsia* (horned dinosaurs like *Triceratops;* herbivorous, quadrupedal dinosaurs with beaklike jaws; Cretaceous only)

CLASS AVES (birds; warm-blooded, breathe by lungs; covered by feathers; Jurassic to Recent)

CLASS MAMMALIA (mammals: opposums, bats, rodents, dogs, whales, horses, men, etc.; highest class of vertebrates, breathe by lungs, warm-blooded, suckle young, covered with hair; Jurassic to Recent)

†SUBCLASS ALLOTHERIA (multituberculates; early rodentlike herbivorous mammals; Jurassic to Eocene)

†*Order Multituberculata* (multituberculates; small primitive rodentlike mammals; Jurassic to Eocene)

SUBCLASS THERIA (most of the living mammals; Jurassic to Recent)

Order Primates (lemurs, monkeys, apes, men, etc.; mammals usually having digits with nails rather than claws or hoofs; Paleocene to Recent)

Order Edentata (tree sloths, armadillos, etc.; teeth absent or reduced; Eocene to Recent)

Order Carnivora (dogs, cats, seals, etc.; flesh-eating mammals; Paleocene to Recent)

†*Order Pantodonta* (pantodonts or amblypods; large, primitive, hoofed, extinct mammals; Paleocene to Oligocene)

†*Order Dinocerata* (uintatheres; largest of known mammals; some had horns; Paleocene to Eocene)

Order Proboscidea (elephants, mastodonts, woolly mammoths; with elongated upper nose and lip forming trunk; Eocene to Recent)

Order Perissodactyla (horses, rhinoceroses, titanotheres; odd-toed mammals with hoofs; Eocene to Recent)

Order Artiodactyla (pigs, deer, camels, entelodonts, etc.; even-toed mammals with hoofs; Eocene to Recent)

PLANT FOSSILS

Although members of the plant kingdom have left an abundant and varied fossil record (about 120,000 species of fossil plants have been described), they will not be discussed in detail in this book. Amateur collectors normally do not collect many plant remains, and when collected these fossils are usually fragmental and difficult to identify. The poor condition of the fossils and the lack of uniformity in plant classification have discouraged many amateurs from an active interest in paleobotany. However, in spite of these problems, much is known of the evolution of plants, and plant fossils provide valuable information about life of the past. In addition, certain species are of considerable value as indicators of past climatic conditions, and their remains have played a large part in the formation of our vast coal deposits.

Plants are fossilized in much the same manner as animals and, in general, must meet the same requirements of fossilization (see p. 7). Fossilization usually occurs as petrifactions (or permineralized plants, see p. 20), compressions (usually carbonized, see p. 17), or impressions (see p. 24).

The classification of plants followed in this chapter is a modification of several of the latest classifications, but different systems of classifications are used by various authors.*

* Harry J. Fuller, *General Botany* (New York: Barnes and Noble, Inc., 4th ed., 1955), p. 107. This excellent review of general botany is recommended for those who would know more about the plant kingdom. *An Introduction to Paleobotany* by C. A. Arnold (New York: McGraw-Hill Book Co., 1947) will further introduce the reader to the study of fossil plants.

Subkingdom Thallophyta

Members of this subkingdom (the term subkingdom is an artificial group name) are simple plants without roots, stems, or leaves. Thallophytes (Greek *thallos,* young shoot + *phyton,* plant) are among the most primitive plants, are chiefly aquatic in habitat, and contain many parasitic types. Two *divisions* are recognized in the Thallophyta: the Algae (seaweeds, algae, and diatoms), and the Fungi (bacteria, molds, and mushrooms).

Division Algae

Members of this group have a long geologic history, ranging from the Precambrian to the Recent. Botanists divide the algae into a number of

Fig. 80.—Cross section of Precambrian calcareous algae (about one half natural size).

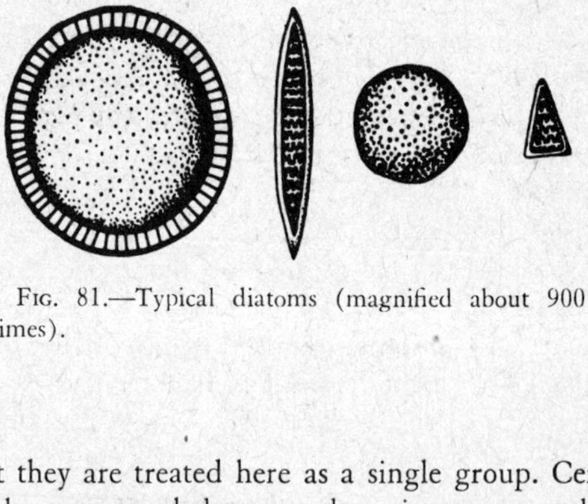

Fig. 81.—Typical diatoms (magnified about 900 times).

lesser taxonomic units, but they are treated here as a single group. Certain of the algae secrete calcareous exoskeletons and are important rock-forming agents in recent and fossil coral reefs. Furthermore, some of these forms built large limestone masses during the Cambrian period. Although much evidence of Precambrian plant life is indirect, primitive algae were present in the Proterozoic (see Fig. 80).

Diatoms. Diatoms are minute, one-celled, aquatic plants which are known from the Jurassic to the Recent (Fig. 81). Because of their ability to secrete a siliceous bivalved exoskeleton, they are often found as fossils. Their shells accumulate in large numbers on the bottoms of present-day seas; these deposits are known as *diatom ooze.* Fossil accumulations of this type have frequently been altered into a type of rock called *diatomite.*

Division Fungi

The fungi show some similarities to algae but lack *chlorophyll* (the green pigment of plants), and most forms depend upon living or dead organic material for food. Fossil fungi are rare and of little value as fossils; there is, however, considerable evidence of their damaging activities on many fossil plants. Their range throughout geologic time is not definitely known, but probable fungus remains have been reported from rocks as old as Middle Devonian.

Subkingdom Embryophyta

(Greek *embryon,* a foetus + *phyton,* plant)

The embryophytes, more advanced than the thallophytes, are chiefly land plants. They form embryos, and most species contain *vascular,* or conducting, tissues. This subkingdom consists of two divisions (or phyla): the Bryophyta and the Tracheophyta.

Division Bryophyta

The Bryophyta (Greek *bryon,* moss + *phyton,* plant) are simple plants with no roots; they include the liverworts and mosses. Although more complex, the bryophytes resemble the algae in some respects. They are rare as fossils, but undoubted bryophytes (liverworts) have been reported from rocks as old as Mississippian, and several Mesozoic and Cenozoic species are known.

Division Tracheophyta

The tracheophytes (Latin *trachia,* pipe + *phyton,* plant) derive their name from the porous vascular nature of their tissues. They may be divided into four subdivisions (or subphyla), each of which contains important fossil species: Psilopsida (largely extinct forms), Lycopsida (club mosses), Sphenopsida (horsetails and scouring rushes), and Pteropsida (ferns, cycads, conifers, and flowering plants).

Subdivision Psilopsida

(Greek *psilos,* slender + *opsidos,* appearance)

These primitive, rootless plants without leaves are the simplest land plants known. Living members of the group are tropical and subtropical land plants, but extinct species grew in many parts of the world. Known Silurian and Devonian psilopsids indicate that early members of this group apparently inhabited a swampy environment.

Although not significant in the world's modern flora (there are only four living species), the psilopsids are important from an evolutionary standpoint, and the genus *Psilophyton* is one of the oldest vascular plants known. They range in age from Silurian to Recent.

Subdivision Lycopsida

(Greek *lycos,* wolf + *opsidos,* appearance)

Members of this subdivision have true roots, stems, and small leaves. Most living lycopods, which measure from three feet, or less, in height, inhabit tropical and subtropical forests. The living species are called club mosses. Paleozoic species of Lycopsida are known as "scale trees," some of which attained heights of as much as one hundred feet. Two Late Paleozoic species, *Lepidodendron* (Figs. 82-*a* and 50) and *Sigillaria*

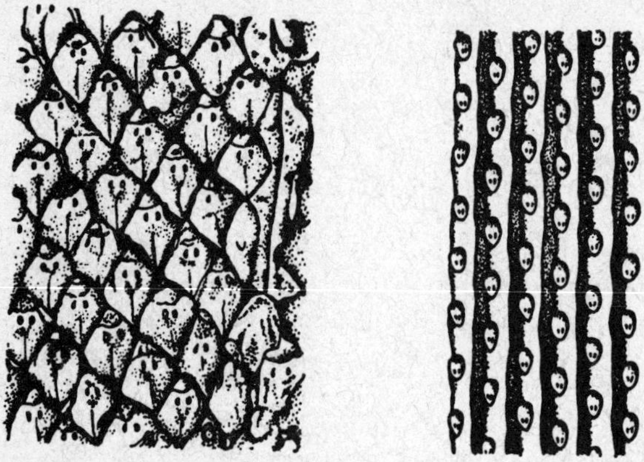

a b

FIG. 82.—Bark patterns of typical Pennsylvanian "coal plants." (*a*) *Lepidodendron.* (*b*) *Sigillaria* (both about one half actual size). (By permission from *Texas Fossils* by W. H. Matthews III, Bureau of Economic Geology, University of Texas, Austin.)

(Figs. 82-*b* and 50), are commonly found in Pennsylvanian and Mississippian coal deposits. Lycopods are known from the Silurian to the present day.

Subdivision Sphenopsida

(Greek *sphenos,* wedge + *opsidos,* appearance)

This group contains the horsetails and scouring rushes. Like the Psilopsida and Lycopsida, these plants were more abundant in the geologic past. Only twenty-five living species are known. Sphenopsids have vascular tissues, true roots, jointed stems with leaflets in whorls at the joints, and usually inhabit moist places. Most living species are not more than five feet tall, but certain extinct species were quite large. The fossil horsetail *Calamites* (Figs. 83 and 50) grew to treelike proportions; it is found in many Mississippian and Pennsylvanian coal deposits.

This group probably originated in the Devonian, became very large and complex in the Mississippian and Pennsylvanian, but are relatively rare today.

Subdivision Pteropsida

(Greek *pteris,* fern + *opsidos,* appearance)

Most of the world's living plants are included in this subdivision. Varying from small herbs to great trees, most are terrestrial, although some species are aquatic. All have vascular tissues, stems, true roots, and leaves. Classes recognized within this subdivision are the Filicineae (ferns), Gymnospermae (seed-ferns, cycads, conifers, ginkgos, etc.), and Angiospermae (flowering plants). Since the latter two classes produce seeds, they are commonly referred to as seed plants.

FIG. 83.—Segment of a stalk of *Calamites,* a fossil horsetail of Pennsylvanian age (about one half actual size). (By permission from *Texas Fossils* by W. H. Matthews III, Bureau of Economic Geology, University of Texas, Austin.)

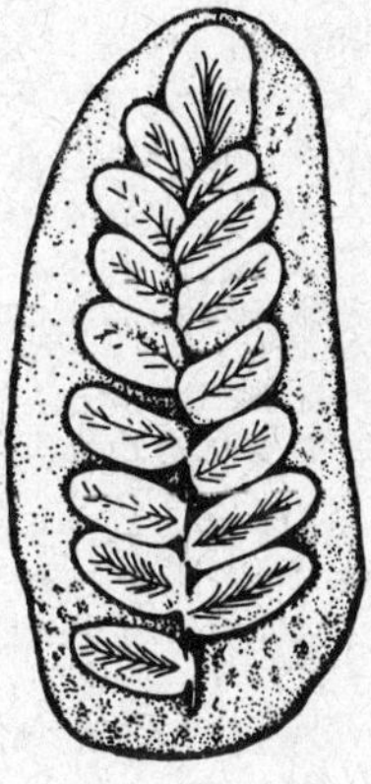

FIG. 84.—*Neuropteris,* a Pennsylvanian seed-fern (about natural size).

FIG. 85.—Leaf of *Cordaites,* a typical Pennsylvanian gymnosperm (about normal size).

Class Filicineae (Latin *filix,* fern). Members of this class, known as "ferns," exhibit a wide variety of body structures. They generally live in moist shaded places and in the tropics often reach heights of thirty to forty feet. Ferns have been very abundant in past geologic ages, and their roots, stems, and leaves are often found as fossils. They first appeared in the Devonian, became abundant during the Mississippian and Pennsylvanian, and are familiar forms of present-day vegetation.

Class Gymnospermae (Greek *gymnos,* naked + *sperma,* seed). These seed plants are chiefly evergreen trees with frondlike, or scalelike leaves. Most species have a dominant main trunk with much smaller branches.

ORDER PTERIDOSPERMALES (*Pteridospermae*) (*Greek, pterido,* fern + *sperma,* seed + *ales,* the ending for plant order names). The pteridosperms are an extinct group representing the oldest known seed-bearing plants. Typically small plants with large fernlike leaves, they are commonly known as seed-ferns. *Neuropteris* (Fig. 84), a typical seed-fern, is a common fossil in certain Pennsylvanian strata. Pteridosperms first appeared in the Early Mississippian and became extinct in Late Jurassic time.

ORDER CYCADEOIDALES (*Bennettitales*) (Greek *cycad,* coco palm + *eidos,* resemblance + *ales,* the ending for plant order names). The cycadeoids closely resemble the cycads (see below) and composed an important part of the Jurassic and Cretaceous flora. The earliest known cycadeoids appeared in the Traissic, and they were extinct by the end of Cretaceous time.

ORDER CYCADALES (Greek, *cycad,* coco palm +*ales,* the ending for plant order names). Cycads are palmlike plants believed to be among the most primitive of living seed plants. Living cycads, called coco palms, or sago palms, are found in limited numbers in tropical areas today, and their fossils have been recovered from rocks of Mesozoic age. Living species are charactertized by cylindrical, erect trunks and large, fernlike leaves on short, thick stems (Fig. 54). Their known geologic range is from Triassic to Recent, but there is some indication that primitive cycads may have been living as far back as Late Permian time.

ORDER CORDAITALES (Corda, Bohemian botanist + Greek, *ales,* the ending for plant order names). This is an extinct group of Paleozoic gymnosperms with tall, slender trunks as much as one hundred feet high. They had long, slender, straplike or pointed leaves and formed extensive forests during Paleozoic time; some had a trunk diameter of as much as five feet. Their known geologic range is from Mississippian to Permian, but questionable Cordaitales have been reported from rocks as old as Devonian and as young as Triassic. Remains of the genus *Cordaites* (Fig. 85) are specially abundant in many Pennsylvanian and Mississippian coal deposits.

ORDER GINKGOALES (Japanese *ginkgo* + *ales,* the ending for plant order names). These are the ginkgos (also spelled *gingkos*) or maidenhair trees (Fig. 86). This order contains only a single living species (*Ginkgo biloba*), but several extinct species have been described. These plants were widespread and abundant during the Mesozoic and probably originated during Late Permian time. The ginkgos are natives of China and Japan; the Japanese consider the tree sacred and plant it near their temples. The primitive characteristics of this plant have resulted in its being called a "living fossil." Their known geologic range is from Permian to Recent, and they attained their maximum abundance during the middle portion of the Mesozoic era.

ORDER CONIFERALES (Latin *conifer,* cone-bearing + *ales,* the ending for plant order names). The conifers (cone-bearing trees) are the largest order of gymnosperms and often attain great size. They include such familiar

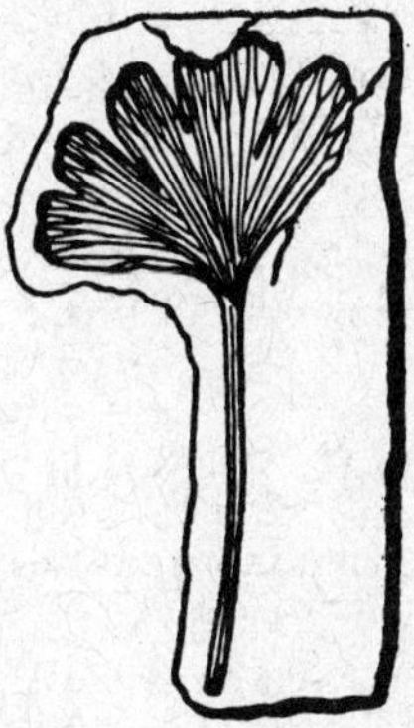

FIG. 86.—Leaf of the *Ginkgo* or maidenhair tree (about one half actual size).

softwoods as pines, junipers, spruce, fir, and redwoods. They are typically evergreens with small needle-shaped leaves and tall, straight trunks. Some conifers, such as the giant redwoods (*Sequoia*), are as much as three hundred feet high with a trunk diameter up to forty feet. Conifers first appeared in the Pennsylvanian, reaching their greatest development during Late Jurassic and Early Cretaceous time. Since the end of Mesozoic time this group has diminished in types and numbers but still constitutes an important part of modern vegetation.

Class Angiospermae (Greek *angeion,* a vessel + *sperma,* seed). The angiosperms, the true flowering plants, are the dominant land plants of the present day. The class is comprised of such familiar forms as the grasses, hardwoods, vegetables, flowers, and fruit. They are the most widely distributed of all land plants, including no less than 250,000 living species, in addition to a large number of fossil forms. Angiosperms are characterized by typically broad leaves with rather complex seeds. They first appeared in the Triassic period, expanded during the Cretaceous, and have dominated the world's vegetation since that time. They are the most complex of all plants and have adapted themselves to a wide variety of environmental conditions. In spite of the great numbers and varieties of living angiosperms, paleobotanists are at a loss to explain their origin and rapid evolutionary expansion. Two subclasses are recognized: the Dicotyledoneae (oaks, roses, carrots, etc.); and the Monocotyledoneae (lilies, palms, grasses, etc.).

Subclass Dicotyledoneae (Greek *di,* two + *kotyledon,* a cup-shaped hollow). The "dicots," as members of this subclass are known, include most of our trees, flowers, and common garden vegetables. They are characterized by netted-veined leaves and an embryo with two seed leaves. Their known geologic range is from Jurassic to Recent.

Subclass Monocotyledoneae (Greek, *mono,* one + *kotyledon,* a hollow cup). The "monocots" are characterized by embryos with one seed leaf and leaves with parallel veins. They include such forms as the cattails, grasses, palms, lilies, and bananas. Their fossil record is rather inadequate; it is believed that most fossil angiosperms differ only slightly from living forms. Fossil angiosperms have been reported from rocks as old as Middle Jurassic, and numerous Cretaceous and Cenozoic species are known.

ANIMAL FOSSILS

Members of the animal kingdom, in contrast to plants, usually exhibit the following characteristics: *

1. Most animals are capable of self-locomotion at some stage in their development.
2. Animals exhibit more rapid and definite response to outside stimuli.
3. Animals grow to rather fixed and definite sizes.
4. Animal bodies are composed primarily of soft body tissues.
5. Animals require complex organic food.

It is difficult in some instances to determine whether an organism is a plant or an animal. For this reason it has been suggested that certain microscopic single-celled organisms of doubtful classification be placed in a separate kingdom, the *Protista.* The protistans possess various characteristics of both plants and animals. Members assigned to this group have a long geologic history (Precambrian to Recent) and contain several forms of paleontological significance. The majority of forms, however, either have little importance or are not known as fossils. Among the organisms which have been assigned to the Protista are: bacteria, algae, diatoms, molds, yeasts, fungi, mushrooms, foraminifers, and radiolarians. Of these, only the foraminifers and radiolarians are important as fossils. (The classification into the kingdom Protista is not recognized in this book; the organisms mentioned above are therefore discussed in their respective positions in the plant and animal kingdoms.)

* Gordon Alexander, *Biology* (New York: Barnes and Noble, Inc., 8th ed., 1962), p. 27. This is an excellent book for a more detailed survey of the plant and animal kingdoms.

Phylum Protozoa

The Protozoa (Greek *protos,* first + *zoion,* animal) differ from other members of the animal kingdom in that they consist of a single cell or colonial aggregate of cells without differentiation of function. Each cell carries on all body functions, including locomotion, digestion, and reproduction. The typical protozoan is microscopic in size, but certain species may attain relatively large sizes. One of these, *Camerina* (known also as *Nummulites*), may attain a diameter of one or two inches. Certain of the fusulinids (Fig. 87) are as much as one to two inches long. Forms of this type are usually referred to as the "larger Foraminifera."

Most protozoans possess no hard covering or exoskeleton and are thus incapable of preservation. Those forms secreting a shell, however, have left a long, varied fossil record and are especially useful as microfossils.

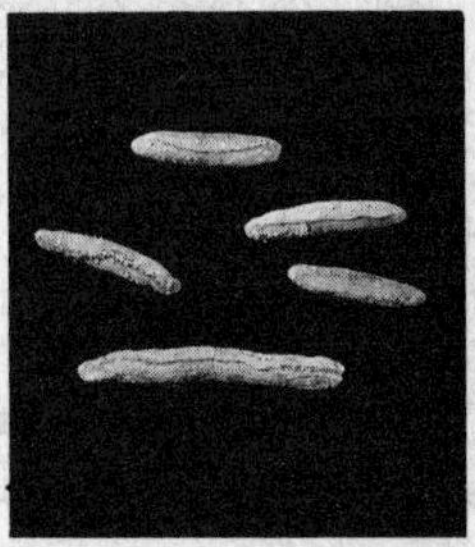

FIG. 87.—*Parafusulina* from the Permian limestones of the Glass Mountains of West Texas. These large foraminifers are shown here only slightly enlarged. (Courtesy of Dr. G. A. Cooper, U. S. National Museum.)

The Protozoa has been divided into four classes: the Mastigophora (or Flagellata), Sarcodina (or Rhizopoda), Sporozoa, and Infusoria (Ciliata or Ciliophora). Of these only the Sarcodina will be discussed here. The only other protozoans known as fossils are certain minor groups within the Mastigophora and Ciliata.

Class Sarcodina (Greek *sarkodes,* flesh). This contains a group of unicellular organisms secreting an *exoskeleton* (external protective covering or *test*), which may be composed of chitin, silica, or calcium carbonate, and it is often fossilized. Included within this class are the foraminifers (commonly called forams) and radiolarians.

ORDER FORAMINIFERA (*Foraminiferida*) (Latin *foramen,* hole + *ferre,* to bear). Members of this order are predominantly marine (salt-water) animals. They commonly secrete a minute (usually microscopic) test made up of many chambers pierced by large numbers of minute pores or perforations (Fig. 88). The test is usually composed of calcium carbonate but may consist of silica or chitin. Certain species build *agglutinated* or *arenaceous* tests—the tests are made by cementing together minute mineral grains or various foreign particles. The composition of the tests and the arrangement of the chambers are important factors in foram classification.

In addition to their value as age-indicators, the forams are of some importance as rock-building agents. Shells of the genus *Globigerina* (Fig. 88-*c*), along with the shells of other forams, have accumulated in great numbers, forming thick deposits over many of our present-day sea floors. This type of sediment has been called *Globigerina ooze* because of the countless numbers of globigerind shells that are present. Other forams, such as the nummulitids and fusulinids, accumulated in much the same manner and are important constituents of certain limestones. This is especially true of the fusulinids, for their small spindle-shaped remains are abundant in many Pennsylvanian and Permian limestones.

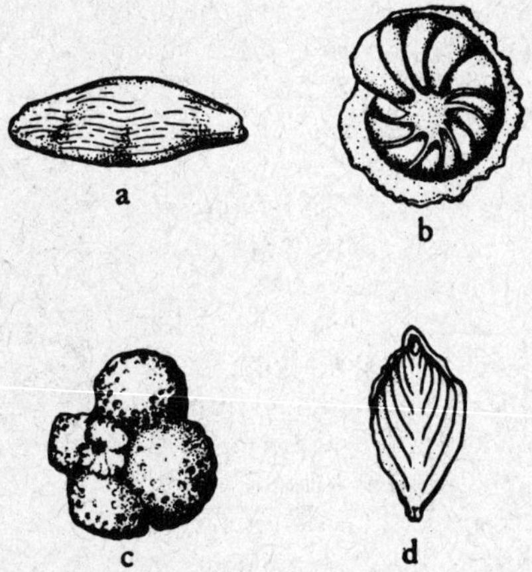

FIG. 88.—Typical foraminifers (all greatly enlarged). (*a*) *Fusulina* (Pennsylvanian). (*b*) *Robulus* (Cretaceous). (*c*) *Globigerina* (Cretaceous). (*d*) *Frondicularia* (Cretaceous). (By permission from *Texas Fossils* by W. H. Matthews III, Bureau of Economic Geology, University of Texas, Austin.)

Foraminifers range from Ordovician to Recent in age, but doubtful Cambrian forms have been reported. They are most abundant in upper Paleozoic, Mesozoic, and Cenozoic formations. Many species are valuable as guide fossils.

ORDER RADIOLARIA (Latin *radiolus,* little ray). The radiolarians are exclusively marine, microscopic protozoans. The radiolarian test is siliceous, unchambered, loosely constructed, and often netlike in appearance (Fig. 89).

There are many thousands of living radiolarians, most of them floating at or near the surface of the oceans. In certain parts of the Pacific and Indian oceans vast numbers of these shells have accumulated on deep sea bottoms, forming thick siliceous deposits of *radiolarian ooze.* Rocks composed of fossil radiolarian ooze are called *radiolarian earth* and have considerable economic importance in the manufacture of certain filtering and insulating materials. Some geologists believe that the siliceous exoskeletons of radiolarians may also be partially responsible for certain chert and flint deposits. The Franciscan chert of California is characterized by radiolarians to the extent that it is called *radiolarite.*

Because of their minute size and the extreme fragility of the test, radiolarians are somewhat limited in their use as fossils. They do, however, have a long geologic range and have been recorded in rocks ranging from Cambrian to Recent.

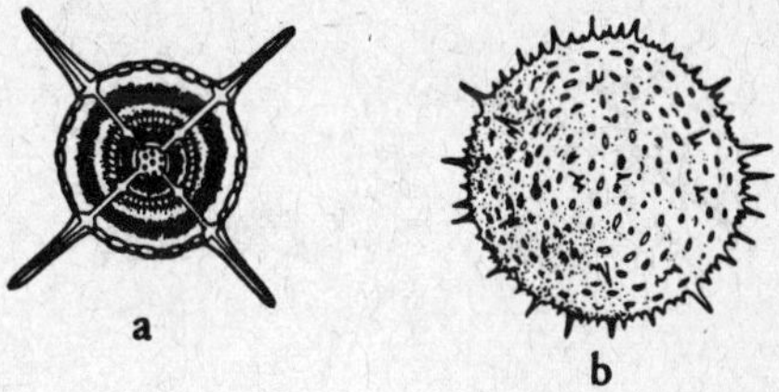

FIG. 89.—Typical radiolarians (greatly enlarged). (*a*) *Actinomma* (Recent). (*b*) *Porodiscus* (Eocene).

Phylum Porifera

The Porifera (Latin *porus,* pore + *ferre,* to bear), or *sponges,* are the simplest of the many-celled animals. The name is derived from the many tiny incurrent canals which penetrate the body of the animal. Sponges are found in both fresh and salt water; they live attached to the bottom as single individuals or in colonies. Most sponges are marine. They vary considerably in size and appearance. Some species are less than one inch in height, whereas others may have a diameter of as much as six feet. Sponges may be branching, vaselike, ball-shaped, encrusting, or fan-shaped, and many of them are plantlike in appearance. Because of this, sponges were once thought to be members of the plant kingdom.

The living animal secretes a skeleton which may consist of calcium carbonate, silica, or horny material known as *spongin.* These needlelike skeletal parts, called *spicules,* assume many different shapes (Fig. 90) and are of prime importance in the classification of the Porifera. The spicules are used to help support the soft tissues of the animal and are either scattered throughout the body tissue or joined together in a rigid supporting framework.

Upon the death of the sponge, the spicules are scattered about the ocean floor, where they are incorporated into the sediments. In addition, certain of the calcareous sponges and spongelike organisms (see below) are known to have added materially to the calcareous deposits of the Lower Paleozoic. Some geologic formations possess chert and flint nodules which contain large numbers of siliceous sponge spicules, and dissolved siliceous spicules are possibly the source of some thick chert and flint beds.

In general, sponges are not particularly common as fossils although they may occur in large numbers locally. They may, however, be collected from certain Paleozoic strata, and their spicules have been encountered in cores and cuttings taken from drilling wells. Certain of these spicules are of some value as microfossils.

Sponges were probably present in the Precambrian, although undisputed

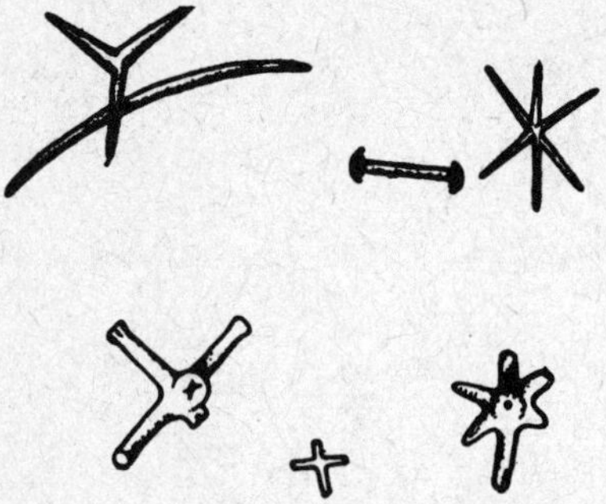

FIG. 90.—Several types of sponge spicules (all greatly enlarged).

evidence of their existence is lacking. The remains of siliceous sponges are numerous in Lower Paleozoic rocks; characteristic genera are *Prismodictya* (Fig. 91–*1*), *Astraeospongium* (Fig. 91–*2*), and *Dictoyospongia* (Fig. 91–*3*). Fossil calcareous sponges are abundant in certain upper Paleozoic, Jurassic, Cretaceous, and lower Teritiary deposits. Three fairly common Paleozic sponges are *Maeandrostia* (Fig. 92–*1*), *Astylospongia* (Fig. 92–*2*), and *Girtyocoelia* (Fig. 92–*3*).

Usually discussed in conjunction with the Porifera are those fossils commonly referred to as *spongelike organisms*. These fossils, because of the lack of living counterparts, are of doubtful zoological affinities; for this reason their taxonomic position is uncertain. In referring to such fossils the paleontologists often place them in a special group—*incertae sedis* (literally meaning "of uncertain position"), a convenient category (facetiously referred to as the "paleontologist's wastebasket"), in discussing fossils of doubtful origin. It is important to note that although we may not know the exact taxonomic position of a given fossil, this does not necessarily minimize its value to the geologist. In the meantime, paleontologists all over the world are continually working on such fossils in an attempt to place them in their proper position in the plant or animal kingdom.

The remains of some of the spongelike organisms are abundant and of considerable use to the paleontologist. Certain reef-forming species are important as rock-builders. One such group, the *archeocyathids* (also

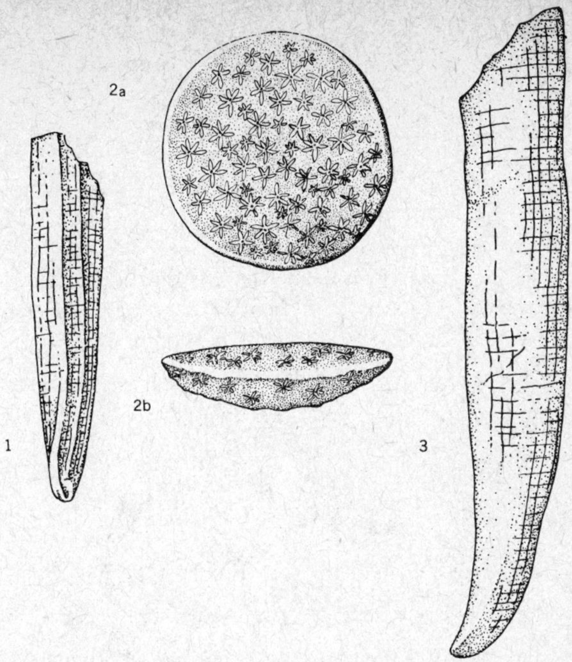

Fig. 91.—Paleozoic siliceous sponges. (*1*) *Prismodictya* (Devonian). (*2*) *Astraeospongium* (*a*) top view, (*b*) side view (Silurian). (*3*) *Dictyospongia* (Devonian). Numbers *1* and *2*, about one half natural size; *3*, about natural size.

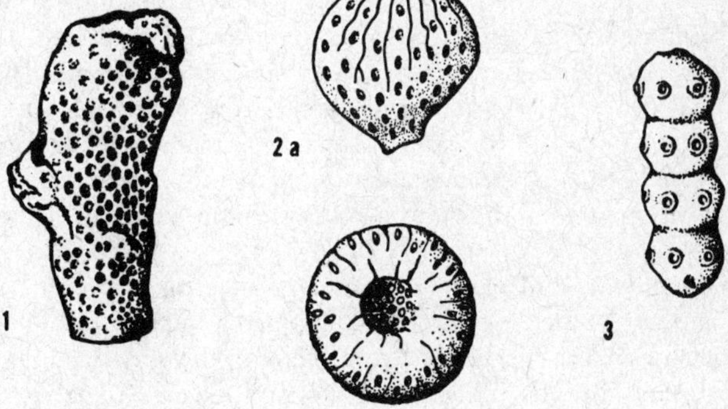

Fig. 92.—Typical Paleozoic sponges. (*1*) *Maeandrostia* (Pennsylvanian). (*2*) *Astylospongia* (*a*) side view, (*b*) top view (Silurian). (*3*) *Girtyocoelia* Pennsylvanian (all about natural size). (Adapted from *Texas Fossils* by W. H. Matthews III, Bureau of Economic Geology, University of Texas, Austin.)

called *pleosponges*), are among the earliest of the reef-building animals and are especially abundant in Lower and Middle Cambrian deposits. Another widespread spongelike fossil is *Receptaculites* (Fig. 93), a fossil previously classified in such diverse groups as the algae, conifers, protozoans, sponges, and corals; its common name, "sunflower coral," has been derived from its alleged affinity with the last group. *Receptaculites* is a relatively common fossil in some of the Middle Ordovician rocks of Missouri, Minnesota, Wisconsin, and Nevada.

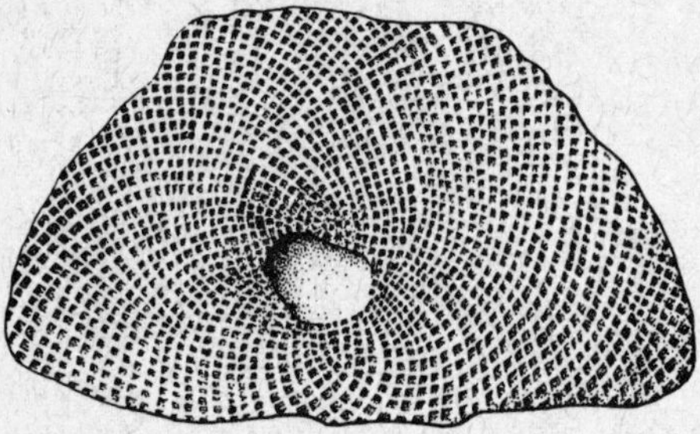

Fig. 93.—Spongelike fossil. *Receptaculites* (Ordovician) (about actual size).

Phylum Coelenterata

Members of the Coelenterata (Greek *koilos,* hollow + *enteron,* intestine) are aquatic forms such as the jellyfishes, sea anemones, and corals. These multicelled animals, though more complex than the sponges, are rather primitive. The living animal is characterized by a tentacles which bear stinging cells. Some forms (for example, the jellyfishes) have umbrella-shaped bodies and are single free-moving organisms. Others, like the colonial corals, are composed of many individuals living together in a colony. Since many coelenterates lack hard parts, their fossil record is scant; others, such as the stony corals, are important fossils and rock-builders.

Most zoologists and paleontologists recognize three classes of coelenterates, although other scientists have proposed as many as six. The classes recognized here are the Hydrozoa, containing the small animals known as hydroids and the extinct stromatoporoids; the Scyphozoa, which includes the jellyfishes and extinct conulariids; and the Anthozoa, which includes the corals and sea anemones. Because of their extreme fragility and lack of hard parts, hydrozoans and scyphozoans are not commonly found as fossils. They do, however, have a long geologic history and may be preserved when unusual conditions of fossilization occur. The Anthozoa, especially the corals, are by far the most important group geologically, and these forms have left a very good paleontological record.

Class Hydrozoa (Greek *hydor,* water + *zoion* animal). Generally not abundant, and relatively unimportant as fossils, this class contains the fresh-water *Hydra* and the colonial form *Obelia.*

ORDER STROMATOPOROIDEA (Greek *stroma, stromatos,* bed + *poros,* pore + *eidos,* resemblance). Most hydrozoans secrete no hard parts and are thus of little significance geologically. Exceptional, however, are the *stromatoporoids,* a group of extinct animals that have been provisionally placed in the class Hydrozoa. These were exclusively marine animals that grew in colonies and secreted variably shaped skeletons consisting of thin layers of calcium carbonate (Fig. 94). Certain of the stromatoporoids

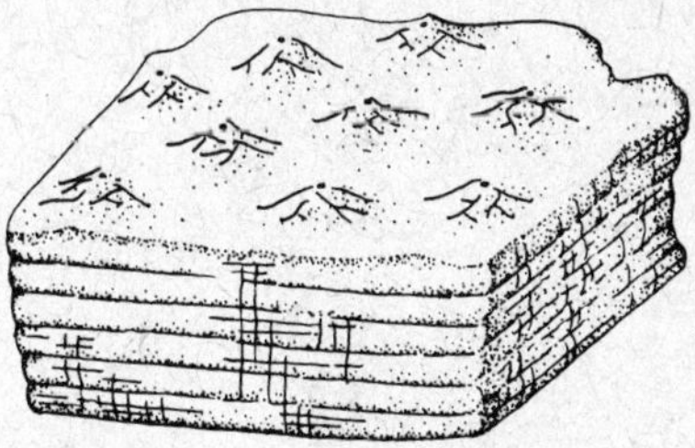

FIG. 94.—A typical stromatoporoid, *Stromatopora* of Devonian age (about actual size).

built reeflike structures and added materially to the sediments of the Silurian and Devonian periods. Their geologic range is Cambrian to Cretaceous).

Class Scyphozoa (Greek *skyphos,* cup + *zoion,* animal). Members of this class are best illustrated by the jellyfishes, which are typically umbrella-shaped and fringed with numerous tentacles. Because of their jellylike bodies, they are rare as fossils. However, unusual finds, in the form of carbon residues or impressions in very fine sediments, have been reported in rocks ranging from Cambrian to Recent in age.

SUBCLASS CONULATA (Latin *conulus,* little cone). The conulariids are an extinct group of animals that are now considered by most paleontologists to be scyphozoans. They have also been placed in such varied groups as the worms, snails, mollusks, and hydrozoans. A typical conulariid is cone- or pyramid-shaped, and the shell is marked by numerous transverse ribs (Fig. 95). They range from Cambrian to Early Triassic in age, but are rare except in certain Ordovician, Silurian, and Devonian formations.

Class Anthozoa (Greek *anthos,* flower + *zoion,* animal). This class is composed of exclusively marine attached organisms and includes the soft-bodied sea anemones and the stony corals. The mouth of the animal is surrounded by a circlet of tentacles which look like flower petals;

hence, these forms are referred to as "flower animals." The corals are among the most important and abundant of fossils. The coral animal or *polyp,* secretes a cup-shaped calcareous exoskeleton, and may be either *solitary* (Fig. 96-*a*) or *colonial* (Fig. 96-*b*) in habitat. The skeleton, called a *corallite,* is usually divided by vertical radially arranged partitions called *septa* (singular *septum*). The polyp inhabits only the upper portion of the corallite known as the *calyx* or *calice* (plural calyces),

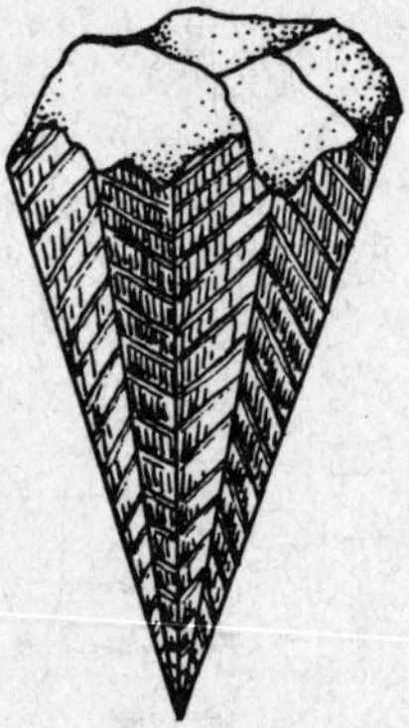

FIG. 95.—A Paleozoic conulariid (about actual size).

which is the central bowl-shaped depression in the top of the corallite (Fig. 96).

Solitary corals form an individual corallite for each polyp, and because of their shape may be given such names as "horn corals" (*Lophophyllidium,* Fig. 97-*b*) or "button corals" (*Micrabacia,* Fig. 99–*3*).

Colonial or *compound* corals live together in colonies which are formed by many individual skeletons attached to each other (Fig. 96-*b*). The mass of coral skeletons formed in this manner is called a *corallum.* Fossil corals commonly occur in marine limestones and in places constitute a large portion of the rock.

Anthozoan classification has recently undergone considerable revision, and several satisfactory classifications may be found in the literature. The nomenclature adopted here is that proposed in the *Treatise on Invertebrate Paleontology* (see p. 308). Only those subclasses that have left a satisfactory fossil record (the Alcyonaria and Zoantharia) will be discussed. For convenience in reference alternative subclass or order names are given in parentheses when advisable.

SUBCLASS ALCYONARIA (*Octocorallia*). The Alcyonaria (Greek *alkyon,* kingfisher; some alcyonarians resemble the nest of this bird), are also called *octocorals* (Greek *okto,* eight) because of the eight symmetrically arranged tentacles and mesenteries. These are exclusively colonial forms, and although they are important constituents among Recent corals, are not important as fossils. Examples of this group include the "sea pens," "sea whips," and "sea fans." Some octocorals possess calcareous spicules, and these can be fossilized. Although questionable Silurian octocorals have been reported, the known geologic range is Permian to Recent.

SUBCLASS ZOANTHARIA (Greek *zoion,* animal + *anthos,* flower). Most corals and all sea anemones belong to this subclass. Zoantharians are

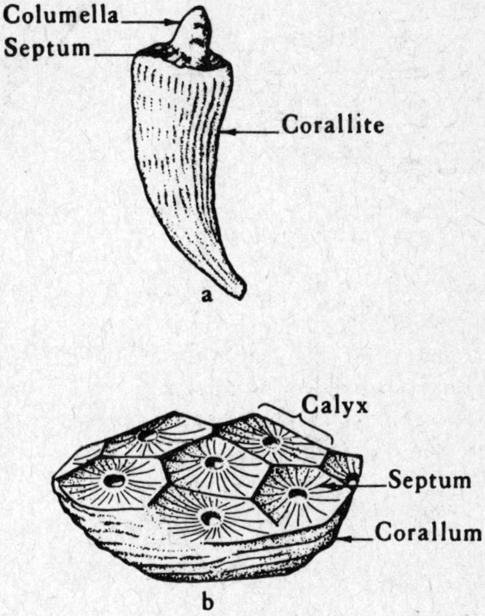

FIG. 96.—Morphology and principal parts of corals. (*a*) Typical solitary or "horn" coral. (*b*) Colonial or compound coral. (By permission from *Texas Fossils* by W. H. Matthews III, Bureau of Economic Geology, University of Texas, Austin.)

either solitary or colonial; and, because most of them possess a hard preservable exoskeleton, they are the most important group of anthozoans geologically. The various orders of the Zoantharia are discussed below.

ORDER RUGOSA (Latin *rugosus,* wrinkled) (*Tetracoralla*). The rugose corals are an extinct group of solitary or colonial corals. The septa are arranged in cycles of four; hence these forms have been called tetracorals (Greek *tetras,* four). They are found only in rocks of Paleozoic age and are abundant in many Paleozoic formations. *Lophophyllidium* (Fig. 97-*b*) and *Caninia* (Fig. 97-*a*) are typical Pennsylvanian rugose corals. The geologic range of the Rugosa is Ordovician to Permian.

ORDER SCLERACTINIA (Greek *skleros,* hard + *aktinos,* ray) (*Hexa-*

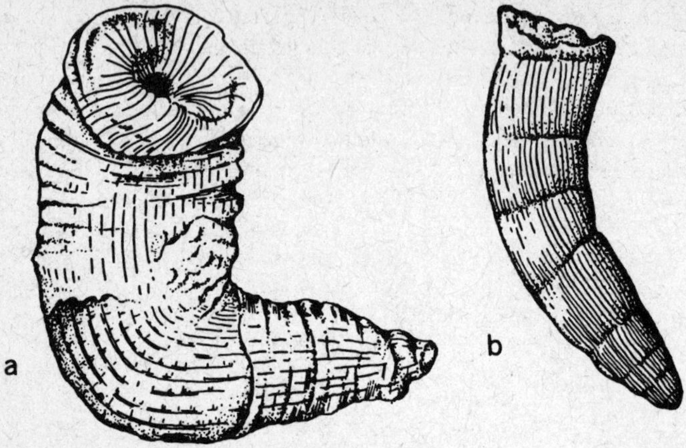

FIG. 97.—Pennsylvanian rugose corals. (*a*) *Caninia* (reduced one half). (*b*) *Lophophyllidium proliferum* (about actual size).

coralla). The scleractinians (or *hexacorals*) are solitary or colonial corals in which the septa grow in multiples of six (Greek *hexa,* six). They are the most important and abundant of the modern corals. These corals were the dominant reef-builders of Mesozoic and Cenozoic seas, and their remains are common in many marine formations. *Cladophyllia, Parasmilia,* and *Pleurocora* (Fig. 98) are typical Cretaceous scleractinians.

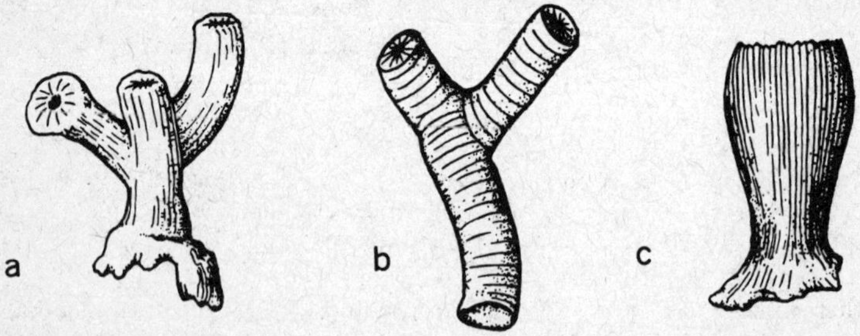

FIG. 98.—Cretaceous scleractinian corals. (*a*) *Cladophyllia.* (*b*) *Pleurocora.* (*c*) *Parasmilia* (all about actual size). (By permission from *Texas Fossils* by W. H. Matthews III, Bureau of Economic Geology, University of Texas, Austin.)

Typical Tertiary forms are *Endopachys, Micrabacia, Flabellum, Astrhelia,* and *Trochosmilia* (Fig. 99). Scleractinians range from Triassic to Recent in age.

ORDER TABULATA (Latin *tabulatus,* floored). These are corals that are now extinct but are known from fossils in both Paleozoic and Cenozoic rocks. Tabulate corals are exclusively colonial, characterized by hori-

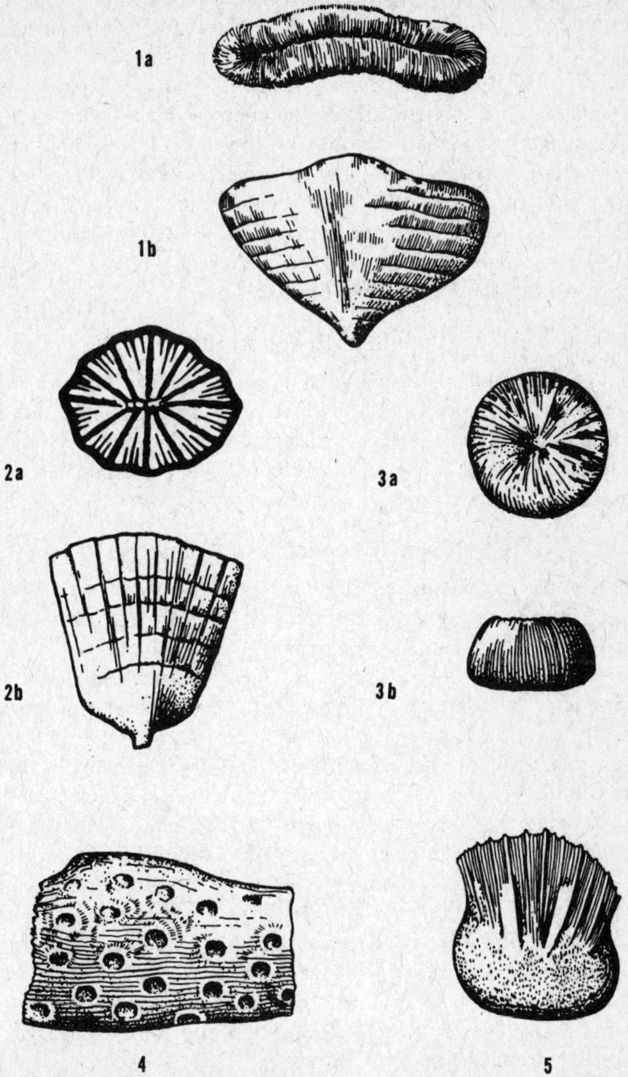

FIG. 99.—Tertiary scleractinian corals. (*1*) *Trochosmilia* (*a*) top view, (*b*) side view. (*2*) *Flabellum* (*a*) top view, (*b*) side view. (*3*) *Micrabacia* (*a*) top view, (*b*) side view. (*4*) *Astrhelia.* (*5*) *Endopachys* (all about actual size). (By permission from *Texas Fossils* by W. H. Matthews III, Bureau of Economic Geology, University of Texas, Austin.)

zontal floorlike partitions called *tabulae,* and with septa either absent or poorly developed. They were the most abundant reef-building corals during Paleozoic time and are common in rocks of this age. *Cladochonus, Halysites, Favosites,* and *Striatopora* (Fig. 100) are examples of Paleozoic tabulates. The earliest known tabulates, which appeared in the Ordovician, were apparently extinct by the end of the Permian. One family, however, persisted until Eocene time. *Halysites* (Fig. 100–*3*) is relatively common and is called the "chain coral" because it closely resembles the links of a chain. *Favosites* (Fig. 100–*2*), another common colonial coral of Paleozoic age, has been referred to as the "honey-comb coral" because of its resemblance to honeycomb.

Phylum Platyhelminthes

The Platyhelminthes (Greek *platys,* flat + *helminthos,* worm) are elongated flattened worms.* They include the parasitic liver fluke and tapeworm, and the fresh-water planarian worm. Because they lack hard parts, the flatworms have left no fossil record. There is a possibility, however, that fossil flatworms may be found.

Phylum Nemathelminthes (Nematoda)

Members of the Nemathelminthes (Greek *nematos,* thread + *helminthos,* worm) are known as round- or threadworms. They are typically cylindrical, elongated, unsegmented, and pointed at both ends. They are both free-living and parasitic (the hookworm and pork worm are examples of the latter). Composed almost exclusively of soft parts, these forms have apparently left no fossil record. It has been suggested, however, that fossil roundworms might some day be found as parasites in some of the frozen mammals of Pleistocene age. Unfortunately, to date, close examination of the remains of such animals as the frozen woolly mammoth has yielded no evidence of such worms.

Phylum Trochelminthes (Rotifera)

The Trochelminthes (Greek *trochos,* wheel + *helminthos,* worm) include the minute animals known as rotifers or "wheel animalcules." While these forms have left no fossil record, they resemble certain larval stages that many other animals pass through and thus may be of some evolutionary significance.

Phylum Bryozoa (Polyzoa)

The Bryozoans (Greek *bryon,* moss + *zoion,* animal) are colonial animals that are often referred to as "sea mats" because they are com-

* All of the worm phyla were at one time placed in the old phylum Vermes (Latin for worms).

monly found matted on shells, rocks, fossils, and other objects. They are abundant in modern seas and a few species live in fresh water. The individual living animals (known as *zooids*) are quite small and have a tentacle-bearing ridge (*lophophore*) surrounding the mouth. Each tiny animal secretes its own cuplike chitinous or calcareous exoskeleton which is often preserved as a fossil. The zooid lives in small boxlike chambers known as *zooecia* (or *autopores*) which are seen as small pits on the surface of the bryozoan colony. The zooecia grow together to

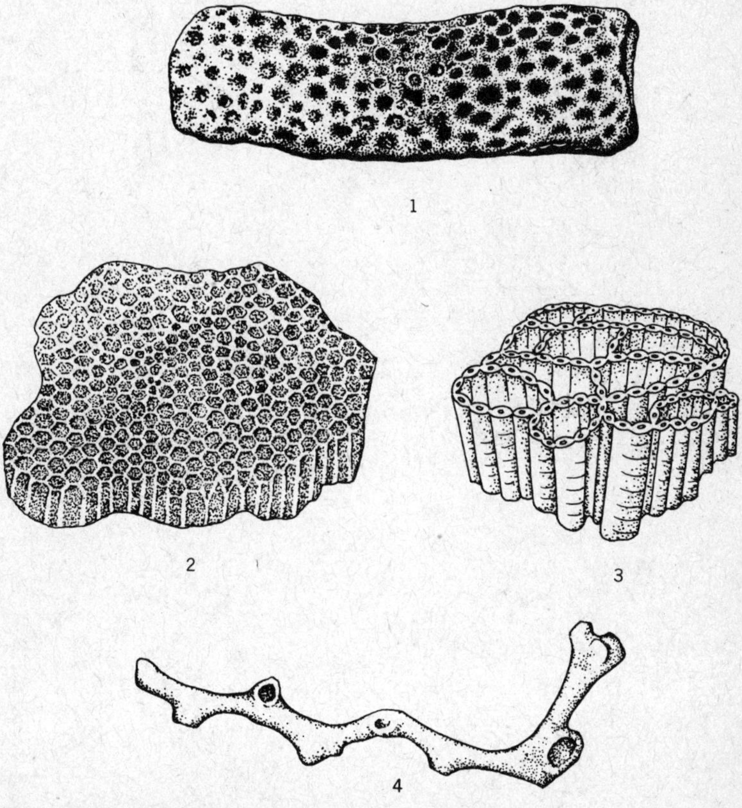

FIG. 100.—Paleozoic tabulate corals. (*1*) *Striatopora* (Pennsylvanian). (*2*) *Favosites* (Silurian). (*3*) *Halysites* (Silurian). (*4*) *Cladochonus* (Pennsylvanian) (all about natural size). (By permission from *Texas Fossils* by W. H. Matthews III, Bureau of Economic Geology, University of Texas, Austin.)

form the *zoarium,* as the colony is called, and some fossil zoaria grow to be as much as two feet across. Such colonies may be lacelike (Fig. 101-*1*), spiral (Fig. 101-*2*), or branching (Fig. 101-*3*). Bryozoans are structurally complex and often present considerable difficulty in identification. Several thousand fossil species have been described, however, and some are valuable guide fossils.

Bryozoans range from Ordovician to Recent in age, though questionable Cambrian forms have been described. Figure 100 illustrates some typical Paleozoic species.

FIG. 101.—Paleozoic bryozoans. (*1*) *Polypora,* a lacy or fenestellid type (Pennsylvanian). (*2*) *Archimedes,* a spiral type (Mississippian). (*3*) *Rhombopora,* a branching type (all about actual size).

Phylum Brachiopoda

Brachiopods (Greek *brachion,* arm + *pous, podos,* foot) are commonly called "lamp shells" because of their resemblance to ancient Grecian lamps. They are exclusively marine animals possessing a shell composed of two valves (Fig. 102) which enclose the soft parts of the

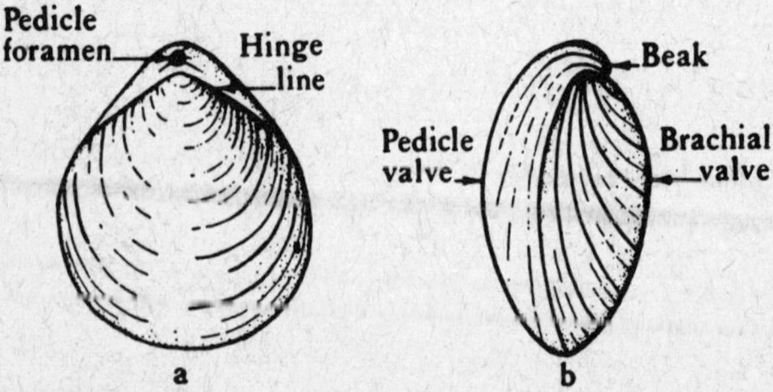

FIG. 102.—Morphology and principal parts of articulate brachiopods. (*a*) Pedicle view. (*b*) Side view. (By permission from *Texas Fossils* by W. H. Matthews III, Bureau of Economic Geology, University of Texas, Austin.)

animal. The valves are composed of calcareous or phosphatic material or a mixture of chitin and calcium phosphate. They are of unequal size, but a line passed through the mid-length of the valves will divide them into equal halves.

The soft parts are composed of muscles, the *mantle* (which secretes the valves), digestive, respiratory, reproductive, and excretory organs, and the tentacle-bearing *lophophore.* The lophophore is similar to that of the bryozoans; and, on the basis of this similarity, Bryozoa and Brachiopoda were once considered to be classes of phylum Molluscoidea —a group which is no longer considered valid.

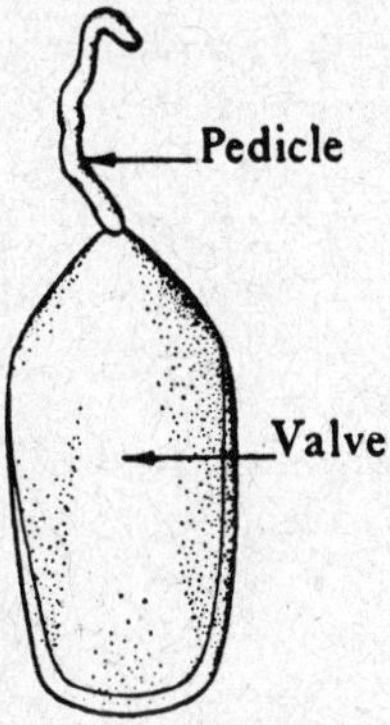

Fig. 103.—*Lingula,* a typical Recent inarticulate brachiopod showing extended pedicle (about actual size).

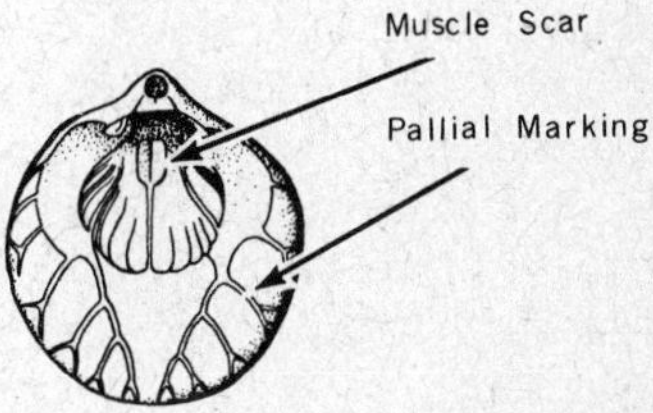

Fig. 104.—Interior of articulate brachiopod valve showing muscle scar and pallial markings.

In adult life the typical brachiopod is attached to the sea bottom by means of a fleshy stalk or *pedicle* (Fig. 103). The pedicle is typically extruded through a hole (the *pedicle foramen*) which is located in the *pedicle* (or *ventral*) valve (Fig. 102). The prominent upturned area which is commonly present on the pedicle valve is called the *beak* (Fig. 102). The other valve, known as the *brachial* (or *dorsal*) valve, is usually the smaller of the two (Fig. 102). The two valves are opened by means of muscles, and since death usually results in relaxation of these muscles, fossil brachiopods are typically found with the valves closed. The interior of brachiopod shells commonly reveal markings called *muscle scars* which mark the position of muscle attachment. Other markings present on the valve's interior include the *brachidia* (see below), muscle scars, and *pallial markings* (Fig. 104). The latter mark tubular extensions of the body cavity which extended into the mantle.

These impressions tell us much about the soft parts of the once-living animal.

Mature brachiopods are *sessile,* or *sedentary* (attached), forms. They may be attached to other shells, rocks, or other solid objects. Most are attached by means of the pedicle, but others are attached by means of spines or direct cementation of the shell.

Brachiopods vary greatly in size and shape and exhibit a wide variety of *ornamentation* such as spines, ribs, nodes, and other structures. Brachiopods range from Cambrian to Recent in age, but are a minor constituent of modern marine faunas. Approximately 3,200 species have been described; of these only two hundred are living today. They are among the most common Paleozoic fossils and are found to a lesser extent in Mesozoic and Cenozoic rocks. Because brachiopods are usually common, well-preserved, relatively easy to identify, and somewhat restricted stratigraphically, they are among the most important of all fossils.

The phylum has been divided into two classes: the Inarticulata and the Articulata. This classification is based on the presence or absence of the *hinge line*—the edge of the shell where the two valves articulate (Fig. 102)—and differences in the muscles of the two groups.

Class Inarticulata (Latin *in,* not + *articulatus,* articulate). The inarticulate brachiopods are rather primitive and have a long geologic history ([?] Precambrian, or Cambrian to Recent). They are characterized by valves which are not provided with *hinge teeth*, the valves being held together by muscles, and a hinge line is lacking. The pedicle opening is small or absent, the pedicle extruding between the two valves. Most inarticulate brachiopods are circular, oval, or tonguelike in shape and commonly composed of chitinous and phosphatic material. Undoubted inarticulate brachiopods range from Early Cambrian to Recent in age, but questionable Precambrian forms have been reported. They were never as common as the articulate brachiopods which are discussed below. *Lingula,* a typical Recent inarticulate brachiopod is illustrated in Fig. 103, and representative fossil forms in Fig. 105.

Class Articulata (Latin *articulatus,* articulate). Articulate brachiopods differ from inarticulate forms in that the valves are hinged and composed primarily of calcium carbonate. One valve has well-developed *teeth* which articulate with sockets in the opposing valve. There is also a well-developed muscle system which aids in opening and closing the shell. In more advanced forms the lophophore is divided into two elongate extensions called *brachia*. These are attached to a supporting calcareous structure termed the *brachidium* (plural, *brachidia*). These supports may be seen on the interior of the brachial valve.

For convenience in study, members of the Articulata have been divided into several orders based upon the position of the pedicle foramen and the nature of shell growth. These orders are further broken down into suborders based upon features found on the inner surfaces of the valves, and the general *morphology* (form) of the shell. (This classification becomes somewhat technical and will not be considered here. Students and more serious collectors who are interested in more specific determinations should refer to the list of publications at the end of this book.)

In addition to the characteristics and structures mentioned above, various external shell features are also used in brachiopod identification.

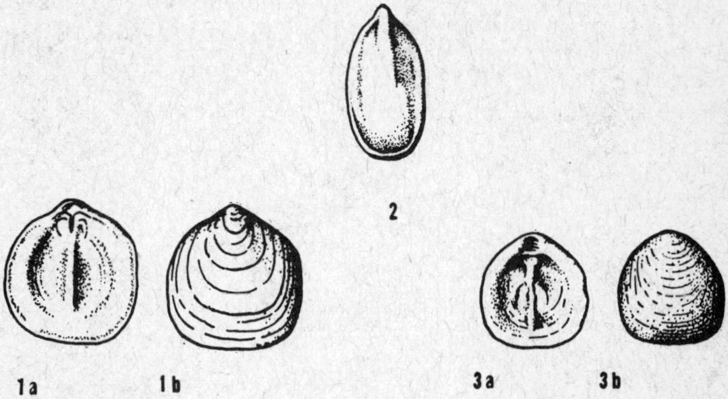

FIG. 105.—Cambrian inarticulate brachiopods. (*1*) *Angulotreta* (*a*) interior of valve, (*b*) exterior of valve. (*2*) *Lingula* (note resemblance to Recent *Lingula* in Fig. 103). (*3*) *Apsotreta* (*a*) interior of valve, (*b*) exterior of valve. (All about natural size.) (By permission from *Texas Fossils* by W. H. Matthews III, Bureau of Economic Geology, University of Texas, Austin.)

The size, degree of curvature of the valves, and surface ornamentation (spines, ribs, grooves, etc.) of the shell play a part in the identification of various species. Figure 106 illustrates several typical articulate brachiopods.

It is possible that certain brachiopods may be confused with clams or mussels (phylum Mollusca, class Pelecypoda, p. 217) because of superficial resemblances between the shells (compare Figs. 106 and 114). The following differences between brachiopods and clams should be noted:

1. The internal body structures of brachiopods and clams are completely different.

2. The valves of articulate brachiopods are hinged along the *posterior* (to the rear), or pedicle, end of the animal; the valves of clams are hinged along the *dorsal* (top) side of the animal.

3. The valves are on the *dorsal* (back) and *ventral* (lower or under) part of the animal in the brachiopods (Fig. 102), and *lateral* (on the sides) in the clams and mussels.

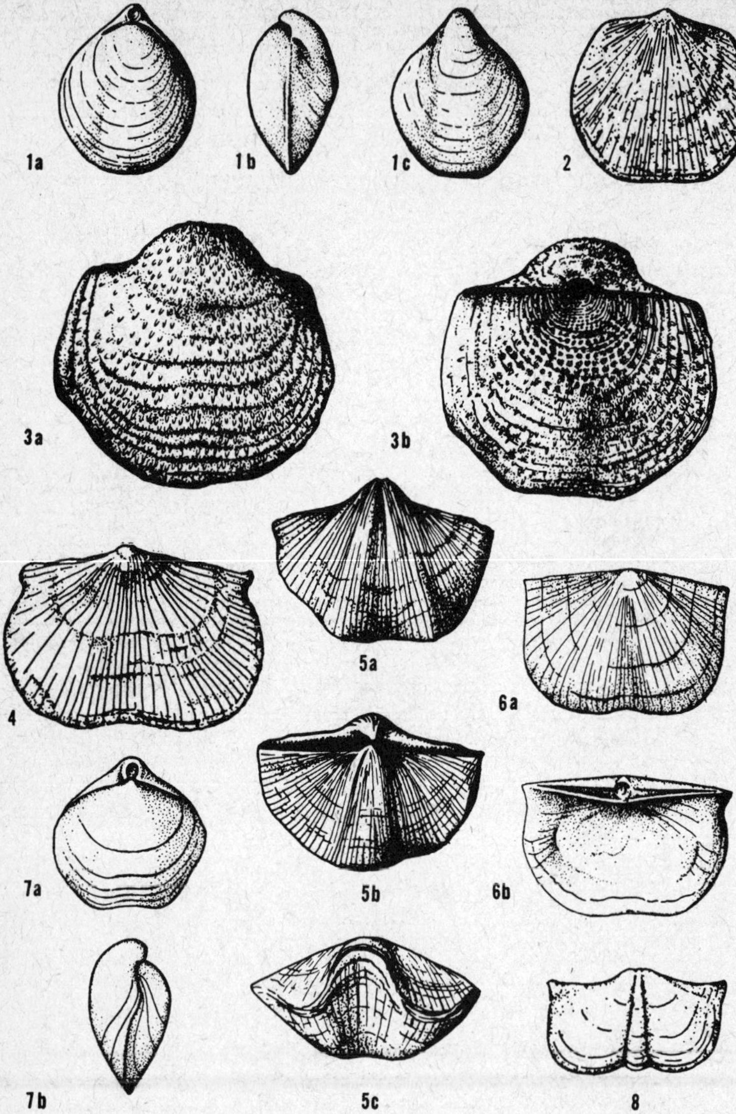

FIG. 106.—Typical articulate brachiopods. (*1*) *Kingena wacoensis* (Cretaceous), (*a*) brachial view, (*b*) side view, (*c*) pedicle view. (*2*) *Rhipodomella* (Mississippian). (*3*) *Juresania* (Pennsylvanian), (*a*) pedicle view, (*b*) brachial view. (*4*) *Derbya* (Pennsylvanian). (*5*) *Neospirifer cameratus* (Pennsylvanian), (*a*) pedicle view, (*b*) brachial view, (*c*) anterior view. (*6*) *Chonetes* (Pennsylvanian), (*a*) exterior of valve, (*b*) interior of valve. (*7*) *Composita subtilita* (Pennsylvanian), (*a*) brachial view, (*b*) side view. (*8*) *Mesolobus* (Pennsylvanian). (All about actual size.) (Adapted from *Texas Fossils* by W. H. Matthews III, Bureau of Economic Geology, University of Texas, Austin.)

4. The brachiopod valve is *equilateral* (each half is a mirror image of the other) and *inequivalved* (the pedicle and brachial valves being of unequal size or shape, or both). Clam valves are just the opposite (compare Figs. 102 and 114).

Brachiopods are usually found in a good state of preservation, with both valves present, although inarticulate valves are commonly separated after death. Shells composed of calcareous and phosphatic material are particularly likely to be preserved. Many brachiopod shells have been replaced by iron compounds, calcite, or silica, the latter resulting in some rare and remarkable preservations (Fig. 10). What is probably the world's finest silicified brachiopod fauna has been recovered from the Permian limestones of the Glass Mountains in Brewster County, Texas (see p. 21).

Articulate brachiopods range from Early Cambrian to Recent in age but underwent their greatest development during the Paleozoic era. Upper Mesozoic and Cenozoic formations contain relatively few brachiopods.

Phylum Mollusca

The phylum Mollusca (Latin *molluscus,* soft) includes a large group of aquatic and terrestrial invertebrates having a typical *bilateral symmetry* and a fleshy body covering, or *mantle*, which commonly secretes a calcareous external shell. The shell serves as an exoskeleton, and these hard parts are well adapted for preservation as fossils. However, some mollusks (the slugs) have no shells, and others (for example, the squids) have an internal shell. The shell-bearing mollusks are among the most important fossils known, largely because of their hard, readily fossilized, and abundant remains, the characteristic variations in their shells, their adaptation to a wide range of environments, and their long geologic history. Moreover, the remains of certain mollusks, such as the oysters, are of considerable importance as rock-builders.

The phylum is composed of five classes: the Amphineura (chitons or "sea mice"), Scaphopoda ("tusk-shells"), Pelecypoda (clams, oysters, and mussels), Gastropoda (snails and slugs), and Cephalopoda (squids, nautiloids, octopuses, and the extinct ammonoids) (Fig. 107). Of these classes, only the last three are important as fossils, although fossil amphineurans and scaphopods are known.

Class Amphineura (Greek *amphi,* on both sides + *neuron,* nerve). The chitons (also called "sea mice" or "coat-of-mail" shells) are relatively simple mollusks with a shell consisting of eight dorsal plates (Fig. 108). They are *herbivorous* (plant-eating) animals which are common on rocky coasts of our modern seas. They have a long geologic range (Ordovician to Recent) but are not common as fossils, although about a hundred species of fossil chitons have been described.

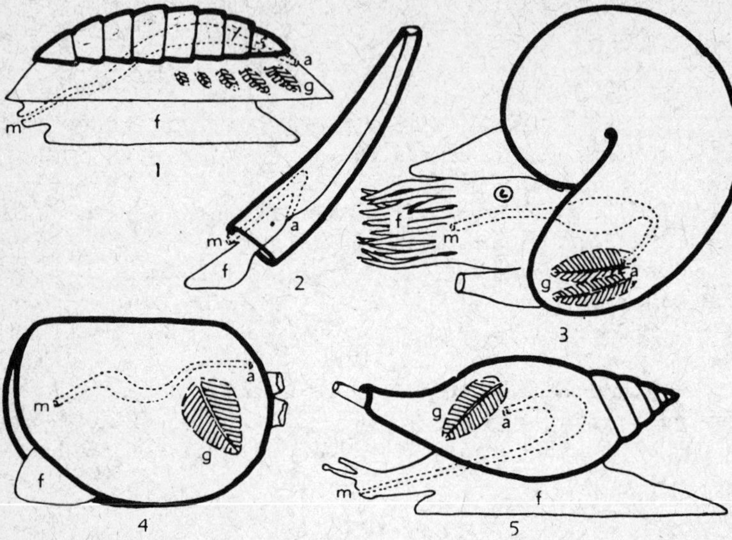

FIG. 107.—Types of mollusks. The diagrams show characteristic forms of the shell (heavy lines) in each of the five molluscan classes and location of the digestive tract and gills (*a,* anus; *f,* foot; *g,* gill; *m,* mouth). (*1*) Amphineura (chitons), with shell consisting of eight transverse plates. (*2*) Scaphopoda (tusk shells) shell elongate, tubular, open at both ends. (*3*) Cephalopoda (nautilus) shell planispirally coiled. (*4*) Pelecypoda (clams), shell composed of two valves hinged dorsally. (*5*) Gastropoda (snails), shell generally coiled in a conical spire. (By permission from *Invertebrate Fossils* by R. C. Moore, C. G. Lalicker, and A. G. Fischer. Copyright, 1952. McGraw-Hill Book Company, Inc.)

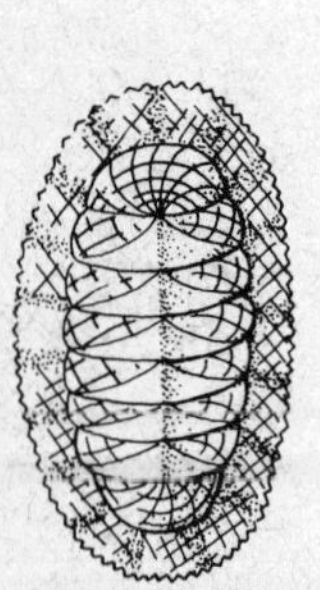

FIG. 108.—Dorsal view of chiton, or amphineuran, showing the eight plates, or valves, on the back of the animal (about actual size).

Class Scaphopoda (Greek *skaphe,* boat + *pous, podos,* foot). The scaphopods are marine mollusks with gently curved, conical, tubular, tusklike shells. The shell consists of one valve, is open at both ends, slightly tapered, and is typically two to three inches long. They have been called "tusk-shells" because of their resemblance to the tusks of certain mammals (Fig. 109).

Living scaphopods comprise an insignificant part of modern molluscan faunas (about two hundred living species are known). Where present they are typically found in shallow waters on sandy or silty bottoms. Some forms, however, have been recovered from depths of as much as 15,000 feet.

Scaphopods are of minor importance as fossils in spite of their long geologic history ([?] Ordovician, Devonian to Recent). Some three hundred species of fossil scaphopods have been described, and certain Tertiary marine strata are known to contain an abundance of these forms. Scaphopods measuring almost two feet long have been found in certain Pennsylvania strata in Texas.

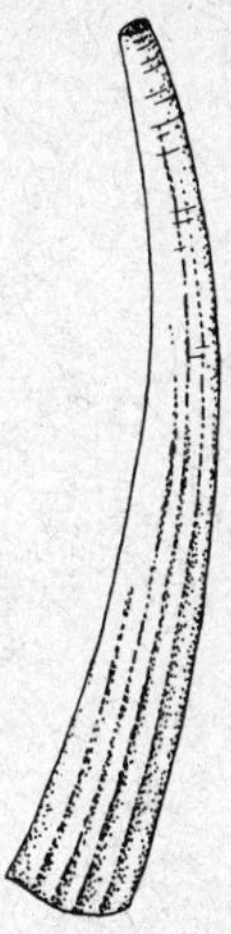

FIG. 109.—Side view of scaphopod, or "tusk shell" (about actual size).

Class Pelecypoda (Greek *pelekys,* hatchet + *pous, podos,* foot) (*Lamellibranchia*). The pelecypods possess a shell composed of two calcareous valves (Fig. 110) which enclose the soft parts of the animal. Members of this class live exclusively in an aquatic habitat and are especially abundant in marine environments. Most pelecypods are slow-moving bottom-dwelling forms, but some (for example, the oyster) are attached, and others (for example, the scallop or *Pecten*) are swimmers (Fig. 111). The Pelecypoda includes such familiar salt-water forms as the clams, oysters, and scallops, as well as the common fresh-water mussel.

The living animal is aquatic, with well-developed soft parts and a muscular, typically hatchet-shaped foot. The soft *mantle* encloses the body and secretes the shell, and in some pelecypods part of the mantle is developed into the *incurrent* and *excurrent siphons.*

Food and fresh water are brought into the *mantle cavity* through the incurrent siphons; waste products are passed out through the excurrent siphons. Respiration is by means of *gills* contained within the mantle cavity.

The more typical pelecypod valves are of equal size and form, but some, such as the scallops and oysters (Fig. 112), have two valves of unequal size and shape. The valves are hinged and held together by a tough elastic *ligament* which runs along the dorsal (top) side of the shell; this ligament spreads the valves apart as the muscles are relaxed. In addition to the ligament, most forms have *hinge teeth* consisting of teeth and sockets located along the *hinge line* (Fig. 110). The teeth in one valve articulate with the socket in the opposite valve, an arrangement which gives added strength to the hinge.

The pelecypod shell is composed of three layers: the *periostracum,* an outer horney layer of *conchiolin* (a chitinlike substance); a middle *prismatic* layer of calcium carbonate (the *ostracum*); and the *hypostracum,* an inner calcareous *laminated* layer of *porcelaneous* or *nacreous* (pearly)

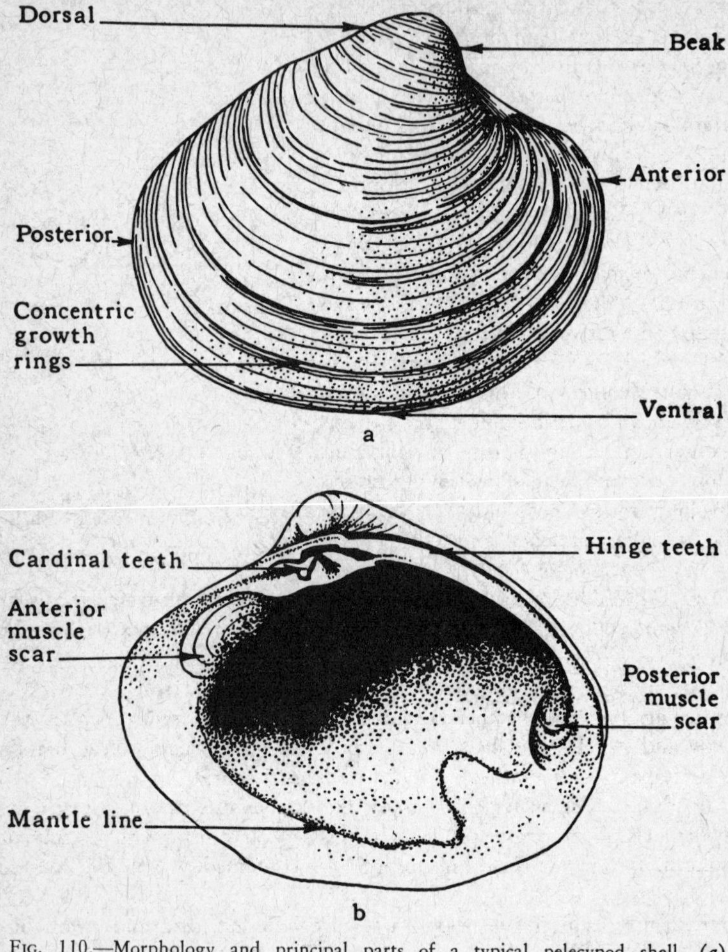

FIG. 110.—Morphology and principal parts of a typical pelecypod shell. (*a*) Exterior view. (*b*) Interior view. (By permission from *Texas Fossils* by W. H. Matthews III, Bureau of Economic Geology, University of Texas, Austin.)

material. The shells of these mollusks vary greatly in shape, but most pelecypods are typically clamlike. However, some forms are round (Fig 112-*1*), others are long and narrow (Fig. 112-*2*), and some have winglike structures (Fig. 112-*4*). Some species like the oysters and certain extinct attached types, *Gryphaea* (Fig. 112-*3*), *Exogyra* (Fig. 112-*5*), and the rudistids (Fig. 56), exhibit unusual shapes. In these forms the larger attached valve is irregular and thick, while the smaller free shell is flat and thin.

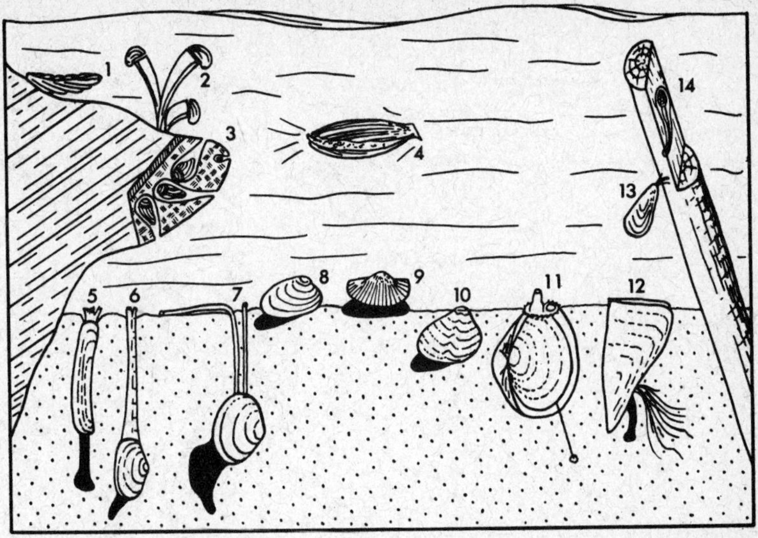

FIG. 111.—Adaptations of marine pelecypods. (*1* and *2*) *Ostrea* and *Coralliochama* cemented to substratum. (*3* and *14*) *Zirphaea* and *Teredo* burrowing in rock and wood. (*4*) *Pecten* swimming. (*5, 6,* and *7*) *Solen, Mya,* and *Scrobicularia* burrowing in soft sediment. (*8* and *9*) *Venus* and *Arca* creeping over substratum. (*10*) *Acila* partly buried. (*11* and *12*) *Notocorbula* and *Atrina* partly buried but attached by byssal threads. (*13*) *Mytilus* attached by byssal threads.

All forms are shown schematically and not to scale. The foot, when present, is shown in black in its extended position. (*5–7* after Yonge, 1949; *11* and *12* after Stenzel, Krause, and Twining, 1957. (By permission from *Invertebrate Paleontology* by W. H. Easton, Harper & Brothers, 1960.)

Most pelecypod shells are characterized by a *beak* which marks the initial point of shell growth and thus represents the oldest part of the shell. The beak is commonly located on the *dorsal* margin of the shell, and the end opposite this is designated *posterior* (the rear). The hinge line and ligament are located *dorsally* (along the top), and the lower margin of the shell where the valves open is called *ventral* (Fig. 110-*a*).

The inner surface of the shell (Fig. 110-*b*) has certain markings which, along with the shell form and *dentition* (the nature and arrangement of the teeth and sockets), are important in classification. *Muscle scars* are present on the inside of most valves; the *anterior muscle scars* are located near the front of the shell, and the *posterior muscle scars* are situated near the rear. These scars mark the place of attachment of muscles which were used to close the shell and aid in locomotion. Along the ventral margin of some shells there is a line or scar extending from the anterior muscle scar to the posterior muscle scar. This *mantle line*

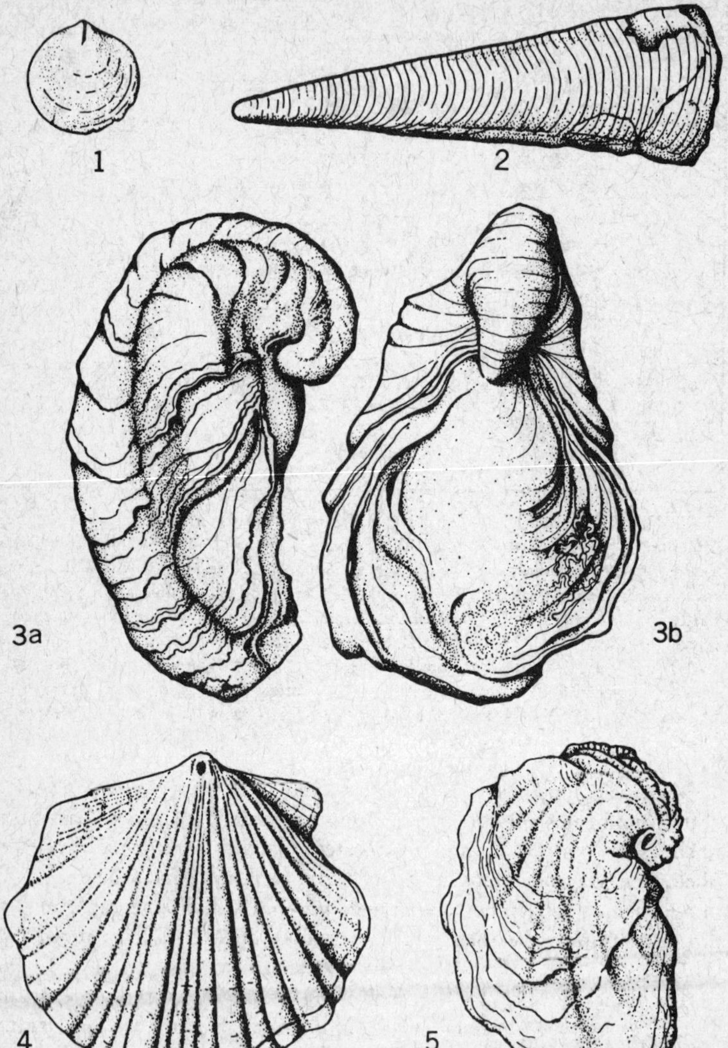

FIG. 112.—Types of pelecypod shells. (*1*) *Anomia,* round-shelled clam. (*2*) *Pinna,* clam with a long narrow shell. (*3*) *Gryphaea,* Cretaceous form with valves of unequal size. (*4*) *Neithea,* Cretaceous scallop with winglike "ears." (*5*) *Exogyra,* Cretaceous oysterlike attached pelecypod (all about natural size). (Adapted from *Texas Fossils* by W. H. Matthews III, Bureau of Economic Geology, Austin.)

or *pallial line* (Fig. 110-*b*) marks the place of attachment of the mantle. In addition to the previously mentioned hinge teeth, certain species have more prominent *cardinal teeth* (Fig. 110-*b*) located below and in front of the hinge teeth.

The exterior of most shells is marked by a series of *concentric growth lines* (Fig. 110-*a*) which show points of periodic addition of shell material. The external surface of many shells is also marked by various types of ornamentation, including ribs, spines, nodes, grooves, and ridges.

Pelecypods are primarily marine animals, though certain fresh-water clams and mussels are common. The pelecypods have become adapted to several types of existence and both *mobile* (free-moving) and *sedentary* (attached) forms are common (Fig. 111). Some forms crawl over the bottom sediments; others may burrow into mud, rock, wood, or even other shells. A few, such as the scallops, are able to swim by clapping the valves together and expelling water. Others (for example, the oysters) are attached by cementation of the shell to such objects as rocks, pilings, and other shells. Some are attached by means of a *byssus,* a series of fine, tough threads that anchor the shell to the bottom. The type of life led by the animal is often reflected in the shape of the shell. The shells of pelecypods attached by a byssus have a *byssal notch* (Fig. 113) marking the point at which the byssus was extruded from the shell. Cemented forms such as the oysters have the attached valve greatly enlarged and often distorted (Fig. 112-*3*). Burrowing forms typically have shells that are shaped to facilitate rapid burrowing into the bottom sediments (Fig. 111-*5*).

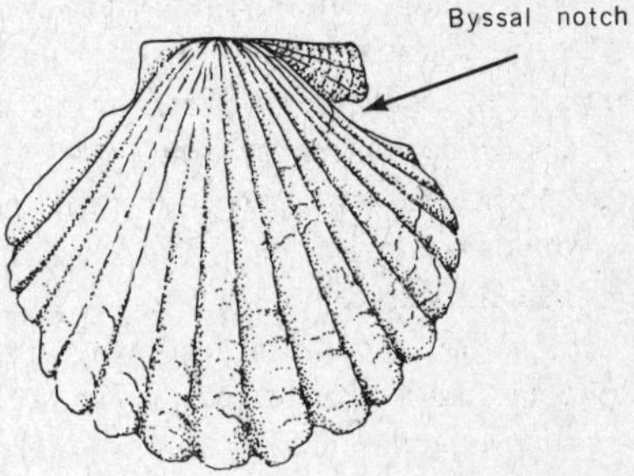

FIG. 113.—Scallop shell showing byssal notch or byssal sinus (about one half actual size).

Pelecypods vary greatly in size, ranging from tiny clams a fraction of an inch in length and diameter, to the great *Tridacna* of the South Seas.

The shell of this huge clam may attain a length of as much as six feet, a width of almost two feet, and a weight of several hundred pounds.

Many Paleozoic and Early Mesozoic pelecypods are found preserved as casts and molds, the original shell material having been dissolved or eroded away. Certain Cretaceous and Cenozoic pelecypods, however, may be found with the original shell perfectly preserved, in some cases unaltered. Fossil-collectors commonly find only one valve of the pelecypod shell because the shell normally opens when the animal dies, and the valves may easily become separated. The shell is thus made more susceptible to damage or destruction by currents, wave action, and crushing by heavy, coarse sediments. Sometimes, however, if the animal dies while burrowed in the mud, or is covered quickly by sediments, both valves will be found in place.

Fossil pelecypods first appear in Ordovician deposits and have become increasingly abundant and varied since that time. They are relatively common in fossiliferous strata of all ages, but especially in Cretaceous, Tertiary and Quaternary strata (Fig. 114).

Class Gastropoda (Greek *gaster, gastros,* stomach + *pous, podos,* foot). The gastropods comprise the largest class of mollusks and include such forms as the snails, slugs, whelks, limpets, and abalones.

The living animal has a distinct head with one pair of eyes, one or two pairs of tentacles, and a broad, flat foot. It is typically enclosed in a coiled, single-valved, unchambered shell which is secreted by the mantle and carried on the animal's back. Most gastropods have gills and live in shallow marine waters, but some inhabit fresh water. Others (the pulmonates) are terrestrial and breathe by means of lungs.

Gastropod shells, both Recent and fossil, exhibit a great variety of size, shape, and ornamentation. The typical gastropod secretes a spirally coiled shell, but some forms occupy ear-shaped, cap-shaped, wormlike, or slipper-shaped shells (Fig. 115). More often the shell is cone-shaped, flat, turreted or cylindrical (Fig. 116). The shell is commonly wound in a spiral around a central axial pillar (the *columella*). The closed pointed end of the shell is called the *apex,* and each turn, or *volution,* of the shell is called a *whorl.* The line dividing two whorls is called a *suture* (Fig. 117). The last-formed and largest whorl, called the *body whorl,* contains the *aperture*—the opening of the shell. The aperture is usually round but may be marked by canals, notches, ridges, or other indentations. The combined whorls, exclusive of the body whorl, are known as the *spire*. The spire may be high or low, and the degree of pointedness is expressed by the *apical,* or *spiral, angle*. The inner and outer margins of the aperture are designated the *inner lip* and *outer lip*, respectively. In some snails the aperture is closed by means of the *operculum*—a calcareous or horny plate attached to the foot of the animal. This plate effectively seals the aperture when the animal is withdrawn into its shell. Some gastropods have shells that are loosely coiled, and in these forms

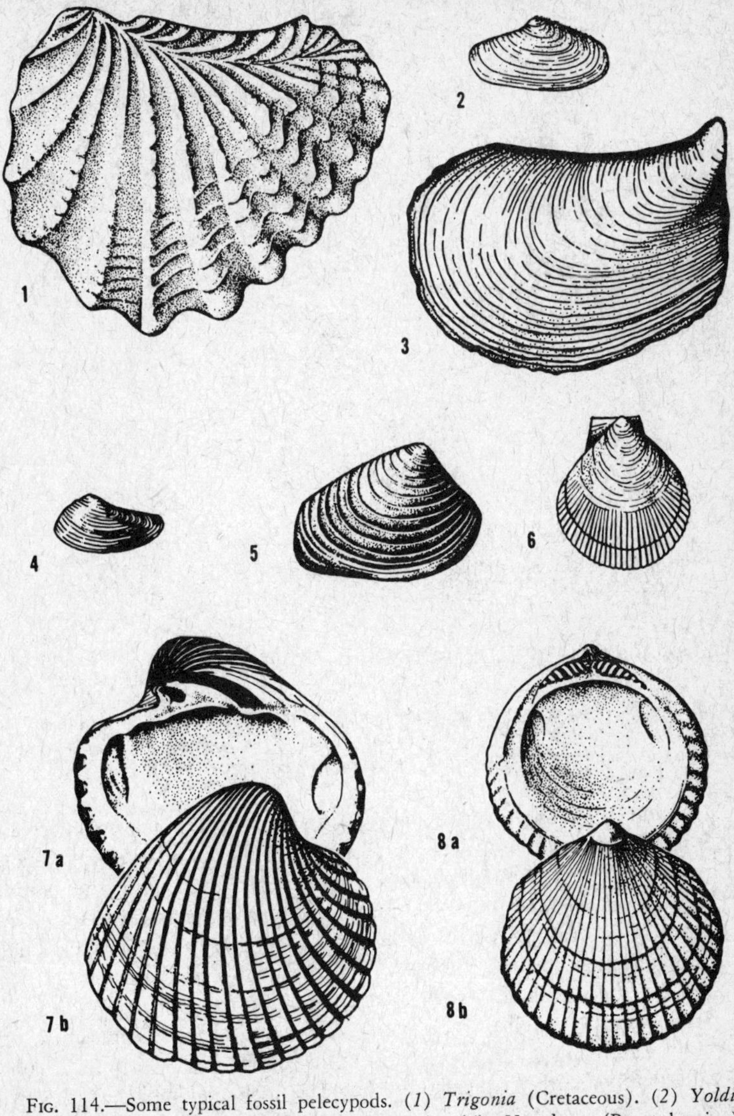

FIG. 114.—Some typical fossil pelecypods. (*1*) *Trigonia* (Cretaceous). (*2*) *Yoldia* (Pennsylvanian). (*3*) *Myalina* (Pennsylvanian). (*4*) *Nuculana* (Pennsylvanian). (*5*) *Astartella* (Pennsylvanian). (*6*) *Pecten* (Tertiary). (*7a, b*) *Venericardia* (Tertiary). (*8a, b*) *Glycymeris* (Tertiary). (*1, 2, 4, 5, 6,* and *8* about actual size; *3* and *7* reduced one half.) (Adapted from *Texas Fossils* by W. H. Matthews III, Bureau of Economic Geology, University of Texas, Austin.)

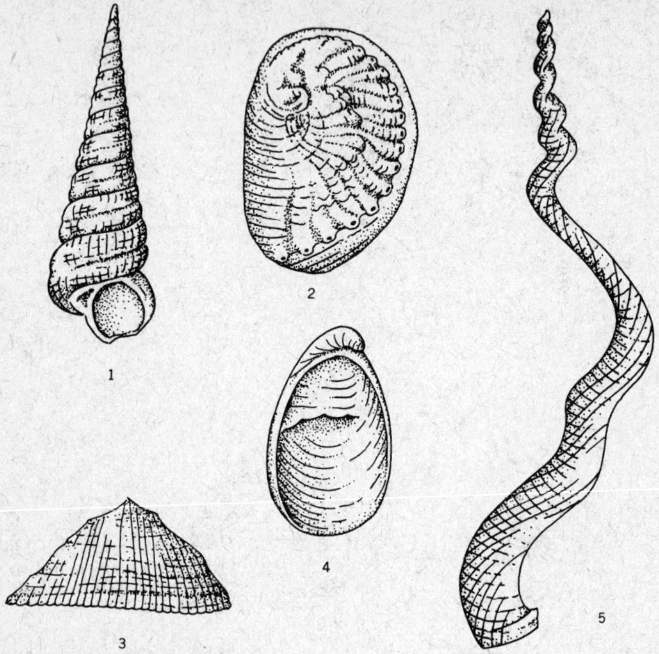

FIG. 115.—Types of gastropod shells. (*1*) Turreted (*Turritella*). (*2*) Auriform or ear-shaped (*Haliotis,* the abalone). (*3*) Patelliform or cap-shaped (*Diodora,* a limpet). (*4*) Slipper-shaped (*Crepidula,* the "slipper shell"). (*5*) Vermiform, or wormlike, or irregularly coiled (*Vermetus*). (All forms shown are Recent. All are about actual size except *2,* which is about one fourth actual size.)

the columella is absent. If the whorls of such shells are not in contact on the inner surface, there is an open space called the *umbilicus* (Fig. 117). The umbilicus is commonly seen as an opening in the base of the gastropod shell, but in some forms the umbilical opening may be partially or completely covered by a thick growth of shell, the *callus.* The external surface of the gastropod shell may be marked by ribs, grooves, nodes, spines, or other distinctive types of ornamentation.

Most gastropod shells are composed of aragonite, an unstable form of calcium carbonate; therefore, the shell is rather easily dissolved, and fossil gastropods are frequently preserved as casts and molds. This type of preservation occurs after the death of the animal, when the decomposition of the soft parts enables the shell to become filled with sediment. This filling later becomes solidified, whereupon the outer shell may be removed by weathering or solution. An internal mold of this type, called a *steinkern,* normally does not reflect the external shell characteristics of the shell (Figs. 8-6 and 118-6). However, in many instances gastropods

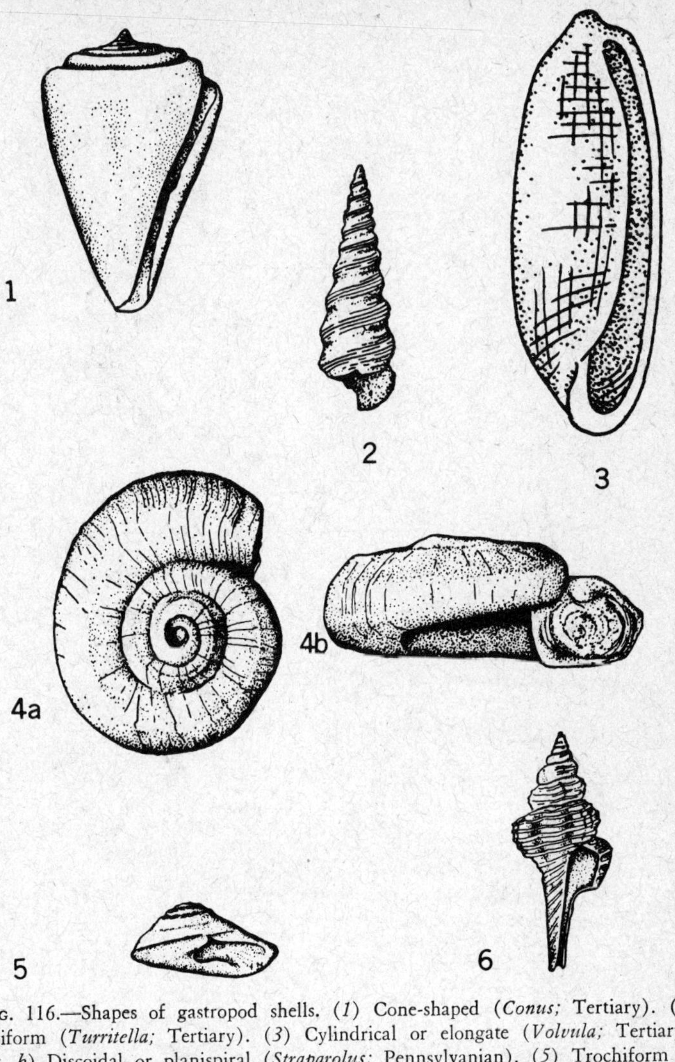

FIG. 116.—Shapes of gastropod shells. (*1*) Cone-shaped (*Conus;* Tertiary). (*2*) Turriform (*Turritella;* Tertiary). (*3*) Cylindrical or elongate (*Volvula;* Tertiary). (*4 a, b*) Discoidal or planispiral (*Straparolus;* Pennsylvanian). (*5*) Trochiform or top-shaped (*Trepospira;* Pennsylvanian). (*6*) Fusiform or spindle-shaped (*Fusus;* Tertiary). (All shells about actual size). (Adapted from *Texas Fossils* by W. H. Matthews III, Bureau of Economic Geology, University of Texas, Austin.)

may be collected with their original shell in an excellent state of preservation.

Indirect fossil evidence of gastropods is sometimes seen in the form of fossil snail trails that were made as the animal moved over soft sedi-

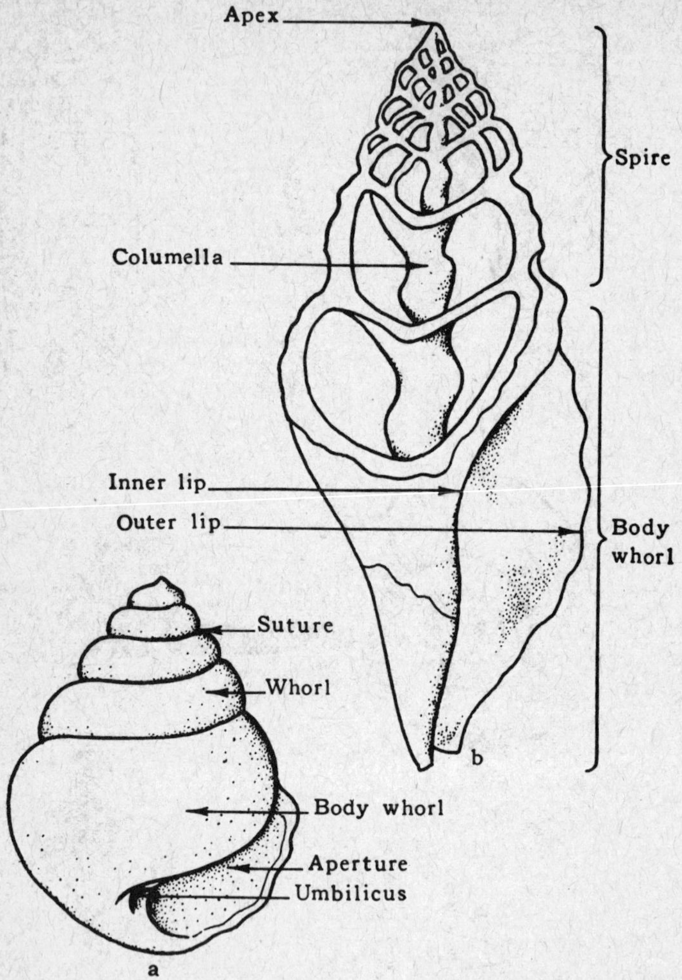

FIG. 117.—Morphology and principal parts of gastropods. (*a*) Low-spired form with umbilicus. (*b*) Section of spirally coiled shell showing columella. (By permission from *Texas Fossils* by W. H. Matthews III, Bureau of Economic Geology, University of Texas, Austin.)

ments. In addition, the neatly drilled, countersunk holes (Fig. 7) made by *carnivorous* (meat-eating) snails are found on many recent and fossil mollusk shells and are valid evidence of the presence of these animals even though their shells are not to be found.

The earliest fossil gastropods were those of the Early Cambrian, at

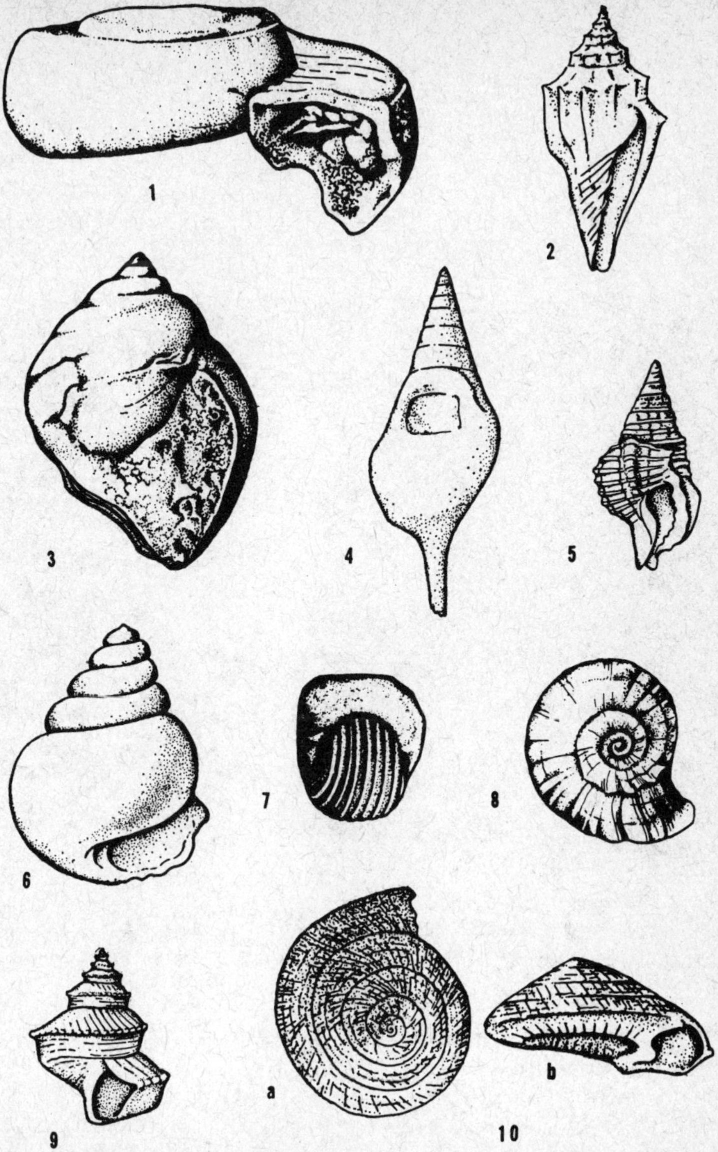

FIG. 118.—Typical fossil gastropods. (*1*) *Euomphalus* (Pennsylvanian). (*2*) *Volutospina* (Tertiary). (*3*) *Strobeus* (Pennsylvanian). (*4*) *Calyptraphorus* (Tertiary). (*5*) *Distorsio* (Tertiary). (*6*) *Tylostoma* (Cretaceous). (*7*) *Euphemites* (Pennsylvanian). (*8*) *Amphiscapha* (Pennsylvanian). (*9*) *Worthenia* (Pennsylvanian). (*10 a, b*) *Architectonica* (Tertiary). (All about natural size.) (Adapted from *Texas Fossils* by W. H. Matthews III, Bureau of Economic Geology, University of Texas, Austin.)

which time they were exclusively marine and relatively rare. Because of the degree of shell development in these early forms, it appears likely that gastropods were also present in Precambrian time. Gastropod remains become increasingly abundant from Ordovician until Recent time, and are found in both marine and fresh-water deposits.

Class Cephalopoda (Greek *kephale,* head + *pous, podos,* foot). The cephalopods are among the most important and interesting fossils

FIG. 119.—Modern cephalopods. *Nautilus* in center foreground, a school of squids in the background, and an octopus at lower left. (By permission from *Invertebrate Fossils* by R. C. Moore, C. G. Lalicker, and A. G. Fischer. Copyright 1952. McGraw-Hill Book Company, Inc.)

known. They are exclusively marine, free-living, carnivorous mollusks with a high degree of body organization. They attain the largest size of any invertebrates, living or fossil. Fossil cephalopods fifteen feet in length have been found in Ordovician rocks; the present-day deep-sea squid may reach a length of thirty feet. Class Cephalopoda includes such forms as the squids, octopuses, the pearly nautilus, and the extinct ammonoids.

The typical living cephalopod has a well-developed head, with eyes, horny jaws, and many tentacles (Fig. 119). The tentacles surround the mouth and are fused with the *foot,* hence the name "head-foot." Respiration is by means of gills. The shell, if present, is secreted by the mantle and may be either internal or external.

Cephalopods constitute one of the most useful groups of fossils. Some three hundred fossil genera have been described. Their shells are widespread and common and are very useful in the study of evolution, as well as for purposes of stratigraphic correlation. Members of this class range from Cambrian to Recent in age but were much more abundant in ancient seas than they are today. Their remains are particularly useful as fossils in rocks of Paleozoic and Mesozoic age.

Most paleontologists have divided the Cephalopoda into three subclasses: the Nautiloidea (pearly nautilus); the Ammonoidea (extinct

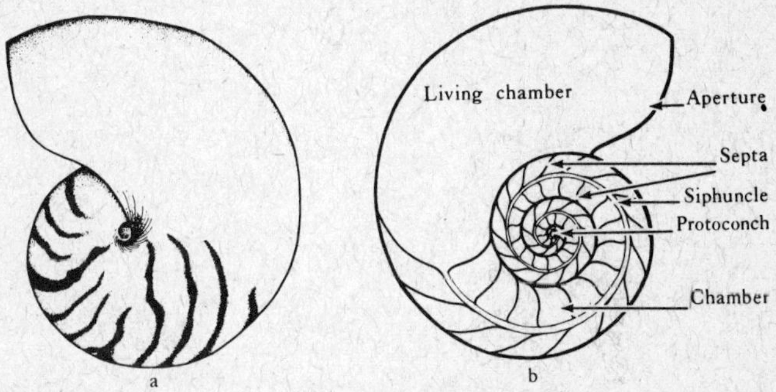

FIG. 120.—Morphology and principal parts of the pearly nautilus. (*a*) Exterior view of a Recent shell. (*b*) Sectioned view of the same shell to show internal structures. (By permission from *Texas Fossils* by W. H. Matthews III, Bureau of Economic Geology, University of Texas, Austin.)

ammonoids); and the Coleoidea (squids, octopuses, and extinct belemnoids). The subclass Coleoidea is equivalent to subclass Dibranchiata or subclass Decapoda of other classifications.

SUBCLASS NAUTILOIDEA (Greek *nautiolus,* a sailor + *eidos,* resemblance). The nautiloids are represented by a single living genus *Nautilus,* plus a large number of fossil species. Most of the latter are from Paleozoic rocks.

The body of the animal is enclosed in a coiled, chambered shell which is secreted by the mantle. The last and largest chamber encloses the soft body and is known as the *living chamber* or *body* chamber. The opening into the living chamber is called the *aperture.* In life the body chamber is connected with the other chambers (or *camerae*) by means of the *siphuncle,* a calcareous tube that extends back to the *protoconch,* the smallest and earliest-formed chamber (Fig. 120-*b*). The mouth of *Nautilus,* bearing two horny, beaklike jaws, is surrounded by about ninety tentacles. A thick, fleshy *hood* lies above the head and acts as a covering for the *aperture* when the animal withdraws into the living chamber (Fig. 119).

In *Nautilus* the shell, which is composed of calcium carbonate, is coiled in a flat spiral (Fig. 120-*a*). Internally the shell is divided into chambers by a series of calcareous partitions known as *septa.* Where

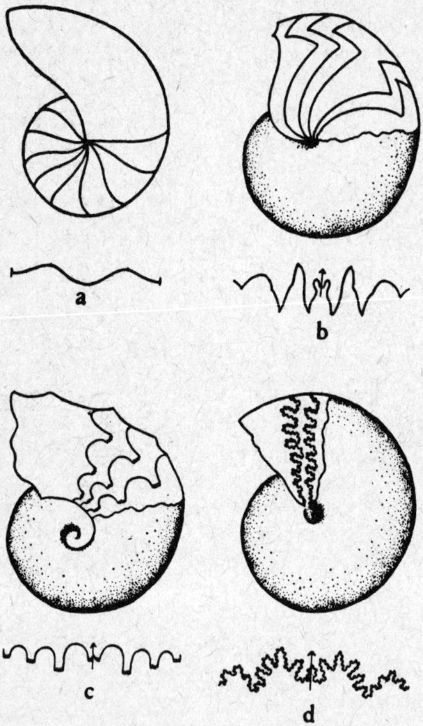

FIG. 121.—Characteristic features of the various types of cephalopod sutures. (*a*) Nautiloid type. (*b*) Goniatite type. (*c*) Ceratite type. (*d*) Ammonite type. (By permission from *Texas Fossils* by W. H. Matthews III, Bureau of Economic Geology, University of Texas, Austin.)

the siphuncle passes through each partition, there is a backward extension of the septum called a *septal neck.* A line known as the *suture* is formed where the septum joins the inner surface of the shell. These *suture lines,* or *patterns,* are not visible from the outside unless the outer shell has been removed. They are more often seen on the internal molds, or steinkerns, of fossil cephalopods where the original shell material has been removed by erosion (Fig. 121). Nautiloid sutures are very simple and smoothly curved, but ammonoids are characterized by more complex and wrinkled sutures. Suture patterns are of great value in cephalopod classification, for different fossil forms possess distinctive and characteristic patterns. Flexures of the suture directed toward the aperture are called *saddles,* and flexures directed away from the aperture are called *lobes* (Fig. 121). An *umbilicus* is present in some nautiloid shells and is seen as a depression or opening in the center of coiling.

Although the shell of the only living nautiloid is coiled, many of the early forms had straight cone-shaped shells (*Orthoceras,* Fig. 122-*b*),

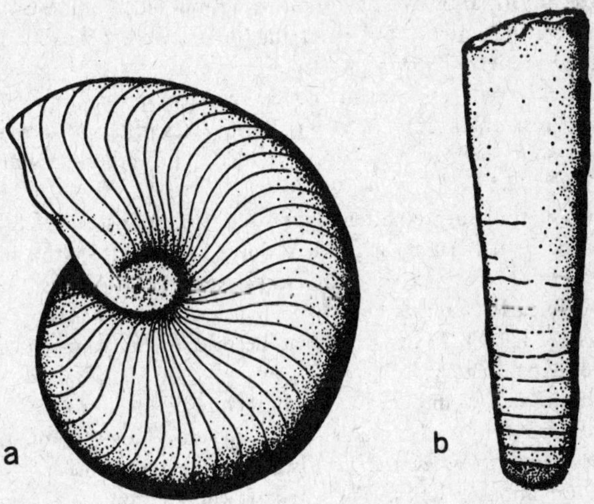

Fig. 122.—Typical fossil nautiloids. (*a*) *Cymatoceras* (Cretaceous). (*b*) *Orthoceras* (Pennsylvanian). (Both reduced about one half.) (By permission from *Texas Fossils* by W. H. Matthews III, Bureau of Economic Geology, University of Texas, Austin.)

and these are common in many fossiliferous strata of Paleozoic age. Externally the nautiloid shell may exhibit ornamentation in the form of nodes, ribs, spines, and growth lines; however, most such shells are smooth (Fig. 122-*a*).

Nautilus is an especially important animal; some scientists have referred to it as a "living fossil." It is of particular value to the paleontologist because it provides the only living link between the nautiloids and the ammonoids. It is interesting to note that the relatively simple nautiloids have remained virtually unchanged from the Cambrian to the present day, whereas the more complexly developed members of subclass Ammonoidea have been extinct for approximately 60 million years.

The nautiloids first appeared in Early Cambrian time, reached their maximum development in the Ordovician, and thereafter started a steady decline.

Subclass Ammonoidea (Greek *Ammon,* the Egyptian ram-headed deity + *eidos,* resemblance). The ammonoids are a group of extinct cephalopods which are related to the nautiloids but are characterized by more complex suture patterns (compare Figs. 121-*a* and 121-*d*).

Since there are no living representatives of this group, knowledge of the original animal is limited to what can be learned from fossils and the rocks in which they are found. Detailed studies of the fossils and comparison of these remains with living nautiloids have provided us with what little information we have on the ammonoid animal. Such studies indicate that the animal and its living habits were probably similar to those of the modern *Nautilus.*

Ammonoid shells are typically coiled in a flat spiral (Fig. 123-*3*); this superficial resemblance to a ram's horn gives the subclass its name. However, some forms are spirally coiled, and others essentially uncoiled (Fig. 123-*5*).

The ammonoid suture pattern is quite complex; instead of following a simple curving pattern as in the nautiloids (Fig. 121-*a*), the sutures become exceedingly wrinkled and complicated (Figs. 121-*b,* 121-*c,* and 121-*d*). The earlier ammonoids display suture patterns that are relatively simple (Fig. 121-*b*), but the patterns become more complicated in later periods of earth history.

Most Paleozoic ammonoids are characterized by a relatively simple, combination curved and angular suture pattern. This type of suture pattern is referred to as *goniatitic* (Fig. 121-*b*) and consists of rounded saddles and angular lobes. The earliest known goniatites appeared in Early Devonian time, and they had disappeared by the end of the Permian. They were, however, the dominant ammonoids of the Paleozoic.

Ceratite sutures are somewhat more complex than the goniatite pattern, and are typified by smooth, rounded saddles and lobes that are *serrate* (with sharp notches like a saw) or *crenulated* (marked in places by a series of toothlike indentations) (Fig. 121-*c*). Ceratitic suture patterns are commonly indicative of Late Paleozoic and Early Mesozoic species, the earliest known forms being from Upper Devonian strata and the most recent from Upper Triassic rocks.

The most complex and advanced pattern is that of the *ammonite* suture, composed of very wrinkled saddles and lobes which show many variations among different species (Fig. 121-*d*). The ammonite suture appeared first in Permian time, although some Pennsylvanian forms had suture patterns transitional between ceratitic and ammonitic. During Mesozoic time, however, the most abundant cephalopods were those

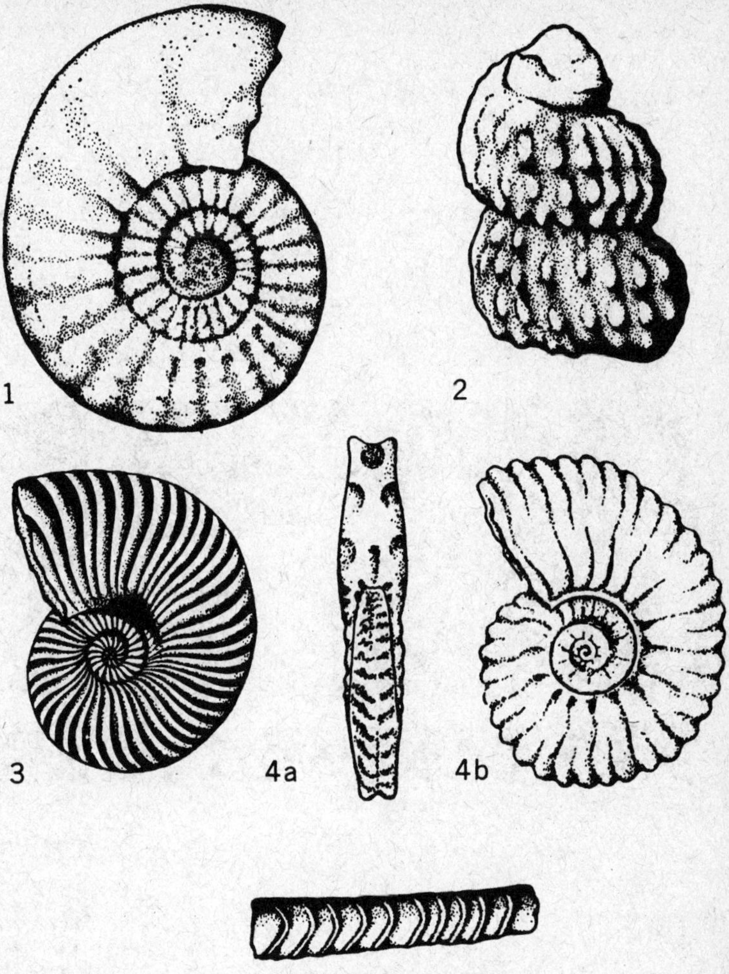

FIG. 123.—Typical Cretaceous cephalopods (ammonoids). (*1*) *Texanites.* (*2*) *Turrilites.* (*3*) *Oxytropidoceras.* (*4 a, b*) *Dufrenoyia.* (*5*) *Baculites.* (Adapted from *Texas Fossils* by W. H. Matthews III, Bureau of Economic Geology, University of Texas, Austin.)

with ammonitic suture patterns. These persisted until the extinction of the Ammonoidea at the end of the Cretaceous.

External ornamentation among ammonoids may consist of ribs, nodes, keels, or spines. Most Paleozoic species started with relatively simple unornamented shells and gradually developed into the more ornate and sculptured forms of the Mesozoic.

Ammonoids occur as fossils in many parts of the world and are abundant in many Mesozoic rocks. Because they attained almost worldwide distribution and lived but a relatively short time geologically, they are important guide fossils that accurately "label" the rocks in which they are found.

Subclass Coleoidea (Greek *koleos,* sheath + *eidos,* resemblance) (*Dibranchiata* or *Decapoda*). This group, while not especially useful as fossils, contains a large number of recent species including the squids, octopuses, cuttlefishes, and the extinct *belemnoids.* Of these only the belemnoids are helpful to the paleontologists. Some forms of coleoid cephalopods have internal skeletons; others have no skeleton. The

Courtesy of Ward's Natural Science Establishment

Fig. 124.—*Pachyteuthis,* a belemnoid from the Jurassic of Wyoming (reduced one half).

subclass has been divided into four orders: the Belemnoidea (Belemnitida) (belemnoids); the Sepioidea (Sepiida) (cuttlefishes); the Teuthoidea (Teuthida) (squids); and the Octopoida (Octopoda, Octopodida) (octopuses).

Order Belemnoidea (Greek *belemnon,* dart or javelin + *eidos,* resemblance) (*Belemnitida*). The belemnoids appear to be the oldest and most primitive of the coleoid cephalopods. The living animal was probably similar to the present-day cuttlefish and was abundant in the seas of the Jurassic and Cretaceous periods. Belemnoids (also called *belemnites*) were among the first fossils noted by early man. Their sharp, dartlike appearance (Fig. 124) led to the superstition that they represented the points of thunderstorms. Because of their shape, they have also been referred to as "fossil cigars" or "finger stones."

The oldest known belemnoid was collected from rocks of Late Mississippian age. The group became extinct at the end of the Cretaceous. Belemnoids are especially valuable as guide fossils for Jurassic and Cretaceous strata.

Phylum Annelida

The annelid (Latin *annulus,* ring), or segmented, worms include such familiar forms as the leeches and the common earthworm. The typical annelid worm has a long cylindrical body composed of a varying number of rings or *segments.* They are marine, fresh-water, or terrestrial forms that have apparently been common through much of geologic time.

Worms are not usually preserved as fossils because of their lack of hard parts. Some forms, however, have horny or siliceous jaws called *scolecodonts* (Greek *skolex,* worm + *odon, odontos,* tooth) (Fig. 125). The microscopic jaws are commonly found in certain shales of Ordovician, Devonian, and Pennsylvanian age. Some species secrete straight or coiled calcareous tubes (Fig. 126) commonly found attached to brachiopods, mollusks, and other objects. Worms have also left evidence of their presence consisting of burrows, trails, tracks, impressions of soft parts, and castings.

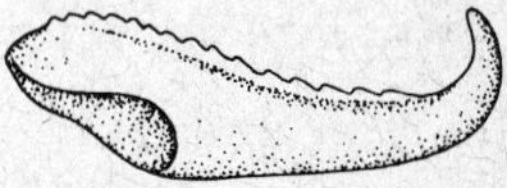

FIG. 125.—*Arabellites,* a scolecodont of Silurian age. These objects represent the jaws of fossil worms. (Enlarged about 20 times.)

Annelid worms have been found in rocks that range from Cambrian to Recent in age. However, there is evidence, principally tracks and burrows, that these forms were present in the Precambrian, although no actual remains have been found.

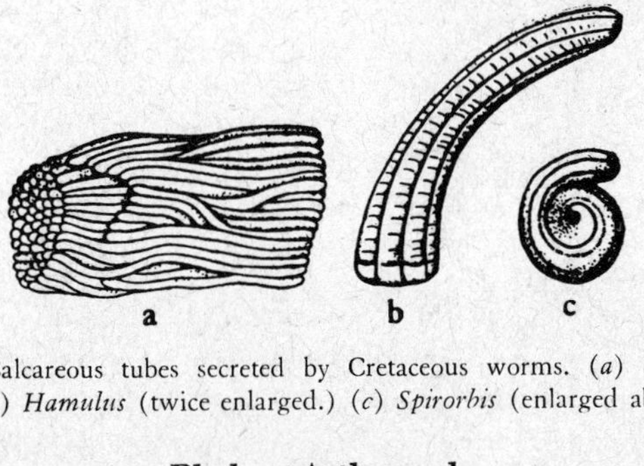

FIG. 126.—Calcareous tubes secreted by Cretaceous worms. (*a*) *Serpula* (about actual size.) (*b*) *Hamulus* (twice enlarged.) (*c*) *Spirorbis* (enlarged about 15 times.)

Phylum Arthropoda

The Arthropoda (Greek *arthron,* joint + *pous, podos,* foot) are a group of highly specialized invertebrates which, numerically, make up the largest subdivision of the animal kingdom. Arthropods vary greatly in size and shape and include such common forms as the crayfishes, crabs, spiders, scorpions, millipedes, centipedes, insects, and the extinct trilobites.

The typical arthropod body is segmented, bilaterally symmetrical, and covered by a chitinous exoskeleton which, in some forms, contains calcium carbonate. Locomotion is by means of jointed appendages which often include legs with pincers. As arthropods grow they keep shedding their exoskeletons until maturity; thus an arthropod might shed several external skeletons capable of fossilization. This process of *ecdysis* explains why many fossil arthropods consist of parts of the body rather than a complete specimen.

Arthropods have become successfully adapted to a wide variety of environments and live on land, in water, and in the air. They are of great importance in nature today, but, in spite of their long geologic history (Cambrian to Recent), only a few forms are important as fossils. These include the classes Trilobita (extinct trilobites), Merostomata (extinct eurypterids), and Ostracoda (ostracodes).

Subphylum Trilobitomorpha

(Greek *tri,* three + *lobos,* lobe + *ate,* possessing + *morphe,* shape)

This subphylum, deriving its name from the typical three-lobed appearance of its members, includes the extinct trilobites and a few lesser-known animals of little importance as fossils. They were most abundant during Paleozoic time.

Class Trilobita (Greek *tri,* three + *lobos,* lobe + *ate,* possessing). The trilobites are extinct, exclusively marine arthropods which derive their name from the typical three-lobed appearance of their bodies. Two long grooves, running from the head to the tail of the animal, divide the body into three distinct segments. This three-lobed feature is usually more distinct on the *thorax,* or middle portion of the body (Fig. 127). The lobe running down the center of the trilobite is called the *central,* or *axial,* lobe; the lobes on either side of the axial lobe are known as the *pleural,* or *lateral,* lobes (Fig. 127).

The body of the trilobite was encased in a chitinous exoskeleton, the top part of which was very thick and known as the *carapace.* It is this part that is usually preserved.

The trilobite is divided into three segments from front to back. The anterior, or head, segment is called the *cephalon;* the *compound eyes* are located on each side of this segment. The central portion of the cephalon is known as the *glabella.* The part of the body behind the cephalon is the *thorax,* which consists of from two to twenty-nine segments, these being joined—in certain of the forms—in such a manner as to enable the animal to roll up like the modern sow bug. Many trilobites are found in this enrolled position (Figs. 127-*b* and 128-5*b*). The posterior, or tail part, of the body is known as the *pygidium,* which is usually composed of several segments fused together. Trilobites assumed a wide variety of shapes and sizes; they were adapted to swimming, crawling, and burrowing.

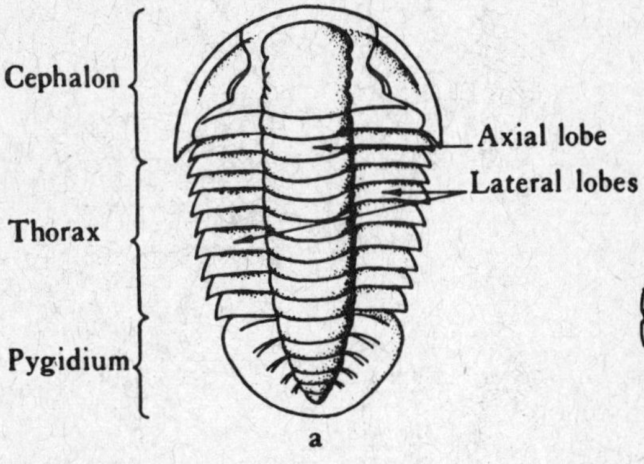

FIG. 127.—Morphology and principal parts of trilobites. (By permission from *Texas Fossils* by W. H. Matthews III, Bureau of Economic Geology, University of Texas, Austin.)

The trilobites first appeared in the Early Cambrian, at which time they were abundant and well developed. While no evidence of Precambrian trilobites has been reported, it appears certain that the group originated at some time prior to the Cambrian. They attained their maximum development during Cambrian and Ordovician time and were probably the dominant form of life during these periods. They diminished in numbers during later Paleozoic time, becoming extinct at the end of the Permian. Some typical trilobites may be seen in Fig. 128.

Subphylum Chelicerata

(Greek *chele,* claw + *keras, keratos,* horn + *ate,* possessing)

The chelicerates are arthropods characterized by the lack of antennae and possession of some appendages which bear pincers. Included are the scorpions, spiders, mites, "king crabs," and the extinct eurypterids. Although some classifications recognize three classes, the Chelicerata is usually divided into two classes: the Merostomata ("king crabs" and extinct eurypterids) and the Arachnida (scorpions, spiders, and ticks). Only the order Eurypterida of class Merostomata is of paleontological significance.

Class Merostomata (Greek *meros,* thigh + *stoma, stomatos,* mouth). This is an ancient group of aquatic chelicerates which breathe by means

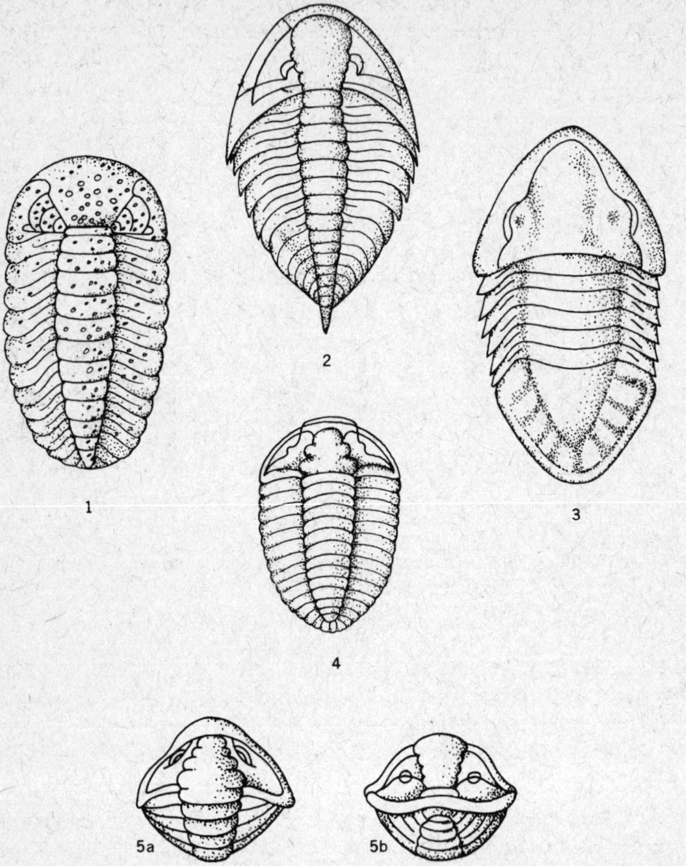

FIG. 128.—Typical trilobites. (*1*) *Phacops* (Devonian). (*2*) *Dalmanites* (Silurian). (*3*) *Isotelus* (Ordovician). (*4*) *Calymene* (Silurian). (*5 a, b*) *Flexicalymene* (Ordovician), specimen shown in enrolled position (all forms about one half actual size). (Adapted from *Guide for Beginning Fossil Hunters* by C. W. Collinson, Illinois State Geological Survey.)

of gills. The merostomes first appeared in the Cambrian, flourished during the Mesozoic, but thereafter declined to their minor position in present-day fauna, Several orders of Merostomata have been recognized, including the Eurypterida.

ORDER EURYPTERIDA (Greek *eurys,* broad + *pteron,* wing). The eurypterids (the name refers to the characteristic broad, winglike appendages, Figs. 129 and 42) are extinct aquatic arthropods. The living animal was scorpionlike and commonly possessed a stinger and a poison gland. In addition, some forms had large claws. At least one species attained a length of more than six feet. Eurypterid remains have been found in rocks ranging from Lower Ordovician to Permian. They are most common, however, in certain Silurian and Devonian formations.

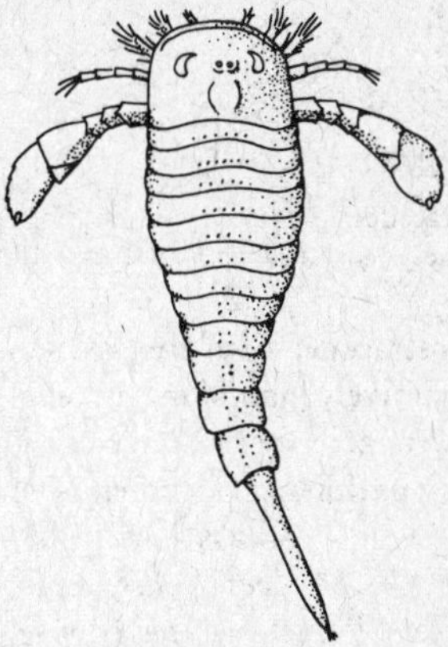

Fig. 129.—A typical eurypterid (about one fourth actual size).

Subphylum Crustacea

(Latin *crusta,* shell + *aceous,* pertaining to)

Crustaceans are characterized by a "crust," or hard exoskeleton which may be preserved as a fossil. This group includes such commonly known form as crayfishes, shrimps, crabs, ostracodes, and barnacles. They range from Cambrian to Recent, forming an important part of the animal life of today. Several classes of crustaceans are recognized, most of which have left a relatively meager fossil record. Nevertheless, the members of the class Ostracoda comprise an important group of crustacean fossils.

Class Ostracoda (Greek *ostrakodes,* testaceous—"shell-bearing"). The ostracodes are a group of small bivalved, aquatic crustaceans which form a very important group of fossils. Externally, ostracodes have the appearance of small clams (Fig. 130), but a typical joint-legged, segmented arthropod body is enclosed in the external shell.

These minute fossils are especially valuable as guide fossils for the petroleum geologist. Because of their small size they are little damaged by the mechanics of oil-well drilling and are brought to the surface with the well cuttings. They are then studied and identified with the aid of a low-power microscope. The amateur collector interested in microfossils will find the ostracodes a varied group worthy of study. Fossil ostracodes are abundant in many marls, shales, and limestones. The fossils may be freed from the surrounding rocks by soaking the material and passing it through a fine-mesh screen (see "Preparation of Microfossils," p. 62).

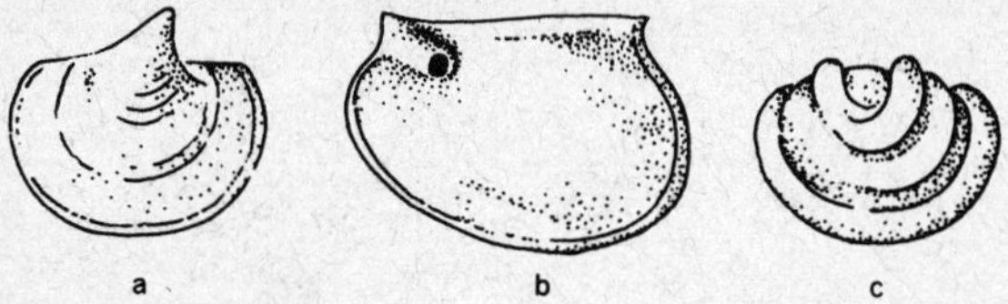

FIG. 130.—Paleozoic ostracodes. (*a*) *Paraechmina* (enlarged 30 times). (*b*) *Leperditia* (enlarged about 4 times). (*c*) *Zygobolba* (enlarged about 10 times.)

The earliest known ostracodes first appeared in the Early Ordovician, and they have been relatively abundant in every subsequent geologic period. Paleozoic and Cenozoic species have been studied in considerable detail and are especially useful for purposes of stratigraphic correlation.

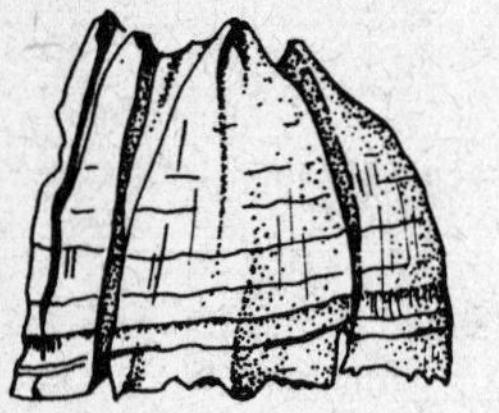

FIG. 131.—*Balanus,* a barnacle (about actual size).

Class Cirripedia (Latin *cirrus,* a curl + *pes, pedis,* foot). Members of this class include the barnacles, a group of degenerate marine arthropods. Externally the barnacles bear little resemblance to other arthropods (Fig. 131), but the soft parts of the creature resemble the typical arthropod animal.

The barnacles have a calcareous exoskeleton consisting of numerous plates. Most barnacles are encrusting organisms, but some (the "gooseneck" barnacles) attach themselves by means of a muscular stalk. Others have become adapted to a parasitic existence.

Barnacles are a common element in modern marine faunas, but are not of paleontological significance. However, certain Cenozoic rocks locally contain numerous fossil barnacles. Some of the Miocene forms grew to almost a foot in length, and isolated skeletal plates of smaller barnacles are sometimes found as microfossils in well cuttings. The geologic range of the Cirripedia is generally considered to be Ordovician to Recent. However, the fossil record is scant and there is some question as to whether the Ordovician forms are true barnacles. Some scientists are of the opinion that the group did not originate until as late as Pennsylvanian time.

Class Malacostraca (Greek *malakos,* soft + *ostrakon,* shell). These familiar arthropods include such forms as the crayfishes, lobsters, shrimps, crabs, and sow bugs, or pill bugs. Most malacostracans have relatively soft shells and are not commonly preserved as fossils. However, certain forms (for example, the crabs) have strong calcareous shells capable of fossilization (Fig. 132), and fragments of these are occasionally found fossilized. In addition, certain Jurassic forms (Fig. 133) have been preserved in the fine-grained limestones of Solnhofen, Bavaria (p. 9).

The geologic range of the Malacostraca, like that of the barnacles, is not definitely agreed upon. The range most commonly quoted is (?)

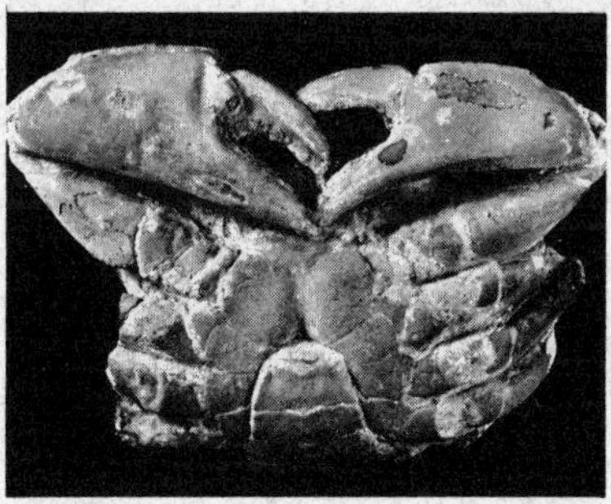

FIG. 132.—*Archaeogeryon peruviana,* a fossil crab from the Oligocene of Patagonia (about one half natural size). (Courtesy of Dr. G. A. Cooper, U. S. National Museum.)

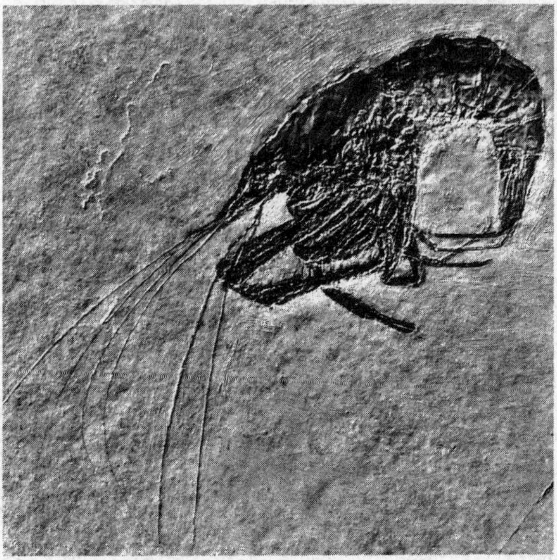

Courtesy of Ward's Natural Science Establishment

FIG. 133.—*Aegar tipularis,* a fossil shrimp from Solnhofen limestone (Upper Jurassic) of Germany (about actual size).

Cambrian or Ordovician to Recent. Other authorities are of the opinion that the earliest malacostracans appeared as late as Devonian time.

Subphylum Insecta

(Latin *in,* into + *secare,* to cut)

Insects are the most abundant and one of the most diverse groups of creatures in the animal kingdom. Though many interesting fossil insects have been described, they are not found in proportion to their past abundance because such fragile forms are rarely preserved. Most fossil insects have been preserved in amber (Fig. 6) or in very fine-grained limestones or shales (Fig. 134).

Fig. 134.—Fossil ant from Miocene beds near Florissant, Colorado (reduced about one half). (Courtesy of Dr. G. A. Cooper, U. S. National Museum.)

Some of the Pennsylvanian insects, which were extremely abundant, grew to be quite large. Dragonflies with a wingspread of as much as two feet and cockroaches three to four inches long were not uncommon. The earliest insects, a primitive wingless group, are reported from Middle Devonian rocks of Scotland. The winged insects appear first in Pennsylvanian rocks and have increased steadily in variety and numbers up to the present day.

Phylum Echinodermata (Echinoderma)

The Echinodermata (Greek *echinos,* a hedgehog, or sea urchin +

derma, skin) derive their name from the typical "spiny skin" which characterizes the phylum. The echinoderms are a large group of exclusively marine animals, including the crinoids, echinoids, sea urchins, sea cucumbers, and starfishes (Fig. 135). Most of them exhibit a marked fivefold radial symmetry.

Living echinoderms are relatively complex organisms, having well-developed nervous and digestive systems and a distinct body cavity. Locomotion is by means of *tube feet* which are part of the *water vascular* system, a well-developed hydrostatic pressure system.

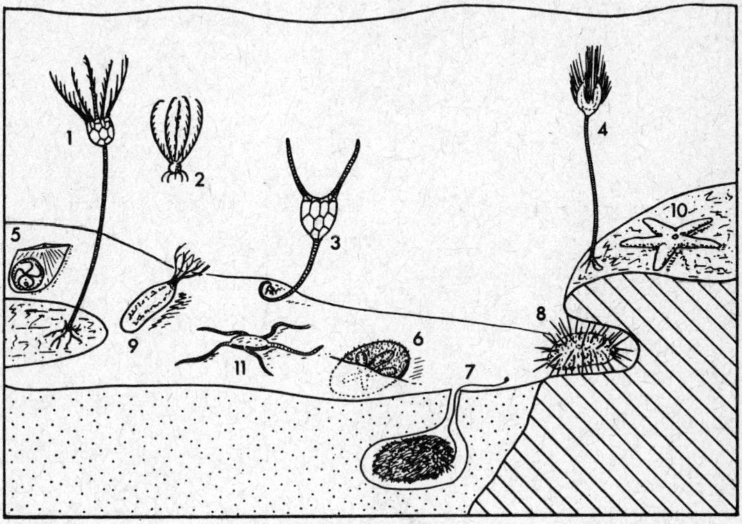

FIG. 135.—Major groups of echinoderms. (*1*) Attached crinoid. (*2*) Free-living crinoid. (*3*) Cystoid. (*4*) Blastoid. (*5*) Edrioasteroid. (*6*) Sand dollar. (*7*) Heart urchin. (*8*) Sea urchin. (*9*) Holothurian. (*10*) Starfish. (*11*) Ophiuroid. (By permission from *Invertebrate Paleontology* by W. H. Easton, Harper & Brothers, 1960.)

The typical echinoderm has a skeleton composed of numerous calcareous *plates* which are intricately fitted together and covered by a leathery outer skin (the *integument*). The echinoderm body often exhibits a typical star-shaped form, but some types may be heart-shaped, biscuit-shaped, or cucumber-shaped.

Members of this phylum range from Cambrian to Recent and are abundant as fossils in marine formations throughout the world.

The phylum Echinodermata has been divided into two subphyla: the Pelmatozoa, or attached forms, which include the classes Cystoidea, Blastoidea, and Crinoidea; and the Eleutherozoa, or free-moving forms, which include classes Stelleroidea, Echinoidea, and Holothuroidea.

Subphylum Pelmatozoa

(Greek *pelmatos,* stalk + *zoion,* animal)

These are echinoderms which are more or less permanently attached to the bottom of the sea by means of a stem, or stalk, which is composed of slightly movable disklike segments (Fig. 136).

Pelmatozoans range from Cambrian to Recent in age. Their fossilized remains are particularly abundant in Paleozoic rocks. The subphylum has been divided into several classes but only three of these—the

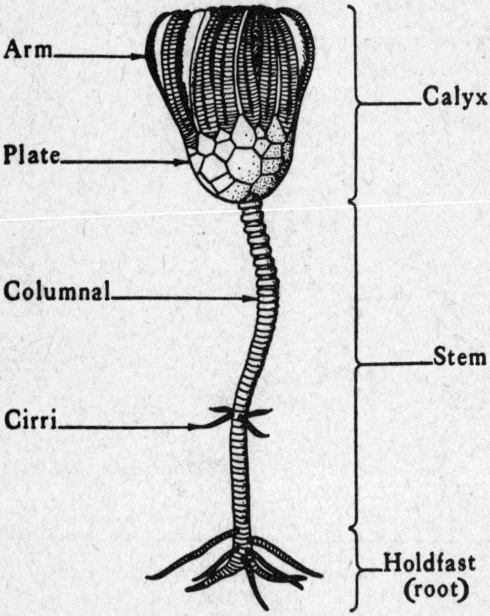

Fig. 136.—Typical modern crinoid, or "sea lily," showing principal parts. (By permission from *Texas Fossils* by W. H. Matthews III, Bureau of Economic Geology, University of Texas, Austin.)

Cystoidea, Blastoidea, and Crinoidea—are discussed here. With the exception of the Crinoidea, all of the attached echinoderms are extinct.

Class Cystoidea (Greek *kystis,* bladder + *eidos,* resemblance). The cystoids are an extinct group of primitive attached echinoderms which were relatively common during early Paleozoic time. The typical cystoid has a somewhat globular or saclike *calyx* (the main body skeleton) composed of numerous irregularly arranged calcareous plates (Fig. 137-*a*). The mouth, located on the top of the calyx, is surrounded by several small *arms.* The plates composing the calyx are usually perforated by pores or slits which were probably used in excretion or respiration. The calyx was attached to the substratum by means of a short *stem.* Although normally rare as fossils, cystoids range from Early Cambrian to Late Devonian and were especially numerous during Ordovician and Silurian times.

Class Blastoidea (Greek *blastos,* sprout or "bud" + *eidos,* resemblance). The "sea buds," as blastoids are often called, are extinct short-stemmed echinoderms with a small, symmetrical, globular to budlike calyx (Figs. 137-*b* and 49). The animal had no arms; the calyx consists of typically thirteen prominent regularly arranged plates placed

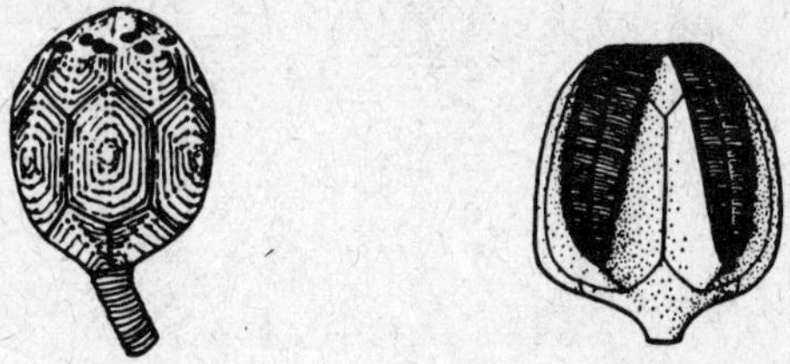

a b

Fig. 137.—Two extinct attached echinoderms. (*a*) *Caryocrinites* (Silurian). (*b*) *Pentremites* (Mississippian). (Both about natural size).

in a typical five-sided pattern. The mouth is located in the center of the calyx and is surrounded by five openings called *spiracles.* Five distinct *ambulacral* or *food grooves* radiate outward from the mouth.

The blastoids first appeared in the Ordovician period and were extinct by the end of Permian time. They are particularly abundant in certain Mississipian formations and in some areas aıe called "fossil acorns."

Some paleontologists place the cystoids and blastoids within a single class, but it appears that enough differences exist between these two forms to justify placing them in separate classes.

Class Crinoidea (Greek *krinon,* lily + *eidos,* resemblance). The crinoids, or "sea lilies," derive their name from their flowerlike appearance. The stemmed calyx with its numerous branching arms resembles a long-stemmed flower (Figs. 136 and 48). Certain of the living crinoids are stemless and free-living in the adult stage and are attached only during the earlier phases of their development. These are called "feather stars." Living stemmed echinoderms are much less abundant than the "feather stars." They are quite similar to earlier attached types and provide much information that can be used in studying fossil forms.

The crinoid skeleton is composed of three main parts: the *stem,* the *calyx,* and the *arms* (Fig. 136). The crinoid calyx is typically cup-shaped; five grooves radiate out from its center. These grooves continue outward along the complexly segmented arms and are used as channels to convey food to the mouth. The calyx encloses the animal's soft parts.

It is composed of numerous symmetrically arranged calcareous plates. The arms, which are usually branched, help in gathering food.

The crinoid stem, attached to the base of the calyx, serves for purposes of support and attachment. It consists of a relatively long flexible stalk

FIG. 138.—Crinoids embedded in Mississippian limestones of Iowa (*Dichocrinus inornatus,* reduced about one half.) (Courtesy of Dr. G. A. Cooper, U. S. National Museum.)

composed of numerous calcareous disklike or buttonlike segments or *columnals* (Figs. 136 and 139), each of which contains a round or star-shaped perforation in its center (Fig. 139). These openings comprise

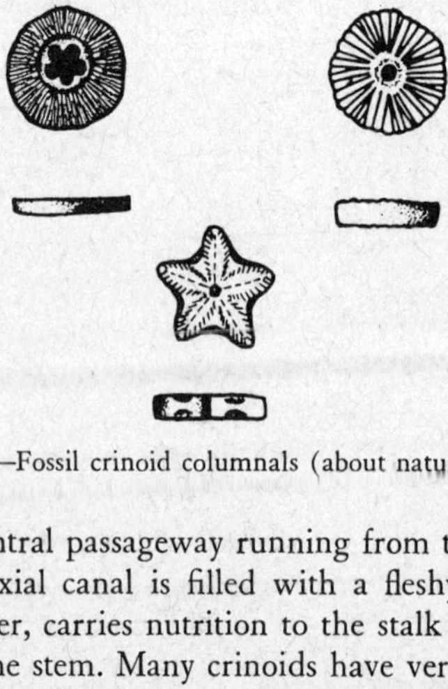

FIG. 139.—Fossil crinoid columnals (about natural size)

the *axial canal*—a central passageway running from the calyx to the root system. In life the axial canal is filled with a fleshy tube which holds the columnals together, carries nutrition to the stalk and roots, and provides flexibility for the stem. Many crinoids have very long stalks (some are as much as fifty feet long), and when the animal dies the columnals become separated and are scattered about on the ocean floor. Paleozoic limestones often contain such great numbers of crinoid columnals that they are referred to as *crinoidal limestones* (Fig. 140). Projections known as *cirri* (singular *cirrus*) frequently extend from the sides of the stalk (Fig. 136); their presence is indicated by small raised areas on the stem.

The stalk is attached to the sea floor or some other object by means of a root system called the *holdfast.* This structure commonly possesses numerous small *rootlets* which branch out into the surrounding sediments (Fig. 136). In this manner the crinoid animal is firmly attached to the bottom of the sea. The holdfast is composed of columnals and cirri

FIG. 140.—Crinoidal limestone of Pennsylvanian age. This rock is composed primarily of segments of crinoid stems.

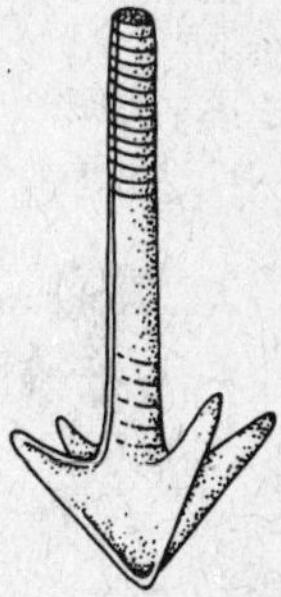

FIG. 141.—*Ancyrocrinus,* a Devonian crinoid. The stem of this crinoid terminated in a structure resembling a grappling hook (about natural size).

and is similar in construction to the stem. Most Recent attached crinoids are cemented to some solid object, such as a rock or shell. Certain fossil crinoids had specialized means of attachment. Some species had the stem terminating in a coil; this was probably looped around some stationary object. On another form, *Ancyrocrinus,* the stem terminated into a structure resembling a grappling hook or grapnel, with several spurs (Fig. 141) which were used to engage objects on the sea floor. Other forms had relatively large bulbous or floatlike roots.

Crinoids, like most echinoderms, are *gregarious* animals—that is, they commonly live together in large assemblages. Because of this tendency, their remains are commonly found concentrated in relatively small areas where they occur in great numbers. Most fossil crinoids occur as stem fragments, as the more fragile calyx and root system are much less likely to be preserved.

The earliest known crinoids have been found in rocks of Ordovician age; their remains are particularly abundant in Paleozoic rocks. Crinoids are living today but, as mentioned earlier, most of them are stemless free-moving "feather stars," which are much less abundant than were their stemmed Paleozoic ancestors. The stemless "feather star" type of crinoid ranges from Triassic to Recent.

Subphylum Eleutherozoa

(Greek *eleutheros,* free + *zoion,* animal)

The eleutherozoans are free-moving, bottom-dwelling echinoderms which are commonly divided into three distinct classes, all represented by forms that are living today. Stelleroidea (starfishes and "brittle stars"), Echinoidea (sea urchins and sand dollars), and Holothuroidea (sea cucumbers). Of these three classes, only the Echinoidea are important as fossils.

Class Stelleroidea (Latin *stella,* star + *eidos,* resemblance). As their name implies, these are typical star-shaped, free-moving echinoderms

Courtesy of Dr. W. W. Newcomb, Jr., Texas Memorial Museum

FIG. 142.—Cretaceous starfishes (*Austinaster mccarteri*) embedded in limestone. Note fountain pen for size comparison.

with body divided into a *central disk* and radiating *arms* (Figs. 135–*10,* 135–*11,* and 142). Members of this class, including the starfishes and the "serpent stars" or "brittle stars," clearly exhibit the characteristic fivefold symmetry of the phylum. The class Stelleroidea is commonly divided into the subclasses Asteroidea and Ophiuroidea.

SUBCLASS ASTEROIDEA (Greek *aster,* star + *eidos,* resemblance). This subclass contains the starfishes which, though not common as fossils, illustrate well the typical echinoderm characteristics (Figs. 135–*10* and 142). Fossil starfishes are found sparsely throughout the geologic column, but well-preserved specimens are quite rare. Asteroids range from Ordovician to Recent.

Subclass Ophiuroidea (Greek *ophis,* serpent + *oura,* tail + *eidos,* resemblance). The ophiuroids are echinoderms with a well-defined central disk and five long, slender, whiplike or serpentlike arms (Figs. 48 and 135–*11*). They have been called "brittle stars" because of their ability to shed their arms when they are disturbed. Their long, slender, snakelike arms have caused them also to be called "serpent stars." Ophiuroids range from Ordovician to Recent, but because of the delicate nature of their bodies they are seldom found as fossils.

Class Echinoidea (Greek *echinos,* a hedgehog, or sea urchin + *eidos,* resemblance). The echinoids are free-moving echinoderms with disk-shaped, heart-shaped, biscuit-shaped, or globular exoskeletons (Figs. 135–*6,* 135–*7,* and 135–*8*). Modern representatives of this group include the familiar sea urchins, heart urchins, and sand dollars.

The echinoid *test* is composed of many intricately fitting calcareous *plates* (Fig. 143–*1*) arranged in more or less radial rows. The exterior of the test is typically covered with large numbers of movable *spines* (Fig. 143–*2*) varying greatly in size. These spines are of some aid in locomotion, support the skeleton of the animal, and provide a measure of protection from enemies.

The echinoid does not have free arms, but the *ambulacral* or *food grooves* on the shell exhibit the typical five-rayed, starlike echinoderm pattern.

The oldest known echinoids have been recorded from rocks of Ordovician age, but it was not until the Mesozoic era that the group began to flourish. They were especially abundant during the Cretaceous and have been abundant and varied from that time until the present. Mesozoic and Cenozoic echinoids are commonly found in an excellent state of preservation. Certain of these species are valuable as Cretaceous and Tertiary guide fossils. The fossil record of echinoids also contains disassociated plates and spines, many of which are small enough to be of some value as microfossils.

Class Holothuroidea (Greek *holothourion,* a sort of water polyp + *eidos,* resemblance). Members of this class, commonly called sea cucumbers, have a rather elongate, leathery, saclike, sausage- or cucumber-shaped body and bear little resemblance to other members of the phylum Echinodermata (Fig. 135–*9*). However, a study of the internal structures and evolutionary development of the holothuroids indicates that they should be classified as members of this phylum.

The sea cucumbers do not have a well-defined skeleton; instead, the body is supported by many small, disconnected, calcareous plates or rods called *ossicles* or *sclerites* (or, less commonly, *spicules*) (Fig. 144). These minute, variably shaped structures are embedded in the tough, flexible body wall of the holothurian and may be preserved as fossils. Such remains are locally abundant in certain formations, but because of their

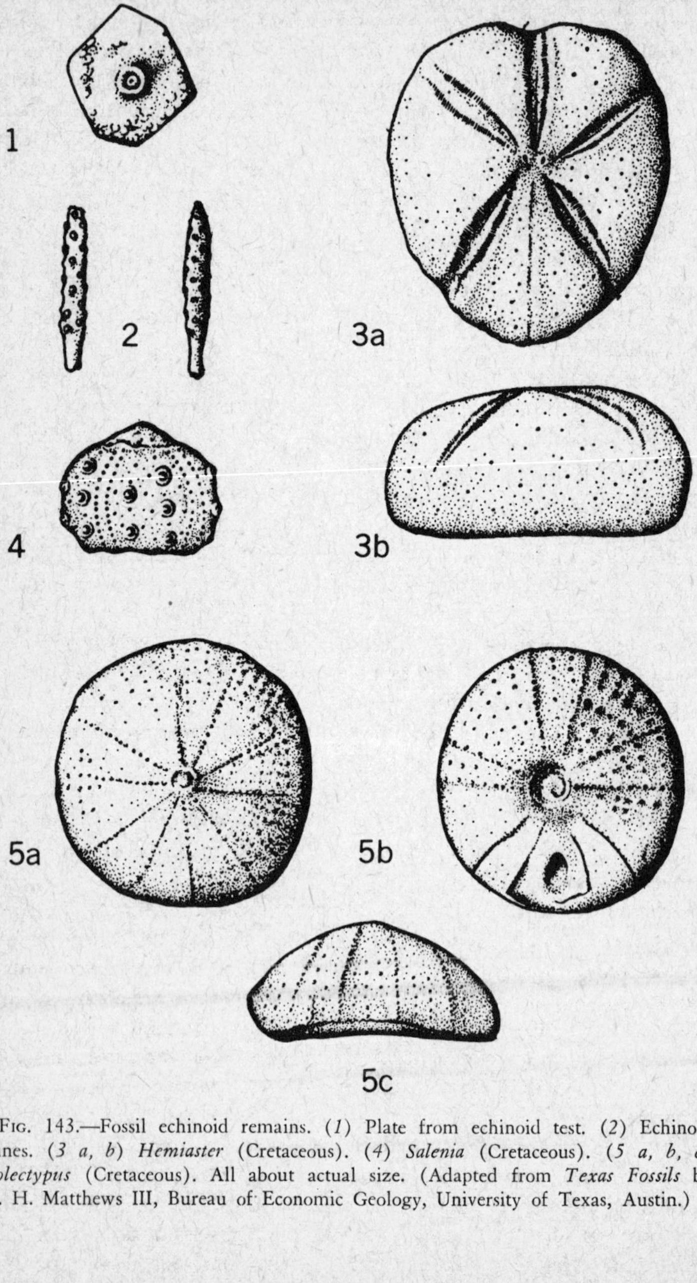

Fig. 143.—Fossil echinoid remains. (*1*) Plate from echinoid test. (*2*) Echinoid spines. (*3 a, b*) *Hemiaster* (Cretaceous). (*4*) *Salenia* (Cretaceous). (*5 a, b, c*) *Holectypus* (Cretaceous). All about actual size. (Adapted from *Texas Fossils* by W. H. Matthews III, Bureau of Economic Geology, University of Texas, Austin.)

small size, scattered occurrence, and problems in classification, this group is of little use to most paleontologists.

The oldest unquestioned holothurian remains are sclerites from rocks of Mississippian age. However, impressions of soft-bodied animals believed to be sea cucumbers have been reported from the Middle Cambrian Burgess Shale of Canada (see p. 17). In addition, structures believed to represent holothurian sclerites have been collected from Middle

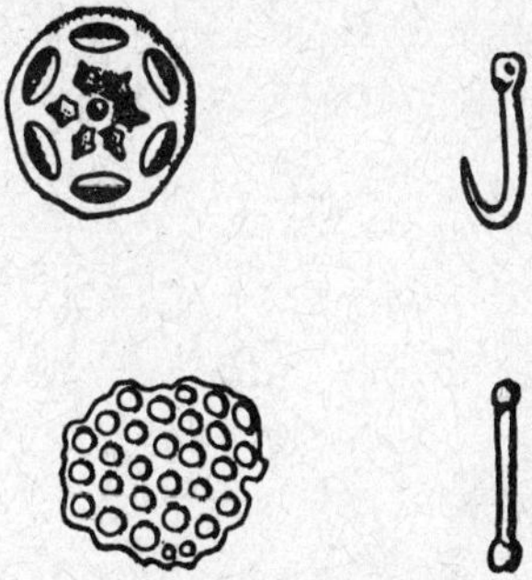

FIG. 144.—Holothurian sclerites (greatly enlarged). These small hard parts are scattered throughout the skin of a sea cucumber.

Ordovician strata. Although some thousand living species have been described, holothurians constitute a minor part of our present-day marine faunas.

Phylum Chordata

The chordates (Latin *chorda,* cord + *ate* possessing), the most advanced of all animals, are characterized by the presence of a well-developed nervous system and a body supported by a bony or cartilaginous *notochord* and/or *spinal column.* In the higher chordates (the vertebrates) the notochord is normally replaced by bone, but in the lower chordates (for example, the graptolites) it remains in a cartilaginous condition.

The phylum Chordata is divided into several subphyla, but only two are of paleontological significance. These are the Hemichordata, composed of primitive chordates (including the graptolites, which are important as fossils), and the Vertebrata, which includes all animals with backbones.

Subphylum Hemichordata

(Greek *hemi,* half + Latin *chorda,* cord + *ate* possessing)

The hemichordates are characterized by a well-defined notochord which runs the length of the body, but they do not possess a true backbone. Several classes of hemichordates are recognized, but only one, the Graptolithina (or Graptozoa), is of paleontological importance.

Class Graptolithina (Graptozoa) (Greek *graptos,* inscribed, painted + *lithos,* stone + *ina,* likeness). The graptolites ("written-stones," so called because of their similarity to pencil marks on the rocks) are an important group of extinct, colonial Lower Paleozoic fossils (Fig. 145). They are characterized by a chitinous exoskeleton which housed the animal in a small cuplike enclosure called the *theca.* These cups are attached to single or branching stalks called *stipes* which in some forms led a fixed existence attached to rocks, seaweeds, or other foreign objects.

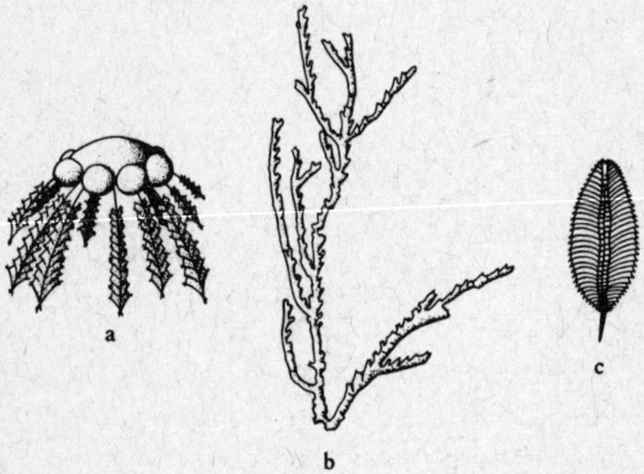

FIG. 145.—Lower Paleozoic graptolites. (*a*) *Diplograptus.* (*b*) *Dendrograptus.* (*c*) *Phyllograptus.* All enlarged about two times. (By permission from *Texas Fossils* by W. H. Matthews III, Bureau of Economic Geology, University of Texas, Austin.)

The stipes of unattached graptolites grew on floats (Fig. 145-*a*), and these floating forms attained wide geographic distribution. It is also possible that some of the attached forms became fixed to floating objects, such as seaweed, and were scattered in this way.

The proper position of graptolites in the animal kingdom has long been uncertain. Most classifications have placed them in phylum Coelenterata. As coelenterates they were assigned, at various times, to the classes Hydrozoa, Scyphozoa, and Graptozoa. In addition, they were classified as bryozoans by certain of the early paleontologists. In accordance with the latest, and most commonly accepted, graptolite classification, these forms are here considered to be an extinct group of hemichordates. This classification is based upon recent research in which uncompressed graptolite remains were dissolved out of chert and studied in great detail. Information derived from these relatively undistorted specimens indicates a much higher degree of body organization than was previously suspected. As a result of these studies, most paleontologists now consider graptolites to be some form of primitive chordate.

The chitinous graptolite exoskeleton is commonly preserved as a flattened carbon residue; their remains may be locally abundant along bedding surfaces of certain black or dark gray shales.

Graptolites are known from rocks that range from Cambrian to Mississipian. They are among the most important guide fossils for Ordovician and Silurian rocks.

Subphylum Vertebrata

(Latin *vertebratus,* jointed, vertebrated)

The vertebrates are the most advanced of all chordates. They are characterized by a skull and a bony or cartilaginous internal skeleton (*endoskeleton*), with a vertebral column of bone or cartilage. The skeleton also includes two pairs of appendages such as fins, legs, or wings. The classification here adopted recognizes two superclasses: the Pisces, including the fishes and their relatives; and the Tetrapoda, consisting principally of animals with four feet.

Though it is not likely that you will find many vertebrate remains, the major types of fossil vertebrates are briefly reviewed to give you some understanding of these important animals. Among this group are giant fishes, primitive amphibians, and an amazing variety of dinosaurs and other extinct reptiles. Included also are such unusual mammals as the giant ground sloths, saber-tooth cats (or "tigers"), mammoths and mastodons—all of which are now extinct. The remains of these, and of numerous other interesting prehistoric vertebrates, may be seen in the fossil exhibits of many American museums (a list of some of these museums may be found on p. 317). Often these exhibits are accompanied by paintings, sketches, or murals (for example, Fig. 165) which depict the scientific restoration of the animal's soft parts and show how the animal is believed to have appeared when it was living. Some of the larger museums also have life-sized models (for example, Figs. 67 and 169) of certain of the extinct vertebrates.

Superclass Pisces

(Latin *piscis,* fish)

Members of this superclass, commonly called fishes, are the simplest and most numerous of all vertebrates. The fishes are aquatic, free-moving, and *cold-blooded* (their blood maintains the temperature of the surrounding water); they breathe primarily by means of gills. However, some forms (the lungfishes) breathe by means of a lung developed from the swim bladder (a gas-filled sac which adds buoyancy to the fish). Most paleontologists believe that the lungfishes cast some light on the evolution of the fishes into primitive amphibians.

Recent fish classifications recognize four major classes: the Agnatha (primitive jawless fishes), Placodermi (armored fishes with primitive jaws), Chondrichthyes (jawed fishes with skeletons of cartilage, and Osteichthyes (jawed fishes with bony skeletons).

Class Agnatha (*Cyclostomata*) (Greek *a,* without + *gnathos,* jaw). Fishes belonging to this class are primitive, jawless, and represented by the living lampreys and hagfishes. The most familiar living member of the Agnatha is the lamprey—an elongated, eel-like parasitic animal. The lamprey attaches itself to living fishes by means of a round, sucking funnel lined with teeth. This organ is used to rasp a hole in the skin of the fish, and its blood is sucked out of the opening. Lampreys live in both salt and fresh water.

The first agnaths were protected by bony armor on the front part of their bodies (Fig. 146). These primitive fishes, called *ostracoderms*

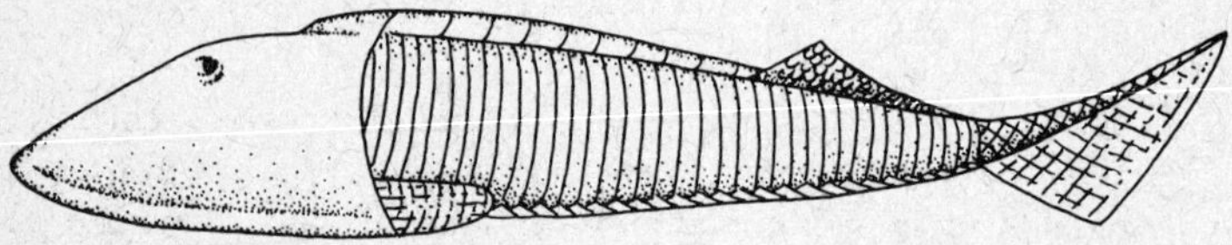

FIG. 146.—Restoration of an ostracoderm, a primitive jawless fish (*Cephalaspis* from the Silurian of England; about one third actual size).

(Greek *ostrakon,* shell + *derma,* skin), are the earliest recorded fishes and, in addition, appear to be the first known vertebrate animals. The ostracoderms appeared first in the Late Ordovician, increased in numbers during Silurian time, and were extinct by the end of the Devonian period. Fragments of the teeth, spines, and bony armor plates of these primitive fishes are abundant in certain Devonian rocks.

Class Placodermi (Greek *plax, plakos,* a flat, round plate + *derma,* skin). These extinct jaw-bearing, armored fishes were more advanced than the ostracoderms (Fig. 147). This class includes the large sharklike *arthrodires,* which were heavily armored and had large, powerful jaws and jointed necks. Some of them grew to be as much as thirty feet in length (Fig. 147).

The geologic range of placoderms is from Late Silurian to Permian. They are believed to have been the dominant vertebrates of the Devonian period.

Class Chondrichthyes (Greek *chondros,* cartilage + *ichthys,* fish). This class includes such modern forms as the sharks, rays, and skates. Abundant in today's marine waters, they are characterized by skeletons composed of cartilage and the absence of a swim bladder. The earliest known representatives of this class are reported from rocks of Devonian age. They have been prevalent up to the present time. Shark teeth (Fig.

FIG. 147.—Joint-necked arthrodire, *Dinichthys*, about thirty feet long. Restoration above, skull below (note man for size comparison). (Reprinted with permission from R. A. Stirton, *Time, Life, and Man*, copyright, 1959, John Wiley & Sons, Inc.)

148) are relatively common fossils in certain Mesozoic and Cenozoic formations and are usually found in an excellent state of preservation.

Class Osteichthyes (Greek *osteon,* bone + *ichthys,* fish). The Osteichthyes includes the true bony fish, the most highly developed and abundant of all fish. They possess an internal bony skeleton, well-developed jaws, a swim bladder, and, typically, an external covering of

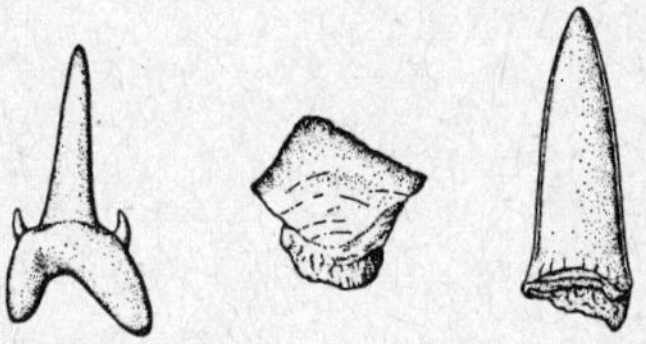

FIG. 148.—Sharks' teeth from the Upper Cretaceous of Texas (about actual size).

overlapping scales. During their long geologic history the bony fish have become adapted to both fresh-water and marine environments. They include such forms as the trout, perch, eels, sea horses, and lungfish.

Also included in this class are a primitive group of fish called *crossopterygians* (Greek *krossi,* fringe + *pteryg,* wing or fin + *ian,* related to). These were very abundant in Devonian time and are believed to be the ancestors of the air-breathing amphibians. These unusual fish were once believed to have been extinct since the end of the Cretaceous period, more than 60 million years ago. Then, in 1938, off the coast of South

Africa, a five-foot *coelacanth* (a member of one of the suborders of order Crossopterygia) was dredged up by a trawler. Since then several other specimens, all belonging to the genus *Latimeria* (Fig. 149), have been caught. These specimens have been most useful in providing us with additional information about a group known previously only as fossils.

The modern lungfish belong to the order Dipnoi (Greek *di,* two + *pneo,* to breathe.) These primitive fish, which are now found only in Australia, South America, and Africa, breathe by means of gills, as well

Courtesy of American Museum of Natural History

FIG. 149.—Cast of a coelacanth fish. These primitive fishes were once believed to have been extinct since the end of Cretaceous time. Then, in 1938, one was caught off the coast of Madagascar. Since that time several have been caught and studied in detail.

as by lungs which have been developed from the swim bladder. Although not abundant as fossils, the remains of these specialized fish have added much to present knowledge concerning the development of certain of the higher vertebrates.

The remains of bony fish have been found in rocks ranging from Middle Devonian to Recent in age. Fish fossils are commonly found in the form of teeth (Fig. 148), vertebrae, scales, and an occasional well-preserved skeleton (Figs. 62 and 150).

One of the most interesting fossils ever discovered is the well-preserved skeleton of a fourteen-foot tarponlike fish collected from Cretaceous rocks in western Kansas. The remains of this fish, named *Portheus,* contain the skeleton of *Gillicus,* another tarponlike fish (Fig. 150). *Portheus* must have swallowed the six-foot *Gillicus* shortly before dying and falling to the sea bottom to become fossilized. It has been suggested that

Portheus may have died as a result of internal injuries inflicted by the death struggles of *Gillicus*. This unusual "fossil in a fossil" may be seen in the museum of Fort Hays Kansas State College Museum at Hays, Kansas.

Fig. 150.—The mounted skeleton of the giant Cretaceous fish, *Portheus molossus,* which measures fourteen feet in length. Enclosed between the ribs of the larger fish is a smaller fish, *Gillicus arcuatus,* which measures six feet in length, indicating that the last meal of *Portheus* was more than he could digest. This unique "fossil within a fossil" was found in the Smoky Hill chalk rock of the Upper Cretaceous of Gove County, Kansas. This remarkable specimen was collected and prepared by Mr. George F. Sternberg, Curator, Museum of Geology and Paleontology, Fort Hays Kansas State College Museum, Hays, Kansas. (Photograph by E. C. Almquist, print courtesy of Fort Hays Kansas State College Museum.)

Conodonts. The *conodonts* (Latin *conus,* cone + Greek *odons,* tooth) are small amber-colored, toothlike fossils (Fig. 151) which are believed to represent the hard parts of some type of extinct fish; they may be teeth or internal supports for soft tissues such as the gills. Although geologists

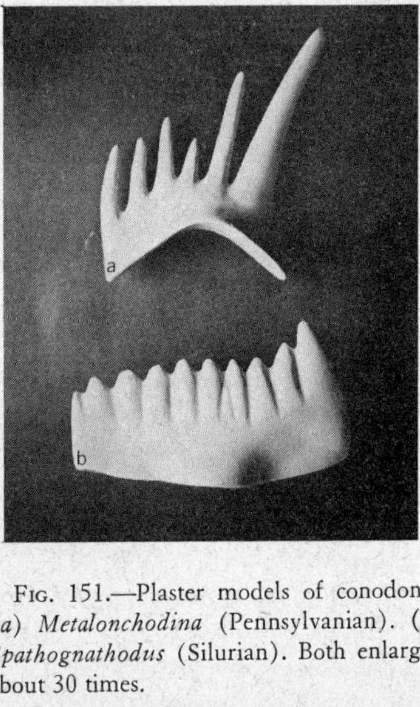

Fig. 151.—Plaster models of conodonts. (*a*) *Metalonchodina* (Pennsylvanian). (*b*) *Spathognathodus* (Silurian). Both enlarged about 30 times.

know little about the origin of these strange fossils, they are of considerable value in micropaleontology. Conodonts, like the previously mentioned spongelike organisms, stromatoporoids, and graptolites, are specimens of doubtful zoological affinities. In the past they have been assigned to such diverse groups as the gastropods, worms, crustaceans, cephalopods, and fishes.

Conodonts first appeared in the Early Ordovician and apparently lived until Triassic time. However, most conodonts were extinct at the end of the Permian period; some scientists believe that conodonts reported from Triassic and Cretaceous rocks are Paleozoic forms that were redeposited with the Mesozoic sediments. Certain species of Ordovician, Devonian, and Mississippian conodonts are especially useful as guide fossils.

Superclass Tetrapoda

(Greek *tetra,* four + *pous, podos,* foot)

Tetrapods, the most advanced chordates, are typified by the presence of lungs, a three- or four-chambered heart, and paired appendages. Included here are the classes Amphibia (frogs, toads, and salamanders), Reptilia (lizards, snakes, turtles, and the extinct dinosaurs), Aves (birds), and Mammalia (dogs, whales, elephants, men, etc.).

Class Amphibia (Greek *amphi,* of both kinds + *bios,* life). The amphibians were the earliest developed four-legged animals and are represented by such living forms as the toads, frogs, and salamanders. They are cold-blooded animals that breathe primarily through lungs and spend most of their life on land. However, during their early stages of development they live in water, where they breathe by means of gills.

Amphibians apparently evolved from crossopterygian fishes in the Late Devonian; they were relatively abundant in the Pennsylvanian, Permian, and Triassic periods. These early forms, varied in shape and size (Figs. 52–4 and 152) and have left an interesting fossil record. Most of the Paleozoic amphibians were *labyrinthodonts* (Greek *labyrinthos,* a tortuous passage + *odons,* tooth), so called because of the complex infolding of the teeth. They have also been called *stegocephalians* (Greek *stegos,* roof or covering + *kephale,* head) amphibians because of their heavily roofed skulls. An interesting feature of these early amphibians is an opening on the top of the skull behind and midway between the eyes. This opening marks the position of the so-called *pineal eye,* which is seen as a vestigial structure in all of the higher vertebrates, including man (see p. 157).

Labyrinthodont amphibians are known from both their footprints and their skeletons and provide much information about the origin of early terrestrial vertebrates.

The geologic range for class Amphibia is from Late Devonian to Recent. The labyrinthodonts appeared first in Devonian time, were abundant in Late Pennsylvanian and Early Permian time, and finally disappeared near the end of the Triassic period.

Class Reptilia (Latin *reptilis,* creeping). The reptiles are cold-blooded, lung-breathing animals with paired five-toed appendages, and a horny or scaly body-covering. Some reptiles (the snakes) have lost all external evidence of four appendages; they move by creeping or slithering. Reptiles have become adapted to permanent life on land and need not rely on an aquatic environment.

The reptiles were apparently derived from labyrinthodont amphibians at some time during the Pennsylvanian period, and steadily increased in kinds and numbers to become the dominant land animals of the Mesozoic era—the "Age of Reptiles." Mesozoic reptiles not only lived successfully on the land but also adapted themselves to life in the sea and in the air. The best-known and most important reptilian fossils are the extinct

FIG. 152.—*Eryops,* a Permian labyrinthodont amphibian, was about six feet long.

dinosaurs which were very numerous during the Mesozoic (see p. 126).

The amateur fossil-collector might possibly discover the remains of dinosaurs or other vertebrates, but in general his collection will be composed largely of invertebrates. The collection of vertebrates requires special care and techniques, which have been discussed in Chapter VI (p. 65). Amateur paleontologists who find interesting and well-preserved accumulations of fossil bones should not disturb them, for fossils of this type are very easily damaged or destroyed. In case you find them, you should notify the nearest natural history museum, college, or university, or the state geological survey in your state capital. If possible send a small portion of bone to show what you have found. In sending material of this sort follow the suggestions outlined on pp. 73–74 and remember that the exact location where the fossils were found is most important. Also include any other information that you might be able to furnish—the geologic age of the rocks, type of rocks the remains were found in, etc. (see p. 73).

The reptiles have been divided into numerous subclasses, orders, and other units of classification, but only the more important groups will be discussed here.

ORDER COTYLOSAURIA (Greek *kotyles,* cup-shaped + *sauros,* lizard). The cotylosaurs were a group of primitive reptiles which, although retaining some amphibian characteristics, become adapted to an exclusively terrestrial existence. Believed to be the forerunners of all reptiles, cotylosaurs range from Pennsylvanian to Triassic. They were especially numerous in the Pennsylvanian and Permian periods. *Seymouria* (Fig. 153) is one of the earlier members of this order.

ORDER CHELONIA (Greek *chelone,* tortoise). This order includes the turtles and tortoises—reptiles in which the body is more or less com-

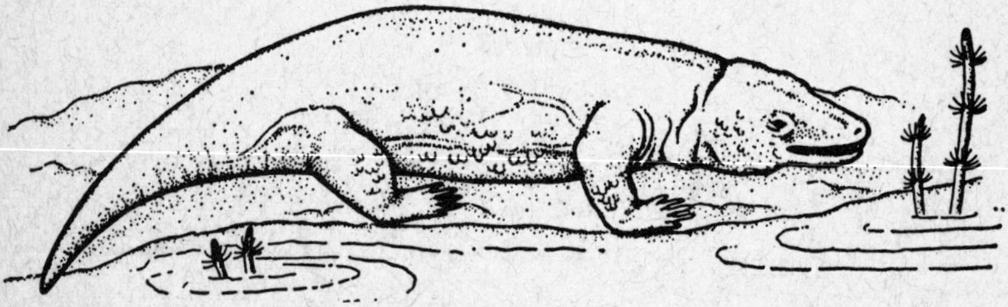

FIG. 153.—Restoration of *Seymouria,* a Permian cotylosaur from Texas. This primitive creature was about two and one half feet long and possessed both reptilian and amphibian characteristics. It is believed to be a connecting link between these two groups of animals. (By permission from *Texas Fossils* by W. H. Matthews III, Bureau of Economic Geology, University of Texas, Austin.)

pletely enclosed by bony plates or a *carapace.* Although large numbers of reptiles became extinct at the end of the Mesozoic, the chelonians were probably able to survive because of their protective shells. They are definitely known as fossils from Middle or Upper Triassic rocks, despite fragmentary evidence of a turtlelike reptile from the Permian of South Africa.

Chelonians have become adapted to a wide variety of environments and have been one of the most successful groups of animals ever to inhabit the earth. Numerous fossil turtles and tortoises have been described. One such fossil, *Archelon* (Greek *archon,* ruler + *chelone,* tortoise) is known as the "King of the Turtles." This huge animal lived during the Cretaceous period; some individuals grew to be as much as twelve feet long and weighed almost three tons. However, marine forms (Fig. 61) were not the only chelonians to attain large size, for certain land tortoises of the Tertiary were three to four feet long (Fig. 69).

ORDER PELYCOSAURIA (Greek *pelyx, pelycos,* a basin + *sauros,* lizard).

The pelycosaurs derive their name from the basinlike shape of their pelvis. They comprise a group of early mammal-like reptiles which lived only during Late Pennsylvanian and Permian times.

The pelycosaurs are normally characterized by a large fin- or sail-like structure on the back, supported by elongated spines of the vertebral column (Figs. 52 and 154). A study of their teeth indicates that both herbivorous and carnivorous forms existed.

ORDER THERAPSIDA (Greek, *ther,* wild beast + *apsis, apsidos,* loop). The therapsids (also called *theromorphs*) were a group of mammal-like rep-

Courtesy of U. S. National Museum

FIG. 154.—*Edaphosaurus,* a "sail-lizard" from Permian strata exposed in Archer County, Texas. Some of these unusual reptiles attained a length of as much as ten to twelve feet.

tiles that appeared after the above mentioned pelycosaurs and were more varied. Therapsids were well adapted for a terrestrial existence; they range from Middle Permian to Triassic. In their relatively short stay on earth these animals developed numerous mammal-like characteristics, as evidenced by the structure of the skull, vertebrae, and teeth. Furthermore, therapsids appear to be the "missing link" between the reptiles and the mammals. *Cynognathus* is a typical carnivorous therapsid which attained the size of a large dog. Although the remains of these primitive reptiles are not especially abundant as fossils, study of them has provided much valuable information about the origin of mammals. They have been found in large numbers in South Africa, and have also been found in Brazil, China, Russia, the United States, and elsewhere.

ORDER ICHTHYOSAURIA (Greek *ichthys,* fish + *sauros,* lizard). The ichthyosaurs ("fish-lizards") are extinct, short-necked, marine reptiles that were fishlike in appearance (Figs. 53 and 155). They looked somewhat like a shark but probably more closely resembled porpoises or dolphins. Despite this superficial resemblance to the shark or porpoise, the muscles, bone, brain, heart, and lungs clearly indicate a true reptile. The average ichthyosaur reached a length of ten or fifteen feet, but specimens thirty feet long have been reported. Their large eyes and sharp, well-developed teeth strongly suggest that ichthyosaurs were beasts of prey. Although they are believed to have been essentially fish-eating reptiles, their fossilized stomach contents show that some of them also ate cephalopods.

These aquatic forms probably could not leave the water and, unlike the typical reptiles, were not able to lay eggs on land. This problem was

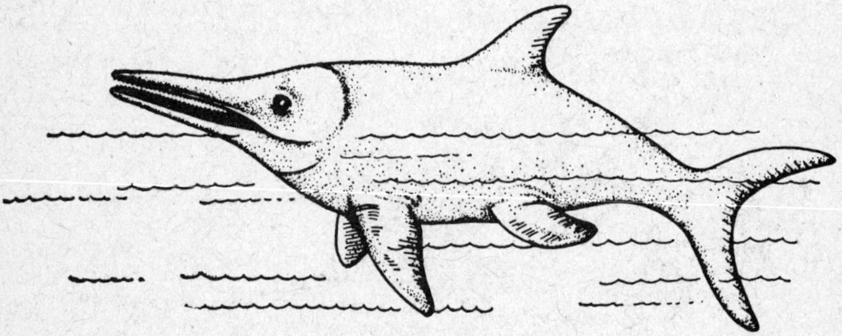

FIG. 155.—Restoration of an ichthyosaur. These fishlike reptiles were abundant during the Cretaceous period. Some were as much as 10 feet long. (By permission from *Texas Fossils* by W. H. Matthews III, Bureau of Economic Geology, University of Texas, Austin.)

apparently solved by the mother's keeping the eggs within her body until they hatched. After the eggs had hatched, the young emerged alive. Animals which reproduce in this manner are said to be *ovoviviparous;* some modern lizards and snakes have this type of reproduction. The ovoviviparous nature of ichthyosaurs is borne out by the remains of a perfectly preserved *Ichthyosaurus* collected near Stuttgart, Germany. This specimen has the remains of five unborn young in the body cavity, and two more are located near the pelvic region. It appears that at least one little ichthyosaur was being born at the time the mother died. The unborn ichthyosaurs are relatively large, and their well-developed paddles and spinal column suggest that they would have been able to swim as soon as they were born.

The ichthyosaurs first appeared in the Middle Triassic and were extinct by the end of the Cretaceous.

ORDER SAUROPTERYGIA (Greek *sauros,* lizard + *pteryx,* fin). The sauropterygians were an order of marine reptiles ranging from Triassic to

Late Cretaceous. Three suborders are usually recognized but only one, the Plesiosauria, will be discussed here.

Suborder Plesiosauria (Greek *plesios,* near + *sauros,* lizard). These were sea-dwelling reptiles with broad, relatively short, turtlelike bodies paddlelike flippers, and, commonly, long necks and tails (Figs. 53 and 156). These reptiles were not as streamlined nor as well-equipped for swimming as the ichthyosaurs or mosasaurs (see p. 128). Some Cretaceous plesiosaurs had serpentlike necks almost twice as long as their bodies, which were useful in darting from side to side to catch fish and other

Fig. 156.—Restoration of a plesiosaur, another of the large marine reptiles of the Mesozoic. Certain species attained lengths up to forty feet.

small animals for food. One of the largest specimens yet discovered was approximately forty feet long with a neck eighteen feet in length.

Plesiosaurs, like ichthyosaurs, were probably ovoviviparous, for skeletons containing embryos have been found. Gastroliths ("stomach-stones") commonly accompany the skeletons of plesiosaurs. One-half bushel of gastroliths (some as much as four inches in diameter) were collected with the skeleton of one plesiosaur. A study of bones and shells in that part of skeleton where the stomach would have been indicates that plesiosaurs ate ammonoids, fish, and flying reptiles.

Both long-necked and short-necked forms are known; and some species, particularly those with exceptionally long necks, grew to be quite long. The fact that some of the Cretaceous plesiosaurs were unusually large was indicated by the discovery of one Australian form which had a skull more than nine feet long, the largest reptile skull ever discovered.

The plesiosaurs first appeared during Triassic time, increased in size and numbers during the Cretaceous period, and became extinct at the end of that period.

ORDER RHYNCHOCEPHALIA (Greek *rhynchos,* beak + *kephalon,* head). The "beak-headed" reptiles first appeared in the Early Triassic, at which time they were abundant, attaining almost world-wide distribution. Today the group is represented by a single species, *Sphenodon punctatum,* which is more commonly called the tuatara. This primitive lizardlike reptile remained virtually unchanged for approximately 180 million years, becoming so important to zoology that it is now protected by law.

Found only on a few small islands off the coast of New Zealand, the tuatara ranges from two to three feet in length; it has a loose-fitting scaly skin and a fringed crust extending from the head to the tip of the tail. One theory suggests that the tuatara has survived as a result of its migration from Australia to remote islands where it faces a minimum of competition from other animals and that its burrowing habit removes it still further from competition.

ORDER SQUAMATA (Latin *squamatus,* scaly). These are the most common, diverse, and abundant of all reptiles. The order includes the lizards and snakes, which are characterized by an external covering of horny scales.

Lizards are four-footed, elongated, sprawling reptiles which range from a few inches to six or eight feet (the huge monitor lizards of Africa) in length. The lizards are an older and more primitive group than the snakes. The first lizardlike reptiles apparently appeared in the Triassic, and the first true lizards in the Early Cretaceous. The latter underwent rapid evolution during Mesozoic and Cenozoic time, as evidenced by the fact that more than thirty-eight hundred species of modern lizards have been discovered.

Snakes are descendants of the lizards—in fact, little more than highly specialized lizards which have lost their legs. Unfortunately, however, the fossil record of this group is poor and much of what we know about fossil snakes is based on inferred relationships with modern forms.

The only members of the Squamata that are of paleontological significance are the marine lizards known as *mosasaurs* (Latin, *Mosa,* the river Meuse, where the first mosasaurs were discovered, + *sauros,* lizard). These were huge lizards which became completely adapted to life in the water. *Tylosaurus* (Figs. 61 and 157), a typical mosasaur, was as large as a small whale, some individuals measuring as much as thirty feet in length.

Mosasaurs had long flexible bodies, powerful tails, and paddle-shaped limbs. Their great gaping jaws were filled with numerous sharp recurved teeth. The head was elongated and pointed; and the tail, laterally compressed, resembled that of an alligator or crocodile. Mosasaurs lived only during Late Cretaceous time, but were apparently relatively abundant during their short (geologically speaking) life span.

ORDER THECODONTIA (Greek *theke,* case or box + *odons,* tooth). The thecodonts are an extinct group of reptiles that somewhat resembled the rhynchocephalians. Many were terrestrial, though some lived in streams and lakes. Thecodonts were limited in both numbers and varieties, and

FIG. 157.—Restoration of Cretaceous mosasaur. These great sea-going lizards must have been excellent swimmers and vicious predators. Some grew to be as much as thirty feet long. (By permission from *Texas Fossils* by W. H. Matthews III, Bureau of Economic Geology, University of Texas, Austin.)

were confined to a single geologic period—the Triassic. In spite of their short stay on earth, these primitive forms are of considerable evolutionary importance and are believed to have given rise to the crocodiles, dinosaurs, and pterosaurs (flying reptiles).

Suborder Phytosauria (Greek *phyton,* plant + *sauros,* lizard). Phytosaurs are thecodont reptiles which ranged from six to twenty-five feet in length. They derive their name ("plant lizards") from the fact that they were originally believed to be plant-eating reptiles. However, the structure of the teeth and jaws clearly indicates that these reptiles were carnivores.

The typical phytosaur had an elongate, slender snout equipped with many sharp teeth, and the body was protected by an armor of heavy bony plates (Fig. 158). They resembled the crocodiles both in appearance and in their mode of life, but this similarity is only superficial, for the phytosaurs and crocodiles represent two distinct groups of reptiles. Phytosaurs are exclusively Triassic and were the dominant reptiles of this period.

ORDER CROCODILIA (Latin *crocodilus,* crocodile). This order includes the crocodiles, alligators, and gavials (a rather large but harmless crocodilian living in northern India). The crocodilians adapted themselves

FIG. 158.—Restoration of a phytosaur, a common reptile of Triassic time. Certain of these animals grew to be twenty feet long, and although they resembled the modern crocodiles these two animals are not closely related. (By permission from *Texas Fossils* by W. H. Matthews III, Bureau of Economic Geology, University of Texas, Austin.)

to the same type habitat that was occupied by the phytosaurs which preceded them. Members of this order are the largest living reptiles (some are as much as twenty feet long) and have persisted from the Triassic to the present with but slight change in form or habits (Fig. 166–2).

Crocodilians are primitive animals closely related to the dinosaurs. Although they are not common as fossils, a study of this group has provided some information as to what the living dinosaurs may have been like.

The Crocodilia were more abundant and widely distributed during the Cretaceous and Cenozoic than they are today. One such crocodile (*Phobosuchus*) represents the remains of the largest crocodile yet discovered (Fig. 159). *Phobosuchus* probably had an over-all length of forty to fifty feet; its broad massive skull was six feet long and possessed exceptionally strong jaws. The remains of this huge animal were collected from exposures of Upper Cretaceous rocks along the Rio Grande River, in Big Bend National Park, in western Texas.

ORDER PTEROSAURIA (Greek *pteron,* wing + *sauros,* lizard). The pterosaurs, or "winged-lizards," were Mesozoic reptiles with batlike wings which were attached to the sides of the body and supported by a greatly

Courtesy of American Museum of Natural History

FIG. 159.—Dr. Brown, R. T. Bird, and Dr. Schaikjer with the skull of *Phobosuchus,* an extinct crocodile, collected from Cretaceous strata in Big Bend National Park in western Texas. Compare with the skull of crocodile in the foreground. When alive, this great reptile was probably fifty feet long.

elongated fourth finger (Fig. 160). The remaining fingers, small and hooklike, were probably used for grasping limbs, etc. These reptiles were well adapted to life in the air; their light-weight bodies and wide, skin-covered wings enabled them to soar or glide for great distances. They had thin, hollow bones, and in their flight probably resembled a bat more than a bird.

Pterosaurs were of many different shapes and sizes. Those of the Jurassic were quite small, some not so large as a sparrow. *Rhamphorhynchus,* a typical Jurassic form about two feet long, had a very long tail with a rudderlike expansion on the end. The beaklike jaws were well supplied

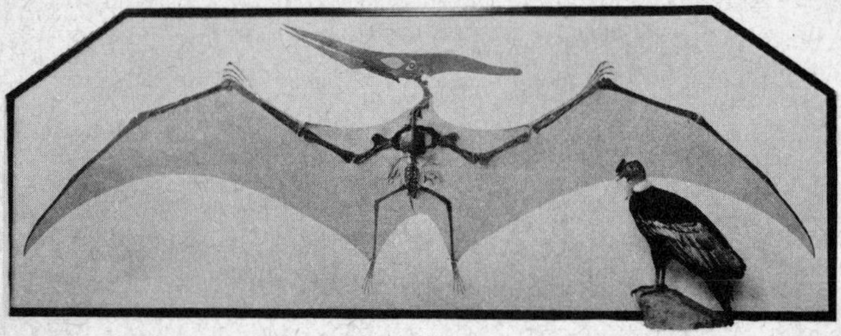

Courtesy of American Museum of Natural History

FIG. 160.—*Pteranodon,* one of the great flying reptiles of Cretaceous time. The largest living bird, the condor, is shown at the right. The body outline has been restored to show how the wings were attached to the body. This specimen is from the Upper Cretaceous chalk beds of Kansas.

with long, pointed teeth (Figs. 54 and 161). Cretaceous pterosaurs were normally larger; some forms such as *Pteranodon* (Figs. 61 and 160), attained a wingspread of as much as twenty-five feet and had a skull over thirty inches long. *Pteranodon* had a long toothless beak, and the back of the skull extended into a triangular crest. The tail of this species was quite short.

There has been considerable speculation on the life habits of the pterosaurs. Most scientists believe that they were carnivores, feeding on fish and insects. They must have been awkward on the ground and, like the bats, may have rested by hanging to cliffs and trees with their claws and wings.

The earliest known pterosaur remains were found in rocks of Early Jurassic age, and the group was extinct by the end of the Cretaceous.

ORDER SAURISCHIA (Greek *sauros,* lizard + *ischion,* hip). The Saurischia are one of two orders of extinct reptiles usually referred to by the collective term "dinosaurs" (Greek *deinos,* terrible + *sauros* lizard). These "terrible lizards," like most of the other "—saurs" that we have discussed, were actually not lizards at all. The dinosaurs comprise a distinctive group of reptiles that were prominent in Mesozoic life for more than 100 million years and are among the most interesting fossils known. Dinosaurs ranged from as little as one foot to more than eighty-five feet in length, and from a few pounds to perhaps forty-five tons in weight. Some were carnivorous, but the majority were herbivorous. Some were *bipedal* (walked on their hind-legs), while others were *quadrupedal* (walked on all fours).

Saurischian dinosaurs are characterized by a hip-girdle similar to that of modern lizards. Members of this order originated in Triassic time and persisted until the end of the Cretaceous. Lizard-hipped dinosaurs are divided into two rather specialized orders: the Theropoda (carnivo-

FIG. 161.—*Rhamphorhynchus,* a Late Jurassic pterosaur (flying reptile). The largest pterosaur of this type was about two and one half feet long. (By permission from *Prehistoric Animals* by J. Augusta and Z. Burian, Spring Books, London.)

rous bipedal dinosaurs that varied greatly in size) and the Sauropoda (herbivorous, quadrupedal, usually gigantic, dinosaurs).

Suborder Theropoda (Greek *ther,* wild beast + *pous, podos,* foot). The theropods walked on their birdlike hind limbs and were carnivores. Some of these dinosaurs were exceptionally large and were undoubtedly vicious beasts of prey. This assumption is borne out by such anatomical features as the small front limbs with long sharp claws adapted for

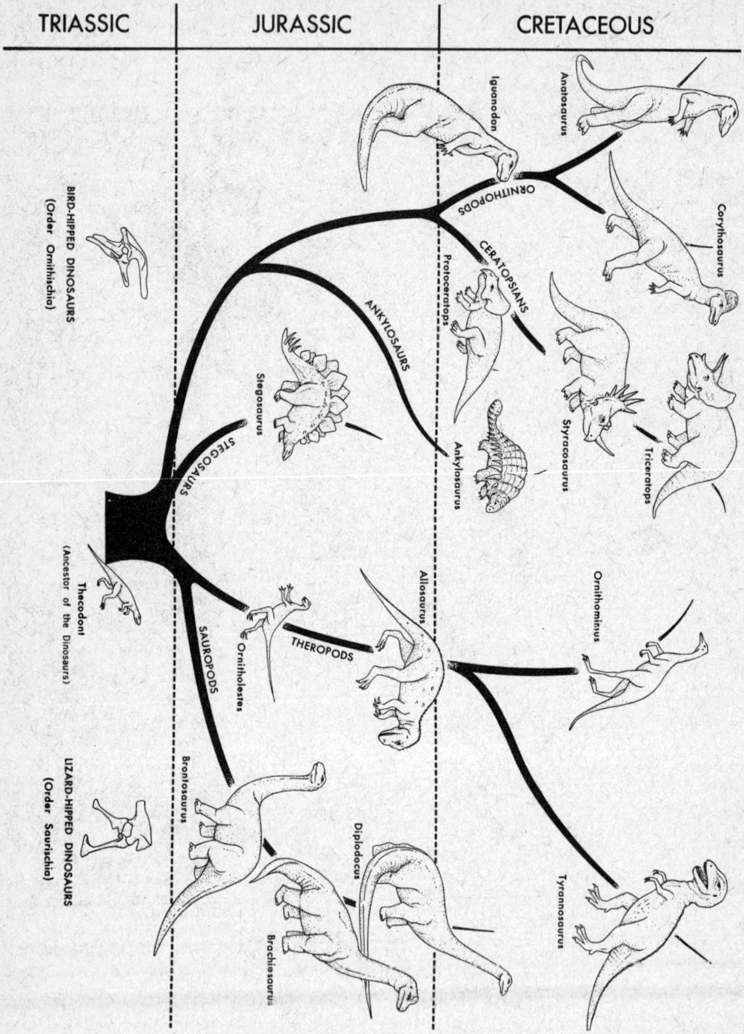

FIG. 162.—The history of the dinosaurs. The earliest (Late Triassic) dinosaurs were saurischians and were well represented by the small *Coelophysis;* they were part of the radiation of the thecodonts. The ornithischian dinosaurs early diverged as a distinct order. (By permission of Dodd, Mead & Company, from *Wonders of the Dinosaur World* by William H. Matthews III, copyright © 1963.)

tearing flesh and the large, strong jaws which were armed with numerous, sharp, daggerlike teeth (Figs. 162, 163, and 164).

Allosaurus (Fig. 164) is a typical Jurassic theropod (see p. 120), but *Tyrannosaurus rex* (Figs. 162 and 165), a Cretaceous form, is the largest and best-known reptile in this group (see p. 125). When standing on his

Courtesy of American Museum of Natural History

FIG. 163.—Skull of *Tyrannosaurus,* the largest known carnivorous dinosaur. The skull shown above is approximately four feet long (note the long sharp teeth).

hind limbs, *Tyrannosaurus* was twenty feet tall; some individuals measured fifty feet from head to tail. This great beast is believed to have been one of the most vicious animals ever to inhabit the earth. Theropod dinosaurs first appeared in the Late Triassic and became extinct at the end of the Cretaceous.

Suborder Sauropoda (Greek *sauros,* lizard + *pous, podos,* foot). The sauropods were the largest of all dinosaurs; some were more than eighty-five feet long, weighing thirty to forty tons. The largest and best-known sauropod was *Brontosaurus* of Jurassic age (Figs. 162 and 166). Most sauropods were quadrupedal, though some forms were apparently bipedal. They were primarily herbivorous reptiles which had become adapted to a semiaquatic existence and probably inhabited rivers, swamps, and lakes.

FIG. 164.—*Allosaurus.* Restoration of one of the common bipedal carnivorous dinosaurs of Jurassic time. These animals had three strong sharp claws on their forelimbs; some grew to be as much as thirty feet long. (By permission from *Texas Fossils* by W. H. Matthews III, Bureau of Economic Geology, University of Texas, Austin.)

Courtesy of Chicago Natural History Museum *C. R. Knight*

FIG. 165.—*Tyrannosaurus* (right) was a huge carnivorous dinosaur which stood almost twenty feet high. *Triceratops* (left) was a quadrupedal plant-eater characterized by its three horns and the bony frill protecting its neck. Both of these reptiles lived during the Cretaceous period.

Not only have well-preserved bones of sauropods (Fig. 166) been found, but they have also left some interesting fossil tracks (Fig. 11).

Sauropods range from Triassic to Cretaceous but were particularly well-developed and numerous in Late Jurassic time.

ORDER ORNITHISCHIA (Greek *ornis, ornithos,* bird + *ischion,* hip). The ornithischian, or bird-hipped, dinosaurs had a hip-girdle similar to that of a bird. These herbivorous reptiles were quite varied in form and size and appear to have been more highly developed than the saurischians. The Ornithischia is divided into four suborders: The Ornithopoda (duck-billed dinosaurs), Stegosauria (plate-bearing dinosaurs), Ankylosauria (armored dinosaurs), and Ceratopsia (horned dinosaurs).

Courtesy of Chicago Natural History Museum *C. R. Knight*

FIG. 166.—*Brontosaurus* (*1*), a huge plant-eating dinosaur of the Jurassic period. This semiaquatic reptile attained a length of about seventy feet and an estimated weight of thirty tons. Crocodilian reptiles (*2*) may be seen in the left foreground.

FIG. 167.—Excavating for dinosaur bones. The larger bone is the femur of a large sauropod. The smaller bone (in circle) is a "finger" bone of a small *Allosaurus*. (Photograph courtesy of J. H. Madsen, Jr., Geology Museum, University of Utah.)

Suborder Ornithopoda (Greek *ornis, ornithos,* bird + *pous, podos,* foot). These unusual dinosaurs were the most primitive ornithischians, and range from Jurassic to Cretaceous. They were primarily bipedal semiaquatic forms, and some (like the trachodonts or duck-billed dinosaurs) were highly specialized. *Trachodon* (known also as *Anatosaurus*) (Figs. 162 and 168) is a typical duck-billed form (see also p. 126).

Courtesy of Chicago Natural History Museum *C. R. Knight*

FIG. 168.—Restoration of *Trachodon,* a typical duck-billed dinosaur of Late Cretaceous time; some were as much as twenty-five feet long.

Suborder Stegosauria (Greek *stegos,* roof or coverings + *sauros,* lizard). The stegosaurs derive their name from the heavy armor which protected their backs. They were herbivorous, quadrupedal ornithischians with large projecting plates down the back and heavy spikes on their tail. (*Stegosaurus,* of Jurrassic age (Fig. 169), the most typical of the plate-bearing forms, is described in more detail on p. 120). The stegosaurs were typically Jurassic dinosaurs which became extinct early in the Cretaceous period.

Suborder Ankylosauria (Greek *ankylos,* curved + *sauros,* lizard). The ankylosaurs were four-footed, herbivorous, Cretaceous dinosaurs with relatively flat bodies (see p. 126). The skull and back of the animal

Courtesy of U. S. National Museum

FIG. 169.—Life-size model of *Stegosaurus,* a Jurassic plated dinosaur. These herbivorous reptiles had large erect bony plates along the back. Some were as much as twenty feet long and weighed ten tons. In spite of their great size, their small heads housed a brain that weighed only about two and one-half ounces.

were protected by bony armor, while the clublike tail was armed with spikes. *Palaeoscincus* (Figs. 58 and 170), a typical ankylosaur, had large spines projecting from the sides of the body and tail. The armored spiked back and the heavy clublike tail probably provided *Palaeoscincus* with much-needed protection from the vicious predatory dinosaurs of Cretaceous time.

Suborder Ceratopsia (Greek, *keras, keratos,* horn + *opsis, opseos,* appearance). The ceratopsians, or horned, dinosaurs are another group of dinosaurs that are known only from rocks of Cretaceous age. These plant-eating dinosaurs possessed beak-like jaws, a bony neck frill which extended back from the skull, and—with some exceptions—one or more horns. *Triceratops* (Figs. 162 and 165) displays the general characteristics of this group (see p. 126).

Class Aves (Latin plural of *avis,* bird). Because of the fragile nature of their bodies, birds are not commonly found as fossils. However, some interesting and important fossil bird remains have been discovered.

The oldest known bird was found in Upper Jurassic rocks exposed in Germany. This primitive bird, named *Archaeopteryx* (Greek *archaios,* ancient + *pteryx,* wing, feather), is little more than a reptile with

FIG. 170.—*Palaeoscincus,* an armored dinosaur of Late Cretaceous time, had a heavy clublike tail and a back covered with numerous bony plates. (By permission from *Texas Fossils* by W. H. Matthews III, Bureau of Economic Geology, University of Texas, Austin.)

feathers (Figs. 54 and 171). *Archaeopteryx* is known from two relatively complete skeletons, and a few fragments and a feather of another. These remains show that this bird was about the size of a crow, had sharp teeth, a relatively long neck, a lizardlike tail, and three sharp claws on each wing. The feathers clearly indicate that *Archaeopteryx* was a bird and that it was warm-blooded. However, such characters as the teeth, skull, hip-girdle, hind limbs, and solid bone construction are wholly reptilian (Fig. 171). These unusual fossils furnish evidence of the close relationship between reptiles and birds and are among the most important paleontological discoveries that have ever been made.

The birds of the Cretaceous were more abundant and more specialized than those of the Jurassic. The structure of the skull, limbs, and bones was definitely more birdlike, but many species still retained teeth.

In addition, Cretaceous birds show considerable evidence of specialization. Some forms, such as *Hesperornis* (Fig. 172), had very small, useless wings, long jaws bearing many sharp teeth, and strong feet which were well suited for paddling. This bird, normally about three feet high and somewhat similar to the modern loon, appears to have been well adapted to swimming and diving. *Ichthyornis,* another Cretaceous bird, was smaller than *Hesperornis,* had well-developed wings, and formed habits that were probably much like those of the present-

b

Courtesy of American Museum of Natural History

FIG. 171.—*Archaeopteryx,* the earliest known bird. (*a*) Restoration from skeleton below. This bird, about the size of a modern crow, bore claws on its wings and had a reptilian tail and toothed beak. (*b*) Skeleton as discovered in fine-grained limestone in Germany (note impression of feathers on tail and wings).

day sea gulls. Much is known about these birds because of unusually well-preserved skeletons collected from Cretaceous limestones in western Kansas.

Birds of the Cenozoic closely resembled the modern birds and must have been almost as varied and abundant though they are relatively rare as fossils. Fossil ducks, vultures, owls, crows, pelicans, and penguins are among the Tertiary birds that have been described. Many of these were about the same size and had the same habits as their modern counterparts. There were exceptions, however, for one extinct species of penguin attained a height of approximately five feet—considerably taller than any of our present-day forms.

Of particular interest are the remains of the large flightless birds of the Tertiary period. One of these, *Diatryma* (Fig. 173), an Eocene form, was about seven feet tall and had strong jaws and a head almost as long as that of a horse. *Dinornis,* the largest known land bird, stood ten to twelve feet tall; its eggs were almost a foot in diameter. These birds lived in New Zealand within historic times, and are believed to have been exterminated by the natives.

Class Mammalia (Latin *mamma,* breast). The mammals are animals that are born alive (that is, do not hatch from eggs) and are fed with milk from the mother's breast. They are warm-blooded and air-breathing, have a protective covering of hair, and include the most advanced of all vertebrates. The features mentioned above are the typical mammalian characteristics, but some of them are lacking in certain mammals (for example, the egg-laying duck-billed platypus).

The first mammals, appeared in the Jurassic and were probably derived from mammal-like reptiles (see p. 121). Mammals were rare during the Mesozoic but multiplied and underwent rapid evolutionary changes during the Cenozoic. Many Cenozoic mammals grew to extremely large sizes and assumed unusual shapes (Figs. 69, 175, and 176), as had the dinosaurs that preceded them. Most of these unusual forms were doomed to early extinction, but they are well known from their fossils.

The mammals expanded rapidly during the Cenozoic, culminating with the appearance of man in the Pleistocene (see p. 164).

When found by the amateur collector, fossil mammalian bones should be treated in the same manner as the bones of other vertebrates (see p. 65).

Recent mammalian classification recognizes several subclasses and numerous orders and suborders. However, the treatment of the mammals in a book of this sort must of necessity be brief and no attempt at detailed classification is made.

Subclass Allotheria (Greek *allos,* strange, different + *ther,* a wild beast). The allotherians originated in the Jurassic period, and under-

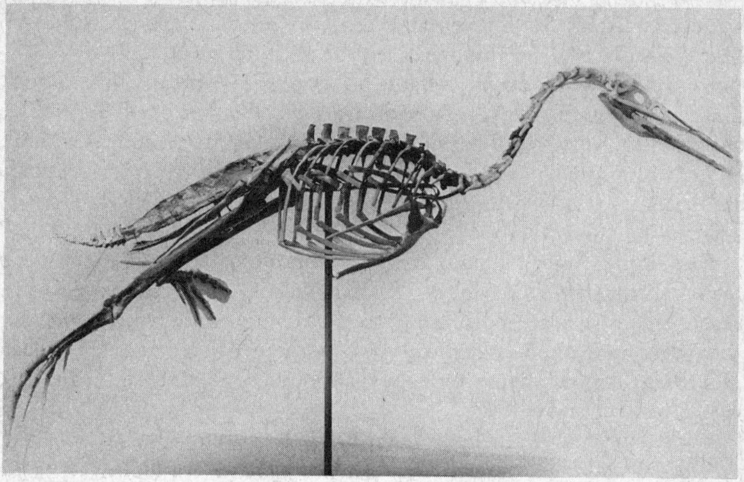

Courtesy of U. S. National Museum

Fig. 172.—*Hesperornis regalis,* an extinct toothed swimming and diving bird from the Upper Cretaceous chalk beds of Kansas. Attaining a maximum length of about six feet, this bird had lost the ability to fly but its legs and feet were well adapted to swimming.

Fig. 173.—*Diatryma,* a large flightless Eocene bird, was seven feet tall and had a skull almost a foot and one-half long. (By permission from *Prehistoric Animals* by J. Augusta and Z. Burian, Spring Books, London.)

went considerable development during Late Cretaceous and Early Eocene time. This subclass contains one order, the Multituberculata.

ORDER MULTITUBERCULATA (Latin *multus, many* + *tuber, tuberculum,* knob). The multituberculates were a group of rather small rodentlike animals that appear to be the earliest herbivorous mammals. These animals originated in the Jurassic, were probably never very numerous, and become extinct during the early part of the Eocene period.

SUBCLASS THERIA (Greek *ther,* wild beast). The therians first appeared during Jurassic time, and they constitute the largest group of mammals that are living today. Therians undergo considerable development before they are born; at birth the young typically resemble the fully developed animal. This subclass has been divided into a number of orders, but only those of some paleontological importance are discussed here.

ORDER PRIMATES (Latin *primus,* first). The primates are tree-dwelling or bipedal walking mammals, which typically have five digits (toes and fingers) provided with flat nails instead of hoofs or claws. These include the lemurs, monkeys, apes, and human beings (Fig. 77). The fossil record of the primates is discussed in Chapter XI.

ORDER EDENTATA (Latin *edentatus,* rendered toothless, from *e,* out + *dens, dentis,* tooth). These are rather primitive mammals which are represented by such living forms as the anteaters, tree sloths, and armadillos. Edentates are characterized by poorly developed teeth, or, in some species, a complete absence of teeth. These somewhat degenerate mammals, which were common in the southern part of the United States during Pliocene and Pleistocene time, have left an interesting fossil record. They range from Eocene to Recent.

One such form was *Megatherium* (Fig. 64), an extinct giant ground sloth. Certain of these huge ground sloths were as large as small elephants, with short wide heads and powerful legs, and undoubtedly weighed several tons. They were the ancestors of the present-day tree sloths of South America.

Another interesting representative of this order was the *glyptodont.* These mammals developed at about the same time as the ground sloths. They are forerunners of the armadillos. *Glyptodon* (Figs. 64 and 174) is characteristic of this group (see p. 137).

ORDER CARNIVORA (Latin *caro, carnis,* fish + *vorare,* to devour). The carnivores are fur-covered, flesh-eating mammals characterized by clawed feet and teeth adapted for tearing and cutting flesh. The earliest known carnivores were an ancient group of Paleocene animals called *creodonts* (see p. 138). These were followed by carnivores that were both more specialized and more numerous. One of the best-known cat fossils is *Smilodon,* the Pleistocene saber-toothed cat or "tiger." *Smilodon* is characterized by a massive body, short tail, and great curved, knifelike canine teeth (Fig. 65). The teeth were adapted more for stabbing than biting, and must have been most effective in bringing down prey. *Smilodon* was about the size of a modern lion.

One of the more interesting members of the dog family was *Canis dirus,* the "dire wolf." This animal, about the size of a modern timber wolf, was quite common in Pleistocene time.

FIG. 174.—Glyptodont. This unusual heavily armored Pleistocene mammal had a spiked clublike tail. (By permission from *Texas Fossils* by W. H. Matthews III, Bureau of Economic Geology, University of Texas, Austin.)

ORDER PANTODONTA (Greek *pantos,* all + *odous, odontos,* tooth). Pantodonts or *amblypods,* were ancient, hoofed, plant-eating animals. They were characterized by a heavy skeleton, short stout limbs, and blunt spreading feet. The pantodonts originated during Paleocene time and had become extinct by the end of the Oligocene.

ORDER DINOCERATA (Greek *deinos,* terrible + *keras, keratos,* horn). The members of this order are an extinct group of gigantic mammals commonly called *uintatheres. Uintatherium* (Fig. 175) was typical of this group and is well known from its fossil record (see p. 138). Uintatheres have a relatively short geologic range; their remains are confined to rocks of Paleocene and Eocene age.

ORDER PROBOSCIDEA (Greek *proboskis,* an elephant's trunk + *idea,* sort). The earliest proboscideans, the elephants and their relatives, were found in Upper Eocene rocks in Africa. They were about the size of a small modern elephant but had larger heads and shorter trunks. The development of the proboscideans is marked by an increase in size, change in tooth and skull structure, and elongation of the trunk. Some of the more interesting members of this order are described in Chapter VIII (p. 138). The *mammoths* (Figs. 66 and 176) and *mastodons* (Fig. 67) are well-known extinct proboscideans whose teeth (Fig. 177) and bones are commonly found as fossils.

FIG. 175.—*Uintatherium,* large extinct mammal of Eocene time. Standing seven feet tall at the shoulder, these animals were characterized by three pairs of blunt horns. (By permission from *Prehistoric Animals* by J. Augusta and Z. Burian, Spring Books, London.)

FIG. 176.—Woolly mammoth. Unlike modern elephants, this huge beast had a thick coat of long, coarse, black hair underlain by a thick brown wool covering. The above restoration is shown about one fiftieth natural size. (By permission from *Texas Fossils* by W. H. Matthews III, Bureau of Economic Geology, University of Texas, Austin.)

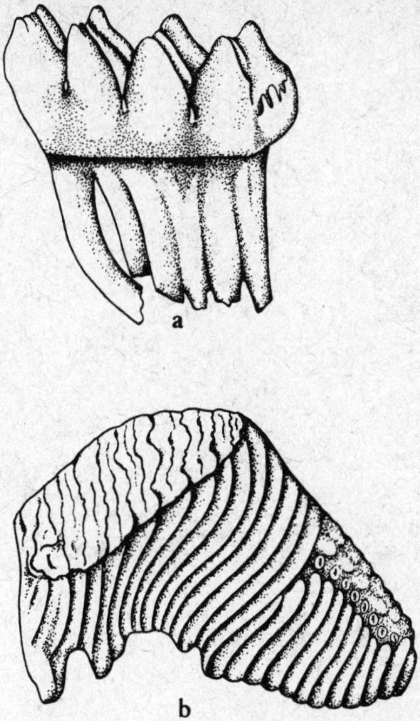

FIG. 177.—(*a*) Tooth of Pleistocene mastodon. (*b*) Tooth of Pleistocene mammoth. Both about one sixth actual size. (By permission from *Texas Fossils* by W. H. Matthews III, Bureau of Economic Geology, University of Texas, Austin.)

ORDER PERISSODACTYLA (Greek *perisso,* odd + *daktylos,* toe). The perissodactyls, or odd-toed animals, are mammals in which the central toe on each limb is greatly enlarged. They include such living forms as the horse and rhinoceros, as well as the extinct *titanotheres* (Fig. 178), *chalicotheres,* and *baluchitheres.* The extinct perissodactyls were exceedingly large and unlike any animals that are living today (see p. 140). Perissodactyls range from Early Eocene to Recent. The fossil record of the horse is especially well known (p. 43) and provides much valuable information on the evolution of these important animals (see p. 42). Fossil horse teeth (Fig. 179) and bones are sometimes found by amateur fossil-collectors.

ORDER ARTIODACTYLA (Greek *artios,* even-numbered + *daktylos,* toe). These are even-toed hoofed mammals, including such familiar forms as pigs, deer, sheep, camels, hippopotamuses, and goats. The artiodactyls comprise a large and varied group of animals, but the basic anatomical structures of the limbs and teeth clearly indicate the relationship between

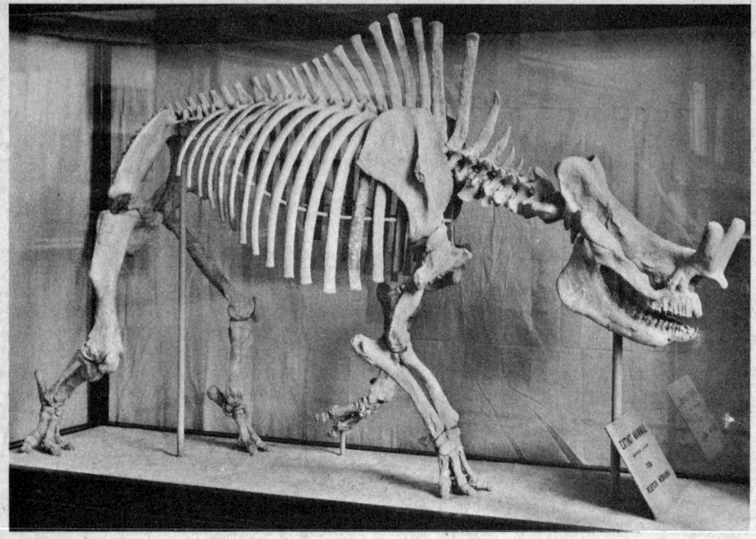

Courtesy of U. S. National Museum

FIG. 178.—Mounted skeleton of *Brontotherium,* an extinct mammal from the Oligocene of Nebraska. Note the flattened divided horn on the front of the skull.

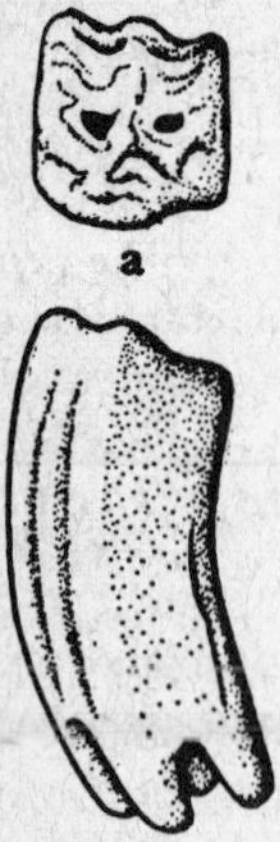

FIG. 179.—Pliocene horse tooth. Top view (*a*) and side view (*b*) of molar tooth (about one half actual size).

the different forms. They are common fossils in rocks ranging from Eocene to Pleistocene and have been found in many different parts of the world. Two of the more interesting and important members of this order are the entelodonts (Greek, *enteles,* complete + *adous, odontos,* tooth) and the camels (Greek *kamelos,* camel).

The entelodonts were giant piglike artiodactyls which lived during the Oligocene and Early Miocene epochs. They were characterized by a long heavy skull that held a relatively small brain. The face was marked by large knobs which were situated beneath the eyes and along the underside of the jaw. Although these knoblike structures were not pointed, they had the appearance of short horns (Fig. 180). Certain of these giant swine attained a height of six to seven feet at the shoulders and were almost eleven feet long. The small brain case of these animals suggests that they were much less intelligent than modern swine.

The earliest known camels were recovered from rocks of Late Eocene age. The ancestral camels were smaller than a lamb and had short limbs. As these forms evolved throughout Cenozoic time, they underwent considerable specialization of teeth and limbs and became increasingly larger. Many camels of Middle Cenozoic time had long legs which would have allowed them to browse on the leaves of trees.

FIG. 180.—Entelodont. These extinct piglike mammals lived during Oligocene and Miocene time. Some of these giant swine stood six feet high at the shoulder. (By permission from *Texas Fossils* by W. H. Matthews III, Bureau of Economic Geology, University of Texas, Austin.)

Appendix B

GLOSSARY

Aberrant: differing radically from the normal.

Aboral: away from the oral opening.

Adapical: opposite the apex, in a direction opposite the apex; oral.

Adaptation: the innate fitness of an organism for the environment in which it lives and thrives. Adaptation develops through various evolutionary mechanisms, and it becomes permanent through inheritance.

Age: any great period of time in earth history; usually of unspecified duration and characterized by certain physical conditions or organic development (for example, the "Age of Reptiles").

Agglutinate: to unite firmly, as though with glue.

Alimentary canal: the digestive tract or canal of some animals.

Amber: a hard, yellowish, transluscent, fossilized plant resin.

Ambulacrum: in the echinoderms the area composed of perforated plates.

Ammonite: ammonoid cephalopod with complexly wrinkled suture pattern; member of subclass Ammonoidea.

Amphibian: an animal capable of living on both land and water; member of class Amphibia of phylum Chordata; includes frogs, toads, and salamanders.

Anal: pertaining to the anus.

Anatomy: the structural make-up of an organism, or of its parts.

Angulated: having angles or corners.

Annulations: rings or ringlike segments.

Anterior: front or fore.

Anthropology: the over-all term for the science of the physical, social, and cultural development of human beings since their appearance on earth.

Anticline: an upfold or arch in rocks.

Anus: the terminal opening of the alimentary canal, through which waste matter is discarded from the body.

Aperture: the opening of shells, cells, etc.

Aragonite: calcium carbonate ($CaCO_3$) crystallizing in the orthorhombic system. In shells it is chalky, opaque, and less stable than calcite.

Archeo-: prefix or combining form meaning ancient; from Gr. *archaios,* ancient.

Archeozoic: the oldest known geological era; early Precambrian time.

Arcuate: arched, bent like a bow.

Arenaceous: of the texture or character of sand.

Arthropod: member of phylum Arthropoda; includes insects, spiders, crabs, shrimp, and trilobites.

Articulated: joined by interlocking processes or by teeth and sockets.

Asymmetrical: without or lacking symmetry.

Asteroid: member of subclass Asteroidea of class Stelleroidea phylum Echinodermata; includes the starfishes.

Auricle: ear.

Auriculate: having ears.

Autopore: see *Zooecium.*

Beak: in brachiopods and pelecypods the more or less pointed extremity marking the initial point of shell growth.

Bed: a tabular rock body lying essentially parallel to the surface on which it was formed; also called a layer or stratum.

Bedding plane: the dividing planes which separate individual layers or beds of sedimentary rocks.

Bidentate: having two teeth.

Bifurcating: dividing into two—forking.

Bilateral: pertaining to the two halves of a body as symmetrical and mirror images of each other.

Binomial nomenclature: system of scientific nomenclature requiring two names: the generic name and the trivial or specific name.

Biogenetic law: the principle stating that ontogeny recapitulates phylogeny: the development of the individual recapitulates, or portrays, the development of the race.

Biserial: having double series in rows.

Blastoid: stalked echinoderm with a budlike calyx usually consisting of 13 plates; member of class Blastoidea.

Brachiole: the slender armlike appendages of certain vertebrates.

Brachiopod: bivalved marine invertebrate; member of phylum Brachiopoda.

Brachium (plural—brachia): an arm.

Brackish: containing a mixture of salt and fresh waters.

Branchial: pertaining to the branchiae or gills.

Breccia: rock composed of angular or broken fragments.

Bryozoan: small, colonial, aquatic animal, usually secreting a calcareous skeleton; member of phylum Bryozoa.

Burrow: a hole in the ground, rock, wood, etc., made by certain animals for shelter or while gathering food.

Byssus: a cluster of threads secreted by certain invertebrates and used to attach themselves to the rocks.

Calcareous: composed of, or containing calcium carbonate; limy.

Calcite: calcium carbonate ($CaCO_3$) crystallizing in the hexagonal system. In shells it is translucent and more stable than aragonite.

Calyx: in corals the bowl-shaped depression in the upper part of the skeleton; in the stalked echinoderms that part of the body which contains most of the soft parts.

Cambrian: the first (oldest) period of the Paleozoic era.

Cancellated: marked by lines crossing one another in a latticelike pattern.

Carapace: the hard protective covering that forms the exoskeleton of many invertebrates; in arthropods it is usually chitinous or calcarochitinous.

Carbonization: the process of fossilization whereby organic remains are reduced to carbon or coal.

Carinated: having a ridge or keel.

Cast: the impression taken from a mold.

Catalogue number: a number assigned to individual fossil specimens in a collection.

Cementation: deposition of mineral material between rock fragments.

-cene: combining form meaning *recent;* from Gr. *ḳainos* (recent).

Ceno-: combining form meaning *recent;* from Gr. *ḳainos* (recent).

Cenozoic: the latest era of the geologic time, following the Mesozoic era and extending to the present.

Cephalon: the head; in trilobites the anterior body segment forming the head.

Cephalopod: marine invertebrate with well-defined head and eyes and with tentacles around the mouth; member of class Cephalopoda, phylum Mollusca; includes squids, octopuses, and the pearly nautilus.

Ceratite: ammonoid cephalopod with suture composed of rounded saddles and jagged lobes; member of subclass Ammonoidea.

Chitin: a hornlike substance, found in the hard parts of all articulated animals, such as beetles and crabs.

Chitinous: composed of chitin.

Chordate: member of phylum Chordata; includes fishes, amphibians, reptiles, birds, and mammals.

Chromosome: in organic cells the bodies of tissue which carry the genes or hereditary determiners. There is a pair of chromosomes in each somatic cell and in each zygote; there is one chromosome in each gamete.

Cilia: minute, microscopic, hairlike processes on the surface of a cell, organ, or organism.

Cirri (singular cirrus): usually applied to certain types of appendages formed by the fusion of setae or cilia.

Class: subdivision of a phylum; a unit of biological classification.

Clastic rock: sedimentary rock consisting of fragments.

Coelenterate: invertebrate characterized by a hollow body cavity, radial symmetry, and stinging cells; a member of phylum Coelenterata; includes jellyfishes, corals, and sea anemones.

Colonial: in biology refers to the way in which some invertebrates (colonial corals, hydroids, etc.) live in close association with, and are more or less dependent upon, each other.

Columella: a small column or central axis; in corals the small rod or axial pillar in the center of the corallite; in gastropods the solid or perforate pillar formed by the union of the successive coils of a conispiral shell.

Columnal: one of the disk-shaped segments of a crinoid stalk.

Compaction: in geology, the process whereby loose sediments are consolidated into firm, hard rocks.

Concentric: having a common center, as circles; refers to shell markings that are parallel to shell margin.

Concretion: an aggregate of nodular or irregular masses in sedimentary rocks, usually formed around a central core, which may be a fossil.

Conglomerate: the rock produced by consolidation of gravel. Constituent rock and mineral fragments are usually varied in composition and size.

Conifers: cone-bearing shrubs or trees.

Conispiral: coiled in the form of a cone.

Conodont: minute toothlike fossils found in certain Paleozoic rocks. Their origin is not definitely known, but they may have been part of some type of extinct fish.

Contact: in geology, the surface which marks the junction of two bodies of rock.

Convergent: approaching.

Coral: bottom-dwelling marine invertebrate that secretes calcareous hard parts; member of class Anthozoa phylum Coelenterata.

Corallite: the skeleton formed by an individual coral animal. May be solitary or form part of a colony.

Corallum: the skeleton of a coral colony.

Corneous: corny.

Corona: crown; in echinoids the main part of the skeleton consisting of symmetrically arranged calcareous plates.

Coronate: somewhat crown-shaped.

Coprolite: the fossilized excrement of animals.

Correlation: the process of demonstrating that certain strata are closely related to each other or that they are stratigraphic equivalents.

Costa (plural—costae): a rib or ridge.
Counter: opposite.
Crenulate: having the margin cut into rounded notches.
Crescentic: shaped like a new moon.
Cretaceous: the third and last period of the Mesozoic era.
Crinoid: member of class Crinoidea of phylum Echinodermata; stemmed attached echinoderms known also as "sea lilies."
Cruciform: cross-shaped.
Cuneate: wedge-shaped.
Cystoid: an extinct stemmed echinoderm with calyx composed of numerous irregularly arranged plates; member of class Cystoidea of phylum Echinodermata.
Cystose: containing or resembling a cyst or bladder.

Dendrite: a branching or treelike figure produced on or in a rock or mineral, usually formed by crystallization of an oxide of manganese.
Dendritic: resembling a tree, branching.
Dendroid: branching after the manner of a tree.
Denticles: small teeth or teethlike ridges.
Denticulate: toothed.
Dentition: the system or arrangement of teeth peculiar to any given animal.
Devonian: the fourth oldest period of the Paleozoic era; follows the Silurian, precedes the Mississippian.
Dextral: right-handed or situated on the right side; in gastropods the more common direction of shell coiling in which, when the apex is directed upward and the aperture faces the observer, the aperture is on the right side of the shell.
Diaphragm: a more or less straight dividing partition, extending horizontally or diagonally from one side of a tube to the other.
Diatomite: a siliceous deposit composed of the remains of microscopic plants called diatoms.
Digitate: branching like the fingers of a hand from a central point.
Dip: the angle of inclination which the bedding plane of rocks makes with a real or imaginary horizontal line.
Dis-: a prefix signifying separation or meaning "not."
Disciform: disc-shaped.
Dissepiment: in corals the horizontal or oblique plates which unite the adjoining septa, usually curved or irregular when seen in transverse section; in bryozoans a crossbar connecting the branches of certain forms; in graptolites a short crossbar connecting adjacent branches of the animal.
Distillation: in fossils, the process by which volatile organic matter is removed, leaving a carbon residue.

Disturbance: in geology, a regional mountain-building event in earth history, commonly separating two periods.

Divergent: parting.

Division: one of the primary divisions of the plant kingdom; equivalent to a phylum.

Dolomite: a mineral composed of calcium magnesium carbonate [$Ca\,Mg(CO_3)_2$].

Dorsal: pertaining to the back.

Echinoderm: marine invertebrate with calcareous exoskeleton and usually a fivefold radial symmetry; member of phylum Echinodermata; includes cystoids, blastoids, crinoids, starfishes, and sea urchins.

Echinoid: bottom-dwelling, unattached marine invertebrate with exoskeleton of calcareous plates covered by movable spines; member of class Echinoidea; includes sea urchins, heart urchins, and biscuit urchins.

Ecology: The study of the relations between organisms and their environment.

Edentulous: without teeth.

Embryo: an organism in the early stage of development.

Embryology: that division of biology that deals with the formation and development of the embryo.

Endoskeleton: the internal supporting structure of an animal.

Environment: the surroundings—physical, chemical, and organic—of an organism.

Eocene: next to earliest of the Tertiary epochs, follows the Paleocene and precedes the Oligocene.

Epoch: a division of geologic time; subdivision of a period.

Era: a division of geologic time; includes one or more periods.

Evolution: a term applied to those methods or processes and to the sum of those processes whereby organisms change through successive generations.

Exfoliate: to remove small portions from the surface.

Exoskeleton: an external skeleton, or hard covering for the protection of soft parts, particularly among invertebrates.

Fasciculate: clustered, grouped in bundles.

Fathom: a measure of length equalling six feet.

Fault: the displacement of rocks along a zone of fracture.

Fauna: an assemblage of animals (living or fossil) associated in a given place at a given time.

Faunal succession, law of: the principle stating that there is a succession of life forms through geologic history so that life of any one period is different from that of preceding and succeeding periods.

Fiber: any fine, thin, threadlike feature.
Fibrous: consisting of fibers.
Filament: a fine thread or fiber.
Filiform: thread-shaped, very thin.
Flabellate: fan-shaped.
Flagellum (plural—flagella): a long lashlike appendage.
Flank: the side or lateral portion of anything.
Flora: an assemblage of plants (living or fossil) in a given place at a given time.
Fold: an elongate elevation.
Foliate: leaflike.
Foramen: in brachiopods, the opening in the pedicle valve near the beak where the pedicle extends through the shell.
Foraminifer: a protozoan usually possessing a calcareous, perforated, chambered shell, but shell may be chitinous or agglutinated; a member of the order Foraminifera phylum Protozoa.
Formation: a rock unit useful for mapping and distinguished primarily on the basis of lithologic characters.
Fossil: the remains or traces of organisms buried by natural causes and preserved in the earth's crust. (See *Guide fossil.*)
Fossiliferous: containing fossilized organic remains.
Fucoid: a seaweed similar to the modern *Fucus.*
Functional: pertaining to the appropriate action of any special organ.
Furcate: branching like a fork.
Fusiform: spindle-shaped; drawn at both ends.

Gamete: a sexual reproduction cell.
Gastral: pertaining to the stomach.
Gastrolith: highly polished well-rounded pebbles found associated with certain reptilian fossils; "stomach stones."
Gastropod: terrestrial or aquatic invertebrate, typically possessing a single-valved, calcareous, coiled shell; member of class Gastropoda phylum Mollusca; includes snails and slugs.
Genal: pertaining to the cheeks.
Gene: the basic building stone of heredity, a hereditary determiner.
Genetic: pertaining to origin.
Genetics: that division of biology which deals with heredity and variation among related organisms.
Genus (plural—genera): a group of closely related species of organisms.
Geologic age: the age of an object as stated in terms of geologic time (e.g., a Pennsylvanian fern, a Cretaceous dinosaur).
Geologic map: a map showing distribution of rock outcrops, structural features, mineral deposits, etc.

Geologic range: the known duration of an organism's existence throughout geologic time (e.g., Cambrian to Recent for brachiopods).

Geologic time scale: the tabular record of the divisions of earth history.

Geosyncline: a great downward flexure of the earth's crust, usually tens of miles wide and hundreds of miles long.

Gibbous: swollen, very convex.

Gills: respiratory organs for gaseous exchange in water.

Glabella: in trilobites the axial portion of the cephalon.

Glauconite: a greenish mineral commonly formed in marine environments, and essentially a hydrous silicate of iron and potassium.

Goniatite: ammonoid cephalopod with suture composed of rounded saddles and angular lobes; member of subclass Ammonoidea.

Granulated: having small and even elevations resembling grains.

Granulose: bearing or resembling grains or granules.

Graptolite: an extinct, marine, colonial organism with chitinous hard parts; believed to belong to subphylum Hemichordata of phylum Chordata.

Guide fossil: a fossil which, because of its limited vertical but wide horizontal distribution, is of value as a guide or index to the age of the rocks in which it is found.

Habitat: the sum of the physical environment in which an organism lives.

Hemi-: a prefix meaning *half.*

Hexa-: a prefix meaning *six.*

Hinge-line: in brachiopods the edge of the shell where the two valves articulate; in pelecypods the dorsal margin of the valve which is in continual contact with the opposite valve.

Hirsute: with hairs, hairy.

Historical geology: the study of geologic history of the earth.

Holo-: a prefix meaning *entire.*

Homologous structure: structures or organs in different animals that have the same fundamental structure, but that are used for different functions.

Igneous rock: rocks which have solidified from lava or molten rock called magma.

Im-: a form of the prefix "in."

Imbricate: to overlap in a series of plates.

Imperforate: without an opening.

In-: a prefix meaning "not" or "in."

Incised: cut into.

Index fossil: see *Guide fossil.*

Inflated: swollen.
Inflected: bent or turned inward or downward.
Infra-: a prefix meaning *below* or *after*.
Inter-: a prefix meaning *between*.
Interstitial: pertaining to an intervening space between lines.
Intra-: a prefix meaning *within*.
Introverted: turned inward.
Invaginated: folded inwardly into self.
Invertebrate: an animal without a backbone or spinal column.
Involute: rolled inward so that later whorls partially or completely hide the preceding whorls.

Keel: a strong carina or ridge.

Lamina: a thin plate or scale.
Lammellar: arranged in plates.
Larva: the early form of some animals before they assume the mature shape.
Lateral: side or to the side.
Lava: molten rock upon the surface.
Linguiform: tongue-shaped.
Linguloid: tongue-shaped.
Lithology: the study and description of rocks based on the megascopic (with the naked eye) examination of samples. Used also to refer to the texture and composition of any given rock sample.
Longitudinal: in a direction parallel with the length.

Macrofossil: a fossil which is, typically, readily visible to the naked eye.
Mantle: the membrane lining the respiratory (mantle) cavity of mollusks and brachiopods.
Median fold: a fold occurring in the middle.
Median sinus: a sinus occurring in the middle.
Megafossil: see *Macrofossil*.
Meso-: a prefix signifying *middle*.
Meta-: a prefix meaning *posterior* or *later*.
Metagenesis: a term referring to those processes of reproduction which result in an alternation of sexual and asexual generations; alternation of generations.
Metamorphic rock: rock formed from igneous or sedimenary rocks that have been subjected to great changes in temperature, pressure, and chemical environment.
Metamorphism: extensive change of rocks or minerals.
Metamorphosis: a marked change in the form or function of an organism by a natural process of growth or development.

Microfossil: a fossil which is, typically, microscopic in size.
Morphology: the study of structure or form.
Mucronate: produced into a long pointed extension.
Multi-: a prefix meaning *many, much,* or *more than two.*
Multicellular: composed of more than one cell.
Mutation: an inherited change transmitted as a result of marked change within the germ plasm.

Nacreous: pearly.
Natural selection: the process by which organisms survive because of their ability to adapt to their surroundings and to changing environmental conditions.
Nautiloid: member of subclass Nautiloidea, class Cephalopoda, phylum Mollusca; represented by the living pearly nautilus.
Nekton: an organism that leads an actively swimming adult life.
Node: a knob.
Nodose: bearing knobs.
Nucleus: in unicellular organisms, and in cells, the central portion of the cell.

Obconical: inversely conical.
Obovate: inversely ovate, or egg-shaped.
Octo: a prefix meaning *eight.*
Occular: pertaining to the eye.
-oid: a suffix meaning *in the form of.*
Ontogeny: the life history or development of an individual organism.
Order: in taxonomy, a subdivision of a class (for example, order Primates of class Mammalia).
Operculum: the lid or covering closing the opening of certain shells.
Oral: referring to the mouth or aperture.
Organ: a part of a plant or animal that functions as a unit—the heart, stomach, eye, etc.
Organic: pertaining to, or derived from, life.
Organism: any living being.
Ossicle: loosely used to mean a small plate.
Ova: egg, the female gamete.

Paleoecology: the study of ancient ecology.
Paleontology: the science that deals with the study of fossils.
Paleozoic: that era of geologic time following the Proterozoic and preceding the Mesozoic.
Palmate: resembling a hand with fingers spread.
Papilla: a minute cone-shaped projection like a pimple.

Parasite: an animal which lives either upon or at the expense of another.

Patelliform: shaped like *Patella;* cap-shaped, a shallow hollow cone.

Pectinate: comblike.

Pedicle opening (pedicle foramen): see *Foramen.*

Pelagic: referring to the open sea at all depths (pelagic animals live in the open sea and are not limited to the ocean bottom).

Pelecypod: bivalved aquatic invertebrate; member of class Pelecypoda phylum Mollusca.

Pendant (also **pendent**): hanging suspended.

Pennsylvanian: the sixth oldest period of the Paleozoic era, follows the Mississippian precedes the Permian.

Pentamerous symmetry: symmetry arranged in a pattern of fives.

Period: the division of geologic time which is next lower in rank than an era, and next above an epoch.

Periostracum: the horny outer covering or epidermis of shells.

Peripheral: relating to the circumference; the outer portion of a surface.

Periphery: the circumference; the boundary line of any closed figure.

Peristome: the edge of an aperture.

Permineralization: in some fossils that process by which mineral matter has been added to the original shell material by precipitation in the interstices rather than replacing the original shell material.

Phosphatic: containing or pertaining to phosphate minerals.

Phyletic: pertaining to a phylum or subordinate group, all of which are united by common descent.

Phylloid: leaf-shaped.

Phyllose: leaf-shaped.

Phyllum: a leaf; a common termination of the generic name of corals.

Phylogeny: the racial history of a group of organisms.

Phylum: one of the primary divisions of the animal or vegetable kingdoms.

Pineal body: small organ located above or between opposite halves of the brain. May have served as a crude eye in certain animals.

Pinnate: divided featherlike.

Planispiral: shell coiled in one plane.

Plankton: marine organism that drifts aimlessly, floating without power to direct its own course.

Planktonic: referring to plankton.

Pleistocene: latest epoch of Quaternary period Cenozoic era; follows Pliocene epoch of Tertiary period, precedes Recent epoch of Quaternary.

Pleural: referring to the side or ribs; in trilobites refers to lateral portions of thorax and pygidium.

Plicate: possessing one or many folds.

Plication: a fold or ridge.

Pliocene: latest epoch of Teritary period of Cenozoic era; follows Miocene epoch and precedes Pleistocene epoch of Quaternary period.

Poly-: a prefix meaning *many.*

Polygonal: having more than four angles.

Polymorphic: assuming several forms or types.

Polyp: a many-tentacled aquatic coelenterate animal, typically cylindrical or cup-shaped, like corals.

Porcelaneous: like porcelain.

Poriferous: pore-bearing.

Posterior: situated behind; to the rear.

Precambrian: that portion of geologic time before the Cambrian; divided into Archeozoic era (Early Precambrian) and Proterozoic era (Late Precambrian).

Predator: a beast of prey.

Prehensile: adapted to seize or grasp.

Preoral: situated in front of the mouth.

Pro-: a prefix meaning *before.*

Produced: drawn out, elongated.

Prolific: producing many young.

Protero-: combining form meaning *fore, former,* or *anterior in time* (Gr. *proteros,* fore).

Proterozoic: youngest era of the Precambrian; follows the Archeozoic era and precedes the Cambrian period of the Paleozoic era.

Protista: the organic kingdom comprising the simplest of all one-celled organisms which possess various characters of both plants and animals; includes bacteria, algae, foraminifers, and radiolarians.

Protoconch: earliest stage of growth in the shell of a mollusk.

Pseudofossils: objects of nonorganic origin which resemble fossils; examples: dendrites, concretious.

Pseudomorph: fossil formed as a replacement of the original organic hard part of an animal.

Pseudopodia (singular—**pseudopodium**): temporary extension of protoplasm in certain one-celled organism; used for taking in food, locomotion, etc.

Pustule: a small blisterlike elevation.

Pustulose: bearing pustules.

Pygidium: the tail or posterior portion of the trilobite body.

Pyrite: a hard, brass-yellow mineral composed of iron sulfide; "fool's gold."

Quadrate: having four equal sides and four right angles; a square.

Quadri-: a prefix meaning *four*.

Quaternary: the youngest period of the Cenozoic era; follows the Tertiary period.

Radial symmetry: see *Symmetry*.

Radioactivity: spontaneous disintegration of atomic nucleus, with release of energy.

Ramification: a branching.

Ramifying: branching.

Ramose: branched.

Recapitulation, law of: see *Biogenetic Law*.

Recent: the latest part of the Pleistocene epoch, Quaternary period, Cenozoic era; includes the present portion of geologic time.

Recrystallization: the process whereby new mineral grains are formed in a rock while it is still in the solid state; the growth of small grains into larger ones.

Reef: a moundlike or ridgelike elevation of the sea bottom, almost reaching the surface of the water, composed primarily of organic material.

Reniform: kidney-shaped.

Replacement: type of fossilization whereby organic hard parts are removed by solution, while there is almost simultaneous deposition of other substances in the resulting voids; mineralization.

Respiration: the process of oxygenation.

Reticulate: resembling a network.

Retractile: capable of being withdrawn.

Revolution: in geology, a major mountain-building movement in earth history, typically of greater magnitude than a disturbance.

Riker mount: a paper-bound, glass-covered box for displaying specimens.

Rock: any naturally formed mass of mineral matter forming an essential part of the earth's crust.

Rock unit: division of rocks based on definite physical and lithologic characteristics and not defined on the basis of geologic time; groups, formations, members.

Rostrate: possessing a shelf.

Rostrum: a shelf.

Rugae: wrinkles.

Rugose: wrinkled.

Sand: small mineral grains, usually quartz.

Saddle: in cephalopods the forward flexure (curved toward the aperture) of the suture line.

Scaphopod: an exclusively marine mollusk with a single-valved tusk-shaped shell; member of class Scaphopoda phylum Mollusca.

Scavenger: an animal that feeds on decaying animal matter.
Sclerite: minute skeletal element of sea cucumbers.
Scolecodonts: the chitinous, horny, or siliceous jaws of worms.
Sedentary: stationary in life, not moving from place to place.
Sediment: material that has been deposited by settling from a transportation agent such as water or air.
Sedimentary rock: rocks formed by the accumulation of sediments.
Segment: one of the parts into which a body naturally separates.
Semilunar: crescentic.
Semiovate: half egg-shaped.
Septal: pertaining to the septum.
Septum (plural—septa): a dividing wall or partition; in fusulinids a partition between chambers in the fusulinid shell; in corals one of the radiating calcareous plates located within the corallite; in cephalopods the transverse partitions between the chambers.
Series: the rocks formed during an epoch; the time-stratigraphic term next in rank below a system.
Serrate: notched like a saw with sharp notches.
Sessile: attached, more or less permanently, to the substratum.
Seta (plural—setae): a bristle.
Sigmoid: curved in two directions like the letter *S*.
Silica: an oxide of silicon (SiO_2).
Siliceous: containing or pertaining to silica.
Silicification: the process of combining or impregnating with silica.
Silurian: the third oldest period of the Paleozoic era; follows the Ordovician precedes the Devonian.
Sinistral: left-handed; in gastropods the opposite of dextral (see above).
Sinuate: waving, winding, sinuous.
Sinuous: wavy, winding.
Sinus: an elongate downbending or depression.
Siphuncle: in cephalopods the segmented horny or calcareous tube which extends from the protoconch to the living chamber.
Slickensides: polished and grooved surfaces that are the result of two rock masses sliding past each other as in faulting.
Soil: broken and decomposed rock and decayed organic matter.
Solitary: living alone; not part of a colony.
Species: one of the smaller natural divisions in classification.
Specific name: the name applied to a species, usually the second of two names applied to a fossil as *wacoensis* in *Kingena wacoensis;* same as trivial name.
Sperm: the germ cell produced by the male.
Spheroidal: pertaining to a spheroid (a distorted sphere).
Spicule: a minute spike or dart, skeletal element in sponges and holothurians.

Spiniform: spinelike.
Spiracle: in blastoids, the round or slitlike openings which surround the mouth.
Spire: the coiled gastropod shell exclusive of the body whorl.
Squamous: covered with scales.
Steinkern: an internal mold.
Stellaroid: having the form of a star; star-shaped.
Stellate: star-shaped or starlike; radiating.
Stratigraphy: geologic subscience dealing with the definition and interpretation of stratified rocks; especially their lithology, sequence, distribution, and correlation.
Stratum (plural—strata): a single bed or layer of sedimentary rock.
Striate: bearing striations.
Striations: closely spaced, fine parallel lines.
Strike: the direction of a real or imaginary line that is formed by the intersection of a bed or stratum with a horizontal plane; strike is perpendicular to the dip.
Sulcate: having a deep furrow or groove.
Superposition, law of: the principle stating that in an undisturbed sequence of rocks younger beds will overlie older beds of rocks.
Supra-: prefix akin to *super*.
Suture: the line of junction between two parts; in crinoids the line of junction between two plates; in gastropods the line of junction of the whorls as seen on the exterior of the shell; in cephalopods the line of junction between a septum and the shell wall.
Symmetry: the reversed repetition of parts with reference to an axis.
Bilateral symmetry: the symmetrical duplication of parts on each side of a vertical anterior-posterior plane; a median sagittal plane.
Radial symmetry: the symmetrical repetition of parts around a common vertical dorso-ventrally disposed axis.
Pentamerous symmetry: symmetry arranged in a pattern of fives.
Syncline: a trough or downfold in the rocks.
System: the rocks formed during a period; the time-stratigraphic term next in rank above a series.

Tabulae (singular—tabula): the transverse interior platforms or diaphragms which extend across the interior of the corallite in tabulate corals; present also in certain hydrozoans.
Taxonomy: that branch of science that deals with classification, especially of plants, animals, or fossils.
Tertiary: the oldest period of the Cenozoic era; follows the Cretaceous period of the Mesozoic and precedes the Quaternary period of the Cenozoic.
Test: the protective covering of certain invertebrate animals.

Theca: a sheath or case; in coelenterates the bounding wall at or near the margin of the exoskeleton; in echinoderms the main body skeleton (or calyx) which houses the animal's soft parts; in graptolites any cup or tube of the colony.

Thorax: in trilobites that part of the body between the cephalon and the pygidium.

Till: unsorted glacial deposit.

Time unit: a portion of continuous geologic time (e.g., eras, periods, epochs, and ages).

Time-rock unit: see *Time-stratigraphic unit.*

Time-stratigraphic unit: term given to rock units with boundaries established by geologic time; strata deposited during definite portions of geologic time (e.g., systems, series, and stages).

Topography: the physical features or configuration of a land surface.

Topographic map: a map showing the physical features of an area, especially the relief and contour of the land.

Transverse: at right angles to length.

Triassic: the youngest period of the Mesozoic era; follows the Permian period of the Paleozoic and precedes the Jurassic period of the Mesozoic.

Trilobite: an extinct marine arthropod having a flattened segmented body covered by a hardened dorsal exoskeleton marked into three lobes.

Trivial name: the Latin or Latinized name added to a generic name to distinguish the species; same as specific name.

Tubercle: a knoblike process.

Tuberculate: provided with tubercles.

Tuberose: having knobs.

Tubule: a small tube or pipe.

Tumid: swollen, inflated.

Turbinate: shaped like a top.

Type locality: the geographic location at which a formation was first described and from which it was named; or from which the type specimen of a fossil species comes.

Type specimen: the individual or specimen on which the original designation of a species was established.

Umbilicus: an external depression or opening at the center of many loosely coiled shells; in gastropods it is usually located at the base of the shell; in cephalopods it is usually located laterally..

Umbo: the arched part of the valve near the beak in bivalve shells.

Unconformity: a break in sedimentation due to erosion or nondeposition; a place in the earth's crust where eroded bedrock is covered by younger sedimentary rocks.

Unicellular: composed of one cell.

Uniformitarianism: the doctrine that the present is the key to the past; that geologic history is best interpreted in the light of what is known about present conditions.

Uniserial: in a row or one series.

Valve: the one or more pieces comprising the shell of animals.

Variety: a subdivision of a species.

Vascular: pertaining to tubes or vessels for circulation of animal or plant fluids.

Vaulted: arched.

Ventral: pertaining to the abdomen; as opposed to dorsal pertaining to the back.

Vertebrate: an animal having a backbone or spinal column.

Vesicle: a bladderlike vessel, a cell.

Vestigial structure: a structure that has been reduced in size and/or usefulness during the course of evolutionary change.

Vulcanism (also volcanism): effects of molten rock and volcanoes.

Whorl: a single turn or volution of a coiled shell.

-zoic: combining form meaning life (Gr. *zoikos,* life).

Zooecium (plural—zooecia): tube or chamber occupied by an individual of the bryozoan colony; also called an autopore.

Zygote: a cell formed by the union of two gametes; a fertilized egg.

APPENDIX C

PUBLICATIONS ABOUT FOSSILS

The following publications are recommended for the reader who would like more information about fossils and fossil-collecting. The books and magazines listed below cover various phases of historical geology and paleontology. They range from children's books to the more technical publications of the professional paleontologist. This list is by no means all-inclusive. Many other interesting and useful publications may be found in public, school, and college libraries.

It is also helpful to refer to articles on Earth History, Geologic History, Paleontology, Fossils, and Organic Evolution in the *Encylopedia Americana, Encyclopaedia Britannica, Collier's Encyclopedia,* and other standard reference works. Consult also the lists of publications of the United States Geological Survey, Washington, D. C., and the Geological Survey of your home state.

HISTORICAL GEOLOGY AND GENERAL BACKGROUND READING

The Story of Our Earth by Richard Carrington, published in 1956 by Harper & Brothers, New York. A popular account of the history of the earth.

Down to Earth by Carey G. Croneis and William G. Krumbein, published in 1936 by the University of Chicago Press, Chicago, Ill. Easily read background text.

Historical Geology by Carl O. Dunbar, 2nd edition published in 1960 by John Wiley & Sons, Inc., New York. A college-level text with numerous illustrations.

Introduction to Evolution by Paul A. Moody, published in 1953 by Harper & Brothers, New York. College-level introductory text on evolution, with considerable emphasis on fosils and their geologic history.

Introduction to Historical Geology by Raymond C. Moore, 2nd edition published in 1958 by McGraw-Hill Book Co., Inc., New

York. College-level presentation of earth history. The book is well illustrated and contains many excellent plates of fossils of all ages.

Man, Time, and Fossils, by Ruth Moore, published in 1953 by Alfred A. Knopf, Inc., New York. A well-written, readable account of fossils and their development through geologic time.

Earth for the Layman by M. W. Pangborn, Jr., published in 1957 by the American Geological Institute, Washington, D. C. This little book contains many valuable references to popular and nontechnical books on earth history, paleontology, and all other phases of geology.

Geology by Richard M. Pearl, published in 1960 by Barnes and Noble, Inc., New York. This well-written book provides the reader with broad background material in both physical and historical geology. Especially useful to students.

Prehistoric Life by Percy E. Raymond, published in 1939 by the Harvard University Press, Cambridge, Mass. This is a college-level text, but it is written in such a manner as to be particularly useful to advanced amateurs.

Record of the Rocks by Horace G. Richards, published in 1953 by Ronald Press Co., New York. College-level but not too technical earth history text.

The Meaning of Evolution by George Gaylord Simpson, published in 1949 by Yale University Press, New Haven, Conn. This book provides much background material on evolution and is a fascinating history of life on earth. Especially for those who want to know more about organic evolution.

Life of the Past by George Gaylord Simpson, published in 1953 by Yale University Press, New Haven, Conn. Thorough, readable, and entertaining, this book presents a wealth of material in a well-organized, authoritative fashion.

Time, Life, and Man: The Fossil Record by R. A. Stirton, published in 1959 by John Wiley & Sons, New York. An introductory college text. Most of its material is of interest to adult-level general readers.

Essentials of Earth History by William L. Stokes, published in 1960 by Prentice-Hall, Englewood Cliffs, N. J. This book is designed for the introductory course in historical geology, but should be of interest to anyone who wants to know more of earth history. It is clearly written and contains many fine illustrations.

History of the Earth; An Introduction to Historical Geology by Bernhard Kummel, published in 1961 by W. F. Freeman and Co.,

San Francisco, Calif. Comprehensive college-level text on historical geology.

NONTECHNICAL AND JUVENILE BOOKS

All About Dinosaurs by Roy Chapman Andrews, published in 1953 by Random House, Inc., New York. An interesting and readable dinosaur book for elementary and junior-high students.

All About Strange Beasts of the Past by Roy Chapman Andrews, published in 1956 by Random House, Inc., New York. This little book deals largely with extinct and unusual mammals. It is interesting and easy to read. For elementary and junior-high level readers.

Ancient Plants and the World They Lived In by H. N. Andrews, published in 1947 by Comstock Publishing Co., Ithaca, N. Y. A popular-type introduction to the field of paleobotany.

Leaves and Stems of Fossil Forests by Raymond E. Janssen, published in 1957 by the Illinois State Museum, Springfield, Ill. Good popular introduction to fossil plants.

Plants of the Past; A Popular Account of Fossil Plants by Frank H. Knowlton, published in 1957 by Princeton University Press, Princeton, N. J. Nontechnical introduction to paleobotany.

Prehistoric Animals by J. Augusta and Z. Burian, published in 1956 by Spring House Books, Ltd., London. This large book contains many beautiful color pictures of plants and animals of the past.

Shelled Invertebrates of the Past and Present by R. S. Bassler, C. E. Resser, W. L. Schmitt, and Paul Bartsch, published in 1934 as Volume X of the Smithsonian Science Series, Smithsonian Institution, Washington, D. C. The first part of this book deals with fossils and the history of the earth.

The Dinosaur Book by E. H. Colbert, published in 1951 by McGraw-Hill Book Co., Inc., New York. An easily understood, clearly written book, this is a "classic" among popular dinosaur books. It is well illustrated and suitable for all age levels.

Dinosaurs by E. H. Colbert, published in 1957 by the American Museum of Natural History, New York. This little booklet provides a factual and well-illustrated introduction to the dinosaurs. For high-school and adult-level readers.

Wonders of the Dinosaur World by W. H. Matthews III, published in 1963 by Dodd, Mead & Co., New York. An easy-to-read, well-illustrated book for elementary and junior-high-school readers.

The World of the Dinosaurs by D. H. Dunkle, published in 1957 by the Smithsonian Institution, Washington, D. C. This little booklet is easy to understand, amply illustrated, and provides much information about all types of dinosaurs. Especially recommended for high-school and adult-level readers.

Prehistoric World by Carroll Lane Fenton, published in 1954 by John Day Co., New York. Stories and discussions of some of the more important fossil animals.

Life Long Ago by Carroll Lane Fenton, published in 1937 by John Day Co., New York. Very good for advanced grade and high-school age.

Dinosaurs by Herbert S. Zim, published in 1954 by William Morrow and Co., Inc., New York. Relatively simple book recommended for lower grades.

The Story of Earth Science by Horace G. Richards, published in 1959 by J. B. Lippincott Co., New York. A high-school level book that provides background material for all phases of earth science. Parts deal with earth history and with fossils.

How the World Began by Edith Heal, published in 1930 by Thomas S. Rockwell Co., Chicago, Ill. Deals with the beginnings and development of life. Particularly for upper grade through high-school age.

Fossils by H. C. Markman, published in 1945 by Denver Museum of Natural History, Denver, Colo. A well-illustrated general survey of fossils. For adult-level readers.

Stories Read From the Rocks by Bertha M. Parker, published in 1942 as part of the Basic Science Education Series of Row, Peterson and Co., Evanston, Ill. A well-written and colorfully illustrated little booklet, especially for grade and junior-high students.

Animals of Yesterday by Bertha M. Parker, published in 1948, as part of the Basic Science Education Series of Row, Peterson and Co., Evanston, Ill. Deals with fossils, especially vertebrates. Contains many colorful illustrations.

The First Mammals by W. E. Scheele, published in 1955 by World Publishing Co., New York. This book deals with fossil mammals and is particularly for junior-high to high-school level readers.

Prehistoric Animals by W. E. Scheele, published in 1954 by World Publishing Co., New York. An introductory presentation to animals of the past. Contains many large illustrations; for high-school age and up.

Real Book of Prehistoric Life by Dorothy Shuttlesworth, published in 1957 by Doubleday & Co., Garden City, New York. This is an easy-to-read survey of prehistoric life which is well suited for grade and junior high school age readers.

REFERENCE WORKS

Index Fossils of North America by H. W. Shimer and R. R. Shrock, published in 1944 by John Wiley & Sons, Inc., New York. This large volume is the most important single source from which to identify fossils. It contains a comprehensive survey of the more common fossils of North America, with pictures of many of them.

Invertebrate Fossils by R. C. Moore, C. G. Lalicker, and A. G. Fisher, published in 1953 by McGraw-Hill Book Co., Inc., New York. This is a college-level paleontology text with many unusually fine illustrations. Good for detailed information on fossil invertebrates and valuable for purposes of identification.

Principles of Invertebrate Paleontology by R. R. Shrock and W. H. Twenhofel, published in 1953 by McGraw-Hill Book Co., Inc., New York. College text that is useful for advanced collectors. Numerous illustrations to assist in identification.

Invertebrate Paleontology by W. H. Easton, published in 1960 by Harper & Brothers, New York. This is another college text which has good general information and many illustrations to help identify fossils.

The Fossil Book by Carroll Lane Fenton and Mildred Adams Fenton, published in 1958 by Doubleday & Co., Inc., New York. This comprehensive, superbly illustrated, easy-to-read book treats all types of fossils. It is valuable for purposes of identification and for learning about fossils in general.

Search for the Past by James R. Beerbower, published in 1960 by Prentice-Hall, Inc., Englewood Cliffs, N. J. This text is good background reading and is well illustrated. Deals with both vertebrate and invertebrate fossils.

Introduction to the Study of Fossils by H. W. Shimer, revised edition published in 1933 by Macmillan Co., New York. A relatively simple college-level presentation of plant and animal fossils.

Foraminifera; Their Classification and Economic Use by Joseph Cushman, 4th edition revised, published in 1948 by Harvard University Press, Cambridge, Mass. A college text and reference book that contains many descriptions and illustrations of foraminifera.

Introduction to Microfossils by Daniel J. Jones, published in 1956 by Harper & Brothers, New York. College text with considerable information on collection, preparation, identification, and the various types of microfossils.

Principles of Micropaleontology by M. F. Glaessner, published in 1947 by John Wiley & Sons, New York. An advanced college text containing much information on micropaleontological techniques and on all types of microfossils.

Textbook of Paleontology by K. A. von Zittel, published in several editions by Macmillan Co., London and New York. An old but still useful college text. Contains many illustrations to aid in fossil identification, but much of the classification is out of date.

Outlines of Paleontology by H. H. Swinnerton, 3rd edition published in 1947 by the Arnold Publishing Co., London. An introductory British text.

Palaeontology: Invertebrate by Henry Woods, published in 1957 by Cambridge University Press, Cambridge, England. Another British introductory text.

Man and the Vertebrates by Alfred S. Romer, published in 1941 by the University of Chicago Press, Chicago, Ill. A well-illustrated survey of both fossil and recent vertebrates.

Vertebrate Paleontology by Alfred S. Romer, 2nd edition published in 1945 by the University of Chicago Press, Chicago. A college-level vertebrate paleontology text with numerous fine illustrations.

Evolution of the Vertebrates by E. H. Colbert, published in 1955 by John Wiley & Sons, New York. A well-written, comprehensive, and technical treatment of the vertebrates and their development throughout geologic time.

An Introduction to Paleobotany by C. A. Arnold, published in 1947 by McGraw-Hill Book Co., Inc., New York. An introductory text on paleobotany; many illustrations.

Principles of Paleobotany by William C. Darrah, 2nd edition, published in 1960 by Ronald Press Co., New York. A college-level text; discusses paleobotanical collecting and preparation techniques.

The Wilmington Coal Flora from a Pennsylvanian Deposit in Will County, Illinois by George Langford, published in 1958 by Esconi Associates, Downers Grove, Ill. A thorough, well-illustrated review of many common Pennsylvanian plant fossils.

Treatise on Invertebrate Paleontology edited by Raymond C. Moore, published by the University of Kansas and the Geological

Society of America. A technical reference for the professional and advanced collector. It is issued in several parts (the first volume in 1953) over a period of several years and is very helpful in identification.

Bibliography of North American Geology, published at intervals by the United States Geological Survey. This important reference series includes references to all aspects of general geology of the continent of North America. Entries are listed by author and are alphabetically arranged. The first of these publications covers the literature beginning in 1785, and the most recent edition brings it up to 1959.

COLLECTING HELPS AND FOSSIL GUIDES

An Illustrated Guide to Fossil Collecting by Richard Casanova, published in 1957 by Natureograph Co., San Martin, Calif. This book contains many hints on fossil-collecting, in addition to a brief section on earth history. Of special interest is the list of collecting areas for each American state.

Methods in Paleontology by C. L. Camp and G. D. Hanna, published in 1937 by the University of California Press, Berkeley, Calif. Excellent discussions of collecting and preparation techniques for all types of fossils.

How to Make a Home Nature Museum by Vinson Brown, published in 1954 by Little, Brown and Co., Boston, Mass. This useful little book contains helpful suggestions for collecting, mounting, displaying, and preparing fossils and other objects of nature.

NOTE: The following books have been written specifically for the states mentioned in each title. In addition to information about the geology and fossils of the respective states, most of them have valuable information about the nature of fossils, how and where to collect them, and suggestions as to their identification and preparation.

Adventures With Fossils by Robert H. Shaver, published in 1959 by the Geological Survey, Indiana Department of Conservation, Bloomington, Ind. Collection hints and general information on fossils, plus a guide to some Indiana collecting localities.

Common Fossils of Missouri by A. G. Unklesbay, published in 1955 as Handbook 4 of the University of Missouri Bulletin, Columbia, Mo. Written for the amateur collector; contains much information of general interest to the beginner or student.

Fossils in Washington by V. E. Livingston, Jr., published in 1959 by the Divisions of Mines and Geology, Department of Conservation, Olympia, Wash. An introduction to the geology and fossils of Washington state. Contains guide to collecting localities.

Field Book, Pennsylvanian Plant Fossils of Illinois by Charles C. Collinson and Romayne Skartvedt, published in 1960 as Educational Series 6 of the Illinois State Geological Survey, Urbana, Ill. Excellent coverage of the plant fossils of Illinois. Contains many illustrations, plus a plant classification, collecting suggestions, and a guide to numerous collecting localities.

Guide for Beginning Fossil Hunters by Charles C. Collinson, published as Educational Series 4 of the Illinois State Geological Survey, Urbana, Ill. A clearly written, well-illustrated guide for the beginner.

Handbook of Paleontology for Beginners and Amateurs, Part I. The Fossils by Winifred Goldring, published in 1950 by the New York State Museum and now available from the Paleontological Research Institution, 109 Dearborn Place, Ithaca, N. Y.

Elementary Guide to the Fossils and Strata of the Ordovician in the Vicinity of Cincinnati, Ohio by Kenneth E. Caster and others, published in 1955 by the Cincinnati Museum of Natural History, Cincinnati, Ohio. Useful book to aid in knowing and identifying Ordovician fossils from the above area.

Fossils: What They Mean and How to Collect Them by L. R. Saul and R. B. Saul, Volume XIII, Number 7, Mineral Information Service, State of California, Division of Mines, San Francisco, Calif. A concise look at fossils and fossil-collecting.

Ohio Fossils by A. L. Rocque and M. F. Marple, published in 1955 as Bulletin 54 of the Ohio Division of Geological Survey, Columbus, Ohio. This publication presents a rather comprehensive treatment of the invertebrates with several keys for fossil identification.

Miocene Fossils of Maryland by Harold E. Vokes, published in 1957 as Bulletin 20 of the Department of Geology, Mines, and Water Resources, Baltimore, Md. Contains descriptions, classification, and excellent figures of the famous Miocene fossils of Maryland.

Texas Fossils by William H. Matthews III, published in 1960 as Guide Book 2 of the Bureau of Economic Geology of the University of Texas, Austin. Contains a complete discussion of fossils of all types with emphasis on the geology and fossils of Texas. Also includes collection, preparation, and identification aids.

Popular Guide to the Nature and the Environment of the Fossil Vertebrates of New York by Roy L. Moodie, published as Handbook 12 of the New York State Museum, Albany, N. Y. Contains a complete discussion of the vertebrate fossils of New York state.

MAGAZINES

Earth Science Digest publishes interesting articles on rocks, minerals, and popular geology; often carries special articles on fossils. It is published bimonthly at Box 1357, Chicago 90, Illinois.

Natural History is a monthly magazine published by the American Museum of Natural History, New York 24, N. Y. Frequently carries stories on fossils and other items of geologic interest.

Rocks and Minerals published by Peter Zodac Box 29, Peekskill, N. Y. Covers rocks, minerals, plus a monthly column on fossils. The fossil column is the source of many good collecting tips and information about fossil-collecting localities.

The Desert Magazine is published monthly at Palm Desert, Calif. This magazine features articles on geologic subjects of the southwestern United States.

NOTE: In addition to the above sources, interesting and authoritative articles on fossils will occasionally be found in *Arizona Highways, Science Digest, Life,* and *National Geographic* magazines.

There are other, more technical, publications which may be consulted in public or college libraries. Among these are the *Journal of Paleontology, Journal of Geology, Bulletin of the Geological Society of America, Micropaleontology,* and *Bulletins of American Paleontology.*

FOSSIL MAN

Meet Your Ancestors; A Biography of Primitive Man by Roy Chapman Andrews, published in 1945 by Viking Press, New York. Good reading for ages fourteen and up.

Fossil Men by Marcellin Boule and Henri Vallois, published in 1957 by Dryden Press, Inc., New York. Excellent relatively advanced study of human fossils.

The Story of Our Ancestors by May Edel. Published in 1955 by Little, Brown and Co., Boston, Mass. Especially for junior- and senior-high-school ages.

Up From the Ape by Earnest A. Hooton, revised edition published in 1946 by Macmillan Co., New York. Thorough treatment of fossil men and anthropology.

Prehistoric Man and the Primates by William E. Scheele, published in 1957 by the World Publishing Co., Cleveland, Ohio. A well-illustrated history of man's development. For high-school age and up.

Early Man in America; A Study in Prehistory by Elias H. Sellards, published in 1952 by the University of Texas Press, Austin, Texas. Interesting reading at the adult level.

Men Before Adam by Anne Terry White, published in 1942 by Random House, New York. High-school and adult reading on early man.

The Piltdown Forgery by Joseph A. Weiner, published in 1955 by Oxford University Press, New York. Interesting account of the famous Piltdown hoax.

Appendix D

SOURCES OF GEOLOGIC INFORMATION FOR THE STATES

The agencies listed below can, in most instances, furnish geologic maps and publications for each of the respective states.

ALABAMA
Geological Survey of Alabama
University of Alabama
University, Alabama

ALASKA
U.S. Geological Survey
210 E. F. Glover Building
Anchorage, Alaska

ARIZONA
Arizona Bureau of Mines
University of Arizona
Tucson, Arizona

ARKANSAS
Arkansas Geological and
Conservation Comm.
446 State Capitol
Little Rock, Arkansas

CALIFORNIA
California Division of Mines
Ferry Building
San Francisco 11, California

U.S. Geological Survey
4 Homewood Place
Menlo Park, California

U.S. Geological Survey
724 Appraisers Building
San Francisco, California

COLORADO
U.S. Geological Survey
Denver Federal Center
Denver, Colorado

CONNECTICUT
Connecticut Geological and
Natural History Survey
University of Connecticut
Storrs, Connecticut

DELAWARE
Delaware Geological Survey
University of Delaware
Newark, Delaware

DISTRICT OF COLUMBIA
U. S. Geological Survey
General Services
Administration Building
18th and 19th Sts., N.W.
Washington, D.C.

FLORIDA
Geological Survey
Tennessee and Woodward
Tallahassee, Florida

GEORGIA
Dept. of Mines, Mining and Geology
Agriculture Building
19 Hunter Street, S.W.
Atlanta 3, Georgia

HAWAII
Division of Hydrography
Department of Public Lands
Honolulu, Hawaii

IDAHO
Idaho Bureau of Mines and Geology
Moscow, Idaho

ILLINOIS
Illinois State Geological Survey
Natural Resources Building
Urbana, Illinois

INDIANA
Indiana Geological Survey
Owen Hall
Indiana University
Bloomington, Indiana

IOWA
Iowa Geological Survey
Geology Annex
Iowa City, Iowa

KANSAS
State Geological Survey of Kansas
Lindley Hall
University of Kansas
Lawrence, Kansas

KENTUCKY
Kentucky Geological Survey
University of Kentucky
Lexington, Kentucky

LOUISIANA
Louisiana Geological Survey
Louisiana State University
Baton Rouge 3, Louisiana

MAINE
Department of Economic Development
State House
Augusta, Maine

MARYLAND
Department of Geology, Mines and Water Resources
The Johns Hopkins University
Baltimore 18, Maryland

MICHIGAN
Geological Survey Division
Department of Conservation
Stevens T. Mason Building
Lansing 26, Michigan

MINNESOTA
Minnesota Geological Survey
University of Minnesota
Minneapolis 14, Minnesota

MISSOURI
Division of Geological Survey and Water Resources
Buehler Building
Rolla, Missouri

MISSISSIPPI
Mississippi Geological Survey
University, Mississippi

MONTANA
Montana Bureau of Mines and Geology
Montana School of Mines
Butte, Montana

NEBRASKA
Conservation and Survey Division
University of Nebraska
Lincoln 8, Nebraska

NEVADA
Nevada Bureau of Mines
University of Nevada
Reno, Nevada

NEW HAMPSHIRE
New Hampshire State Planning and Development Commission
Conant Hall
University of New Hampshire
Durham, New Hampshire

NEW JERSEY
Bureau of Geology and Topography
520 East State Street
Trenton 25, New Jersey

NEW MEXICO
New Mexico Bureau of Mines and Mineral Resources
Socorro, New Mexico

NEW YORK
Geological Survey
New York State Museum and Scientific Service
New York State Education Building
Albany 1, New York

NORTH CAROLINA
Division of Natural Resources
253 Education Building
Raleigh, North Carolina

NORTH DAKOTA
North Dakota Geological Survey
University of North Dakota
Grand Forks, North Dakota

OHIO
Division of Geological Survey
Dept. of Natural Resources
106 Orton Hall
The Ohio State University
Columbus 10, Ohio

OKLAHOMA
Oklahoma Geological Survey
Universty of Oklahoma
Norman, Oklahoma

OREGON
State of Oregon
Dept. of Geology and Mineral Industries
1069 State Office Building
Portland 1, Oregon

PENNSYLVANIA
Bureau of Topographic and Geological Survey
Dept. of Internal Affairs
604 South Office Building
Harrisburg, Pennsylvania

RHODE ISLAND
Rhode Island Development Council
State House
Providence 2, Rhode Island

SOUTH CAROLINA
South Carolina Development Board
Wade Hampton Office Building
Columbia, South Carolina

SOUTH DAKOTA
South Dakota Geological Survey
Union Building
University of South Dakota
Vermillion, South Dakota

TENNESSEE
Division of Geology
G-5 State Office Building
Nashville 3, Tennessee

TEXAS
Bureau of Economic Geology
The University of Texas
18th and Red River Streets
Austin 12, Texas

U.S. Geological Survey
602 Thomas Building
1314 Wood Street
Dallas, Texas

UTAH
Utah Geological and Mineralogical Survey
200 Mines Building
University of Utah
Salt Lake City, Utah

VERMONT
Vermont Geological Survey
East Hall
University of Vermont
Burlington, Vermont

VIRGINIA
Virginia Division of Mineral Resources
Charlottesville, Virginia

WASHINGTON
Division of Mines and Geology
Dept. of Conservation
335 General Administration Bldg.
Olympia, Washington

WEST VIRGINIA
West Virginia Geological and Economic Survey
Morgantown, West Virginia

WISCONSIN
Wisconsin Geological and Natural History Survey
University of Wisconsin
115 Science Hall
Madison, Wisconsin

WYOMING
Geological Survey of Wyoming
University of Wyoming
Geology Hall
Laramie, Wyoming

Appendix E

PARTIAL LIST OF MUSEUMS WHERE FOSSIL EXHIBITS ARE DISPLAYED

The following list includes most of the larger museums which have paleontological exhibits. In addition to the museums listed below there are many smaller museums which have fine collections of fossils from the various areas in which they are located. Most colleges and universities also have fossils on display in their museums or geology buildings.

ALABAMA
Alabama Museum of Natural History, University, Alabama.

ALASKA
Alaska Historical Library and Museum, Juneau, Alaska.
University of Alaska, School of Mines, College, Alaska.

ARIZONA
Arizona State Museum, University of Arizona, Tucson, Arizona.
Museum of Northern Arizona, Fort Valley Road, Flagstaff, Arizona.
Petrified Forest National Monument Museum, Rainbow Forest Visitor Center, Holbrook, Arizona.
Grand Canyon National Park Museum, Visitor Center, Grand Canyon, Arizona.

CALIFORNIA
California Academy of Sciences, San Francisco, California.
Geology Museum, California Institute of Technology, Pasadena, California.
University of California Department of Geology Museum, University of California, Berkeley, California.
Geology Museum, University of California at Los Angeles, California.
Los Angeles County Museum, Los Angeles, California.
San Diego Natural History Museum, San Diego, California.
Santa Barbara Museum of Natural History, Santa Barbara, California.

COLORADO

Denver Museum of Natural History, Denver, Colorado.

Geological Museum, Colorado School of Mines, Golden, Colorado.

University of Colorado Museum, Boulder, Colorado.

CONNECTICUT

Peabody Museum of Natural History, Yale University, New Haven, Connecticut.

DISTRICT OF COLUMBIA

Interior Department Museum, Interior Building, Washington, D.C.

Department of the Interior Museum (Geological Survey Section), Washington, D.C.

U. S. National Museum, Natural History Bldg., Washington 25, D.C.

FLORIDA

Florida Geological Survey, Tennessee and Woodward, Tallahassee, Florida.

Florida State Museum, University of Florida, Gainesville, Florida.

IDAHO

College of Mines, University of Idaho. Moscow, Idaho.

ILLINOIS

Geology Museum of Augustana College, Rock Island, Illinois.

Chicago Natural History Museum, Roosevelt Road, Chicago, Illinois.

Walker Museum of Paleontology, University of Chicago, Chicago, Illinois.

Illinois State Museum, Springfield, Illinois.

Museum of Natural History, University of Illinois, Urbana, Illinois.

Department of Geology, Northwestern University, Evanston, Illinois.

INDIANA

Joseph Moore Museum, Earlham College, Richmond, Indiana.

IOWA

Department of History and Archives, Des Moines, Iowa.

KANSAS

Baker University Museum, Baldwin, Kansas.

Fort Hays Kansas State College Museum, Hays, Kansas.

Kansas State University, Manhattan, Kansas.

University of Kansas, Natural History Museum, Lawrence, Kansas.

KENTUCKY

Department of Geology, University of Kentucky, Lexington, Kentucky.

MAINE
Department of Geology, Bates College, Lewiston, Maine.
Portland Society of Natural History, Portland, Maine.

MARYLAND
Great Falls Museum, Great Falls, Maryland.
Department of Geology, The Johns Hopkins University, Baltimore, Maryland.
Maryland Academy of Sciences, Baltimore, Maryland.

MASSACHUSETTS
Pratt Museum of Geology, Amherst College, Amherst, Massachusetts.
Harvard University Museum, Cambridge, Massachusetts.
Worcester Natural History Museum, Worcester, Mass.

MICHIGAN
Grand Rapids Public Museum, Grand Rapids, Michigan.
Jennison Trailside Museum, Bay City, Michigan.
Kingman Museum of Natural History, Battle Creek, Michigan.
Geology Department Museum, Michigan State University, East Lansing, Michigan.
Museum, Michigan State University, East Lansing, Michigan.
Exhibit Museum, The University of Michigan, North University, Ann Arbor, Michigan.

MINNESOTA
The Science Museum, St. Paul 3, Minnesota.

MISSISSIPPI
Mississippi Geological Survey, University, Mississippi.

MISSOURI
Missouri Resources Museum, State Capitol, Jefferson City, Missouri.
Palmer Little Museum, Webb City, Missouri.
Minerals Museum, Geology Department, Missouri School of Mines, Rolla, Missouri.

NEBRASKA
Cook Museum of Natural History, Agate, Nebraska.
Nebraska State Museum, University of Nebraska, Lincoln, Nebraska.
Oregon Trail Museum, Scotts Bluff National Monument, Gering, Nebraska.

NEVADA
Lake Mead National Recreation Area, Boulder City, Nevada.
Mackay School of Mines Museum, University of Nevada, Reno, Nevada.
Nevada State Museum, Carson City, Nevada.

NEW HAMPSHIRE

Geology Museum, University of New Hampshire, Durham, New Hampshire.

NEW JERSEY

New Jersey State Museum, State House Annex, Trenton, New Jersey.

Paterson Museum, Paterson, New Jersey.

Princeton University Geological Museum, Guyot Hall, Princeton, New Jersey.

NEW MEXICO

Carlsbad Caverns National Park Visitor Center, Carlsbad, New Mexico.

Museum of New Mexico, Santa Fe, New Mexico.

Geology Museum, University of New Mexico, Albuquerque, New Mexico.

NEW YORK

The American Museum of Natural History, New York, New York.

Buffalo Museum of Science, Buffalo, New York.

New York State Museum and Science Service, Albany, New York.

Rochester Museum of Arts and Sciences, Rochester, New York.

NORTH CAROLINA

Department of Geology Museum, Duke University, Durham, North Carolina.

North Carolina State Museum, Raleigh, North Carolina.

Research Laboratory of Anthropology and Museum of Geology, University of North Carolina, Chapel Hill, North Carolina.

NORTH DAKOTA

Department of Geology, University of North Dakota, Grand Forks, North Dakota.

OHIO

Cincinnati Museum of Natural History, Cincinnati, Ohio.

University Geology Museum, University of Cincinnati, Cincinnati, Ohio.

Cleveland Natural History Museum, Cleveland, Ohio.

Geology Museum, Miami University, Oxford, Ohio.

Ohio State Museum, Columbus, Ohio.

Geological Museum, The Ohio State University, Columbus, Ohio.

OKLAHOMA

Stovall Museum of Science and History, University of Oklahoma, Norman, Oklahoma.

OREGON

Museum of Natural History, University of Oregon, Eugene, Oregon.

State of Oregon Department of Geology and Mineral Industries Museum, Portland, Oregon.

PENNSYLVANIA

Academy of Natural Sciences, Philadelphia, Pennsylvania.

Bryn Mawr College, Department of Geology, Bryn Mawr, Pennsylvania.

Lafayette College Geology Museum, Easton, Pennsylvania.

Pennsylvania State Museum, Harrisburg, Pennsylvania.

The Mineral Industries Museum, The Pennsylvania State University, State College, Pennsylvania.

College Museum, State Teachers College, Millersville, Pennsylvania.

RHODE ISLAND

Brown University, Department of Geology Museum, Providence, Rhode Island.

Park Museum, Williams Park, Providence, Rhode Island.

SOUTH CAROLINA

Geology Museum, University of South Carolina, Columbia, South Carolina.

SOUTH DAKOTA

Cedar Pass Visitor Center, Badlands National Monument, South Dakota.

Museum of Geology, South Dakota School of Mines and Technology, Rapid City, South Dakota.

W. H. Over Museum, State University of South Dakota, Vermillion, South Dakota.

TENNESSEE

Geology Museum, University of Tennessee, Knoxville, Tennessee.

TEXAS

Geology Museum, Lamar State College of Technology, Beaumont, Texas.

Houston Museum of Natural History, Houston, Texas.

Panhandle-Plains Historical Museum, Canyon, Texas.

Strecker Museum, Baylor University, Waco, Texas.

Texas A & M College Museum, College Station, Texas.

Texas Christian University Museum, Fort Worth, Texas.

Texas Memorial Museum, Austin, Texas.

University of Texas Geological Museum, Austin, Texas.

Witte Museum, San Antonio, Texas.

UTAH

Bryce Canyon National Park Museum, Bryce Canyon, Utah.

Dinosaur Quarry Visitor Center Museum, Dinosaur National Monument, Jensen, Utah.

Utah Field House of Natural History, Vernal State Park, Vernal, Utah.
University of Utah Geology Museum, Salt Lake City, Utah.
Zion Visitor Center Museum, Zion National Park, Springdale, Utah.

VERMONT

Robert Hull Fleming Museum, University of Vermont, Burlington, Vermont.

VIRGINIA

Holden Geology Museum, Virginia Polytechnic Institute, Blacksburg, Virginia.
Brooks Museum, University of Virginia, Charlottesville, Virginia.
Washington and Lee Geology Department Museum, Washington and Lee University, Lexington, Virginia.

WASHINGTON

Eastern Washington State Historical Society, Spokane, Washington.

WEST VIRGINIA

Geology Museum of Marshall College, Huntington, West Virginia.

WISCONSIN

Thomas A. Greene Memorial Museum, Milwaukee-Downer College, Milwaukee, Wisconsin.

WYOMING

Mammoth Museum, Yellowstone Park, Wyoming.
University of Wyoming Geology Museum, Laramie, Wyoming.

Appendix F

DEALERS IN FOSSILS AND FOSSIL-COLLECTING EQUIPMENT

The dealers listed below carry a variety of fossils of all geologic ages. Most of them also carry a complete line of fossil-collecting equipment such as hammers, hand lenses, sample bags, etc. In addition, they sell books, display trays, display cases, and many other items of interest to the fossil-collector. For additional sources of supply consult the classified advertisement section of the magazines listed under "Publications About Fossils" on page 311.

Fossil Supply Company
6507 Sondra Drive
Dallas 14, Texas

Fossils Unlimited
2905 McKinley Street
Fort Worth 6, Texas

General Biological Supply House
8200 South Hoyne Avenue
Chicago 20, Illinois

Geological Enterprises
Box 926
Ardmore, Oklahoma

Malicks
5514 Plymouth Road
Baltimore 14, Maryland

Paleontological Research
Laboratory
424 South Race Street
Statesville, North Carolina

Ward's Natural Science
Establishment, Inc.
P. O. Box 1712
Rochester, 3, New York

INDEX

Note: Page numbers in **boldface** indicate illustrations.